C000179806

DAMNED
Un-English Machines

DAMNED
Un-English Machines

A HISTORY OF
BARROW-BUILT SUBMARINES

JACK HOOL & KEITH NUTTER

TEMPUS

Cover Illustrations

Front: HMS *Valiant*, as featured on p.162.
Back and spine: Holland 5, as featured on p.27.
Back: A painting by C.E. Turner showing the three O Class submarines (*Capitan O'Brien*, *Capitan Thompson*, and *Almirante Simpson*) with *Araucano*, their depot ship, in the background.

First published 2003

PUBLISHED IN THE UNITED KINGDOM BY:
Tempus Publishing Ltd
The Mill, Brimscombe Port
Stroud, Gloucestershire GL5 2QG

PUBLISHED IN THE UNITED STATES OF AMERICA BY:
Tempus Publishing Inc.
2 Cumberland Street
Charleston, SC 29401

© Jack Hool & Keith Nutter, 2003

The right of Jack Hool & Keith Nutter to be identified as the Authors
of this work has been asserted in accordance with the
Copyrights, Designs and Patents Act 1988.

All rights reserved. No part of this book may be reprinted
or reproduced or utilised in any form or by any electronic,
mechanical or other means, now known or hereafter invented,
including photocopying and recording, or in any information
storage or retrieval system, without the permission in writing
from the Publishers.

British Library Cataloguing in Publication Data.
A catalogue record for this book is available from the British Library.

ISBN 0 7524 2781 4

Typesetting and origination by Tempus Publishing.
Printed in Great Britain by Midway Colour Print, Wiltshire.

Contents

How Many Submarines?

As this book is about Barrow-built submarines, it seems reasonable for the reader to ask just how many such vessels have been built at Barrow. The question is not as simple as it might first appear – there are just too many variables and it is difficult to establish an exact definition of what constitutes a Barrow-built submarine.

The authors have determined that to qualify for the main list at the start of each Class section a submarine must have been launched or, for its first commitment to water, lowered by crane or synchronised shiplift at the Barrow-in-Furness Shipyard.

329 submarines (303 for the Royal Navy, twenty-four for foreign navies and two others – the Nordenfelt boats) fall into this category, though it must be noted that one of these (L32) was subsequently cancelled by the Royal Navy prior to completion while at least another five (K26, L23, L25, L26 and L27) were towed away after their launch to be completed at other shipyards.

To add to the confusion, a minimum of two submarines have been launched at other shipyards (E25 and E26) then towed into the Barrow-in-Furness Shipyard for completion. These have not been included in the main Class section lists but have been referenced in the text. The same applies to the three Type 2400 Class submarines built at Cammell Laird while that yard was owned by the Barrow-in-Furness Shipyard.

Acknowledgements

The authors would like to thank the following individuals and organizations for assistance provided during the preparation of this book:

Our wives, Ann and Tricia, for tolerating us for the last three years as this book developed from the germ of an idea into the finished article. Without their help and encouragement along the way we would never have got this far.

Wendy Tse of Tempus Publishing for giving help and advice at all stages and for having the faith in this book to publish on our behalf.

Roy Redshaw for undertaking an enormous amount of scanning and internet-related work on our behalf. Without question he has contributed as much to this book as the authors and has worked tirelessly alongside us for the last three years.

Dave Eddevane for proofreading the draft of this book – no mean task given the amount of statistical information. Dave's work has improved and tightened up the finished article.

Jim Glasgow for kindly agreeing to write the foreword.

BAE Systems Marine Ltd (referenced throughout the book as BAE) for permitting the use of Shipyard material from a variety of documents, including drawings and photographs. It should be noted that all drawings and photographs used were obtained from sources falling within BAE's ownership with the exception of those specifically referenced elsewhere in these acknowledgements. Particular thanks to BAE's Mike Smith and Mike Vallance for providing much-needed assistance.

Alan Smith for providing the *Turbulent* launch photograph.

Mr A. Hemple, Chief Librarian of Mirror Group Newspapers, for providing articles relating to *Warspite*'s flooding.

The United States Naval Institute (USNI), Annapolis, for providing the photographs used in the Japanese section which are also among illustrations used in the excellent *Submarines of the Imperial Japanese Navy*, USNI, 1986, by Polmar and Carpenter.

The Japanese section also benefited from the assistance given by Mr Sakashita (Director of the Shipbuilding Division) and Kay Anderson (Research/Public Relations Officer) – both of the Japan Ship Centre.

Rumic staff at both Barrow and Renfrew, particularly Garry Binns and Eric Wrightson, for providing information relating to the commercial mini-submarines.

The Cumbria Records Office and its staff for providing help throughout the three years it took to compile this book. A major source of Shipyard material is to be found within the archives of the Cumbria Record Office at Barrow and (under the leadership of Aidan Jones) Chris Robinson, Andrea Fazackerley, Sonya Waplington, Susan Benson and John Houliston assisted in search and copying activities, and undertook the scanning of Submarine Agreements in Appendix V and the Vickers advertisement.

Staff at Barrow Public Library for pursuing our interests across the county and in conjunction with the British Library.

We would like to thank the following who contributed by providing material, answering queries or helping out at some stage during the production of this book: Jimmy Ellis; Keith Glasgow; Keith Gregory; John Harrison; Bob Graham; Jack Lowther; Stuart Walker;

Mark Eilbeck; Maurice Redhead; Garth Harley; Brian Curwen; Bob Moody; Phil Moody; Derek Gawne and Alan Hooper.

The Ministry of Defence and Shipyard personnel (names unknown) who read and checked the book for security reasons prior to its publication.

Barrow's local newspaper the *North West Evening Mail* (particularly Frank Cassidy and Bill Myers) for providing help whenever required and for allowing the use of various articles which are reproduced in this book. (This newspaper was previously known as the *North Western Evening Mail*.)

Ken Wilson, of Baton Wicks Publishing, for providing the quote from *Classic Rock*.

Last (but not least) those private collectors of maritime and naval material for allowing us to view some amazing collections. They were always available to provide advice and loan books, photographs, etc. They prefer to remain anonymous and we respect that wish but nevertheless would like to thank them here. They know who they are.

Foreword

The Shipbuilding Works at Barrow-in-Furness has been the hub of the Royal Navy's submarine-building programme for more than a century.

Keith Nutter and Jack Hool are former employees whose names are familiar to many Barrovians, the former for his books relating to Rugby League and the latter for his contributions to various climbing books, journals and magazines. For both men, this book is an altogether different undertaking and the outcome of their collaboration is a history of submarine construction at Barrow starting before the Royal Navy involvement through to the present day.

Those with even a scant knowledge of the subject will appreciate the enormous amount of research that has been undertaken to uncover information from, in some cases, highly unusual sources and to marshal it with that from more conventional routes into a fascinating story. The authors have produced a narrative that gives an objective account of the submarine-building activities and an encyclopaedic listing of statistics. The comprehensive treatment of the subject has produced an exceptional story that will also become a valuable reference in the future.

The book recognises that the integrated nature of the shipbuilding and engineering activities at Barrow provided an unrivalled facility when coupled with a strong technical team closely linked to their opposite numbers at the Ministry of Defence. These attributes and the foresight of such people as the then Len Redshaw (later Sir Len) ensured that the Barrow Works became the sole builders of nuclear submarines for the Royal Navy.

Despite the tribulations that arose from time to time through industrial relations, the managers, designers, draughtsmen, foremen and tradesmen on the shop floor were linked by an ethos; they were never more than ten minutes away from one another and this resulted in a two-way exchange of views on changes that could make the job easier and produce a better product for the customer.

The Royal Navy Submarine Service has a reputation that is second to none and their standards of training have been a significant factor in attracting overseas navies to have their submarines built in the United Kingdom. In the Vickers era this complemented the export activities of the company and the authors have given due weight to the building of submarines for overseas navies. Over the years many have documented various aspects of work undertaken in Barrow and this record of submarine building in three centuries is an outstanding and welcome addition.

Jim Glasgow
2003

Jim Glasgow retired from the Shipyard (then Vickers Shipbuilding & Engineering Ltd) in March 1990 having risen through the ranks from apprentice ship draughtsman to ultimately become the Deputy Managing Director. He had joined the Yard workforce in 1945, going on to gain an honours degree in Naval Architecture from Newcastle University. In a career spanning forty-five years Jim covered a wide variety of projects, including merchant ships, surface warships and of course submarines, including a spell on the Dounreay Submarine Prototype. His entire working life was spent with the Yard apart from a short (three-year) service commission with the RAF. It was shortly after his return from the RAF (in 1958) that he was appointed as an Assistant Manager on the liner Oriana, *which was followed by his first technical management position. By 1975 he was Shipbuilding Manager and was ultimately appointed to the Board of Directors. In 1977 he became Deputy General Manager (Shipbuilding), one year later General Manager (Shipbuilding) and in 1982 Deputy Managing Director. Following a period in which he also served as Technical Director, he was given the additional and special responsibility for VSEL's quality assurance. Always a popular man with all levels of the Yard workforce (from shop floor through to senior management), the authors felt that Jim epitomised everything that this book is about and were delighted when he agreed to write the above foreword.*

Introduction

Barrow-in-Furness and its Shipyard

The town of Barrow-in-Furness and its Shipyard are situated at the end of the Furness Peninsula on the south-west coast of Cumbria with Morecambe Bay, the Irish Sea and the Duddon Estuary forming saltwater boundaries. Shipbuilding, in one form or another, has been practiced at various sites along the peninsula for several hundred years, but it is the Shipyard founded in 1871 by the Barrow Shipbuilding Co. Ltd (BSCL) and the eventual submarine construction activities that concern this book. Submarine construction first commenced in 1886 with the building of two submarine boats for the Swedish armaments entrepreneur Nordenfelt; they were completed in the next year. From the evidence available it appears the BSCL were not asked to participate in design aspects or in the resolution of stability problems which beset those boats – an unfortunate exclusion. In 1888, the BSCL amalgamated with the Nordenfelt Gun & Ammunition Co. to form the Naval Construction & Armaments Co. The company prospered to the extent that by the mid- and late 1890s a number of 1st and 2nd Class cruisers and various types of destroyers had been constructed.

Consequently, in 1897, the Barrow Shipyard was ripe for a takeover that came via a very progressive steel company – Vickers, Sons & Co. (of Sheffield) – who also possessed significant holdings in the then up-and-coming Maxim Gun & Ammunitions Co. Vickers took over the Shipyard and with Maxim formed the Vickers, Sons & Maxim Ltd company which was to be very successful. Around that time the transition from wooden to steel shipbuilding was taking place and the Royal dockyards, skilled only in wooden shipbuilding, needed alliances with steel companies able to meet the necessary requirements in respect of armour and armour plating – or lose their 'as of right' status to supply the Royal Navy and foreign customers.

Vickers and the Barrow Shipyard were already ahead of the game. They now possessed the necessary shipbuilding and engineering experience, as well as the naval gun mounting and armament experience and up-to-date steel-making prowess. It was with the completion in 1902 of HMS *Vengeance* (Yard No.265), a Canopus Class battleship, that Vickers, Sons & Maxim laid down a unique marker which was quickly taken up by the newspapers. *The Times* commented that it was 'the only ship in the British Navy which had been built, engined, armoured, and supplied with her heavy gun-mounting by one firm.' The interests of first Nordenfelt then Maxim were bought out and by 1911 the Shipyard's owner emerged as Vickers Ltd and, notwithstanding adjustments in the name to indicate political and structural changes, it would be as 'Vickers' that the Barrow Shipyard would be known for the next eighty-seven years until 1998. That name was synonymous with quality (in design and in construction), be it applicable to cargo ship, liner, warship, tanker or submarine.

Between the First and Second World Wars upkeep of equipment and plant was at least as good as, if not better than, most British shipyards. Following the Second World War the Shipyard was completely modernised as the primary customer changed from the Royal Navy to the companies operating passenger liners and cargo vessels and then the tanker operators.

That is not to imply that warship construction ceased – overseas navies such as those of Chile, Venezuela, Iran and Argentina made their way to Barrow to buy destroyers. Additionally, Israel and Brazil came for submarines. The decision to specialise in submarines, particularly nuclear submarines, was vindicated in 1971 when the government of the day determined the Barrow Shipyard to be the sole supplier of nuclear submarines for the Royal Navy. Running parallel with the decision on nuclear submarines was a policy of limited sophisticated warship production – thus the Shipyard progressed into the 1980s. In that decade, with the one exception of the diesel-electric Upholder (which appeared to hold so much promise until financial considerations decided otherwise), nuclear submarine construction became paramount, and so it remained until the mid-1990s – perhaps the nervous nineties.

Changes in ownership ended the long Vickers association; GEC and then their subsidiary Marconi had a brief relationship with the Shipyard before deciding that 'metal bashing' was not a sufficiently sophisticated business. Those companies, however, instituted a welcome return to surface vessel construction, both naval and commercial. Under the guidance of BAE, whose ownership commenced in 1999, the Barrow Shipyard will hopefully have a clearly identifiable future. The enormous modernization programme instituted in the 1980s with the building of the Devonshire Dock Hall and the ship syncro-lift is being further enhanced by BAE's own modernization programme and their stated aim of making the Shipyard a Submarine Centre of Excellence.

Development and Progress

Construction of the two Nordenfelts built at Barrow-in-Furness in the late 1800s appeared to do little to excite the public's interest, the newfangled submarine boats being but novelties at best – novelties invented by a foreigner and a lunatic Mancunian man of the cloth, Thorsten Nordenfelt and George William Garrett, respectively. However, looking back they were very close to a limited form of success with the first Nordenfelt built at Barrow and closer again with the second Barrow boat. Many experts believe that given more time the curate and the Swede would have succeeded. Even more experts believe that had the Barrow Yard's engineers been involved, submarine design and construction would have been advanced by ten years. Be that as it may, those naval engineers critical of the Nordenfelt fleet were swiftly proved correct, but building submarines became the pursuit of a number of nations, including France.

In 1899 concern was registered in Britain about France's submersible fleet, although many believed the French boats more dangerous than French sailors. Amongst many disparaging remarks were those of a correspondent for the *Glasgow Herald* who could see no future for such vessels and damned the French boats by comparison with the Nordenfelts thus: 'If my memory serves me rightly [of the] two of the most promising ships built at Barrow ... the larger one sold to Russia [was] not a success. When underwater she developed nasty tricks. A member of the crew walking forward or aft was sufficient to bring her to the surface.' Well, the French could do whatever they wished, Britain would have nothing to do with submarine boats and the good and the great in public office and other areas of influence were widely quoted as saying so, or so it appeared. A closer glance at the quote can isolate the crux phrase: 'if, however, the vessel can be rendered practical'. The craft became practical in 1901, just two years after the quote, when the newspapers would announce details of specifications, numbers to be built and where. Just how early the government/Admiralty made the decision to build submarine boats would only become public knowledge many years later, but the Admiralty were already holding discussions with the Holland Torpedo Boat Co. in 1899 in respect of submarines for the Royal Navy.

The Admiralty's discussions with Vickers Sons & Maxim Ltd concerning submarine construction were formalised on 13 December 1900 with the written offer of the contract for the first five boats. So it would appear the publicly aired statements of Admiralty and government officials were either an elaborate smoke-screen or the Black Mafia were already at work. The entire matter is made all the more intriguing by virtue of the following press quote. Under the by-line 'Submarine Boat for the British Navy', the *North West Daily Mail* printed that:

The Press Association's Woolwich correspondent states that stores are being drawn from Woolwich and other stations in connection with the trial by the naval authorities of a newly designed submarine boat. So far as the experiments have proceeded the trial has been satisfactory. The boat submerges and travels well, and is so constructed as to admit of its passing under an enemy's heaviest warship. In this way a submarine mine charged with five hundred pounds of gun cotton, equivalent to 2,000 pounds of gunpowder, can be attached to the warship, and time can be allowed for the submarine boat to get out of danger before the explosion acts. The boat is fitted with two tubes for discharging torpedoes both above and below water, and is armed with quick-firing and machine guns. The vessel thus equipped will, when finally approved by the Admiralty, be a formidable engine of war.

It appears to be remarkable that such a quote is dated 29 August 1900 because *Holland 1* was not launched until 2 October 1901. There would appear to be another line of research to be pursued in whatever it was the Woolwich newspaper man reported or believed he had reported. Possibly the Admiralty were blowing hot and cold with regard to confidentiality and were drip-feeding information (or even misinformation). Certainly, prior to the launch of *Holland 1*, newspapers and periodicals featured both factual and fictional articles then, following *Holland 1*'s launch, information dried up. Reporters were not given access to the Yard and would report that the men chosen to work on the Hollands 'were such as are not given to provide details of their work.' In fact to gain any knowledge on the new boats reporters were now reduced to gleaning observations from the Michaelson Road bridge man who overlooked the Buccleuch Dock, and who provided the press with descriptions of the boats' comings and goings.

It would be 1902 before any information emanating from an official source would be available concerning the Holland boats and it would be via America and the Committee on Naval Affairs of the United States House of Representatives. That committee was tasked with making a 'thorough and exhaustive enquiry into the question of submarine boats' via numerous witnesses. Amongst those questioned was Capt. F.T. Cable, who was electrical engineer with the Holland Torpedo Boat Co. and responsible for the construction of Holland boats. Cable advised that he had made some 500 submerged trips in US Hollands and several in the first Vickers Holland, including 'about' thirty dives in the Irish Sea which 'was very rough but the boat was very successful and the Admiralty accepted it.' Capt. Cable went on to describe the responsibilities and enthusiasm of the Royal Navy officers and men and then reported on the British government requirements.

Their special requirements are less than ours. They do not require the speed that the United States government does, and they are not as accurate about the firing of the torpedo. All the British government wanted was to see the boat under water, to see that she could dive and manoeuvre, and that she was capable of being properly handled under water…They do not care anything about whether we fire torpedoes or not. In fact on the first boat that was accepted we did not fire any torpedoes at all. They have had enough torpedo practice to know all about the torpedo. It is only the boat they want to see. They know that if the boat has a tube in her she will fire the torpedo.

Thus the 'experiment' with the Hollands passed by and with the coming of the A Class the ritual damning of the Royal Navy's boats could commence. That highly respected journal *The Engineer* opened the proceedings in January 1903, publishing a scathing article under the heading 'A Submarine Fiasco' in which they advised 'British submarines are next door to failures' and then went on to suppose 'that if the crew could satisfactorily close the boat's hatch and did not pass out from petrol fumes they could submerge and via use of the periscope, which could not accurately convey distance, run themselves into trouble.' Given the history of the Hollands it was a reasonable assessment. However, *The Engineer* was objective. They concluded that 'the experiments must proceed, and in course of time we do not doubt if there is anything of utility in the submarine it will be discovered.'

By the time the C Class arrived, the *Daily Express* would, in July 1907, report that whereas previously 'if a disaster befell a vessel their chances of escape were slight in the extreme, now it was no longer the case.' Cdr S.S. Hall, Inspecting Commander of Submarines, and Staff Surgeon Oswald Rees of HMS *Mercury* had perfected an apparatus which rendered catastrophes such as that which overtook the men of A1 an impossibility, and which would enable the crew of a submarine to escape from a vessel even though it 'be filled with water or poisonous gases.' The new invention was, like a diving helmet, made of light metal, with a canvas jacket, weighed 10lb and could be fitted in seconds. The air breathed by the wearer could be used 'over and over again'. The poisonous carbonic acid gas of the respired air was absorbed by a special substance, 'oxylithe', which also restored to the air the requisite amount of oxygen and rendered it fit again for breathing.

Thus the pace of submarine development in all aspects quickened, so that by September 1912 the departure to Chatham of Yard Craft No.96 (Yard No.413) would mean the Admiralty were in possession of the latest and most up-to-date salvage ship. Consequently, in the event of any mishap, even the D and E Classes then under construction could be lifted.

By Autumn 1913 the V Class were under development and the pace, with war looming, was such that the Hollands were going to the auctioneers – they were obsolete. Interestingly enough, and as the newspapers stated, 'Built in order to sink ships, they are now going to be used to save them.' According to the buyers the boats would be used as 'camels' – large cylinders sunk beneath a wreck then filled with air to raise it.

Holland 1 was sold to Ward for £470, *Holland 2* to Pollock & Brown for £360 and *Holland 3* to Ryadyk (Holland) for £345. They had originally cost £35,000 each, a price revealed by Isaac L. Rice in his statement to the House of Representatives much earlier. The boats were sold with their engines in them but it was a condition that the torpedo tubes should be broken up under Admiralty inspection prior to the boats' removal. *Holland 1* was saved from the salvage operator by virtue of sinking and then being salvaged herself for the benefit of the public in 1982.

With each new class, boats became more complex and sophisticated and, when in 1931 the Admiralty announced the Thames Class, they were heralded in newspapers as the 'super submarines'. 1931 was also the year in which Cdr Charles Craven, one of several great Vickers leaders, became managing director of Vickers-Armstrongs.

The Portuguese submarines built at the Yard in the mid-thirties were the first at Barrow in which welded sections were included in the hull, marking a major step forward. These boats were smaller than contemporary Royal Navy boats but of a similar design and appearance, although the deck gun was in a fully-enclosed shield.

The Estonian boats which followed the Portuguese, although similar to the Royal Navy's S Class, were considered somewhat unusual in that they used what was virtually a First World War system for minelaying in employing vertical minelaying wells or chutes. These boats also had the 'disappearing' anti-aircraft gun mounting systems similar to some Scandinavian boats. The boats were apparently well designed and well built. *Lembit*, for example, has quite clearly lasted the course.

Construction of the Royal Navy's boats in various classes continued steadily and then, with the awareness that war was a possibility, production ramped-up with the construction of T, S, U and V Classes and four boats 'loaned' from the Turkish Navy plus the X, XT and XE Craft.

Although the primary aim of this book is to be a history of Barrow submarine construction, a brief statement will not go amiss with regard to the immense output of the Yard during the Second World War, when a vast and diverse range of much-needed war material for all three services and the Mercantile Marine was produced. The full contribution to the 1939-1945 shipbuilding programme alone is quite astonishing. In that excellent book *A Century of Shipbuilding* the Barrovian author Tom Clark summarised a little under six years of new construction of 137 vessels in a brief statement of immense impact when he wrote: 'A cursory glance has made it four aircraft carriers, three cruisers, ten destroyers, ten cargo ships, eleven landing craft and ninety-nine submarines.' Running parallel with that new construction was an extensive programme of repairs, refits and modifications to existing vessels, often badly battle damaged, both naval and mercantile. The Yard also found time to investigate the hull and machinery of His Majesty's U-Boat *Graph* and set to work on the vessel.

As the chapters in this book unroll to cover the period 1946 to 1958, it perhaps appears that the navy is searching for the boat that contains all the characteristics of the Cold War warriors' weapon. The boat that could run fast and deep, be quiet and dependable, self-sustaining and tough and – if push turned to shove – have enough muscle to make the opposition blink first. By 1959 it was clear that one of Barrow's local newspapers knew what that weapon was. With a headline both provocative and frightening, the *Barrow News* said about *Dreadnought* that: 'Barrow's 'A' Sub Could Destroy a Nation', and went on to put the nation's mind at rest by stating 'Britain's chances of surviving atomic war might rest upon local shipyard skill'.

The man who would be responsible for determining how those skills would be best employed was another of the Yard's, and British industry's, great leaders – Leonard Redshaw. It was clear that *Dreadnought* was the test piece, the real thing would come with the next class, the Valiants.

Although the 'nukes' were now established, the numbers didn't exist and for years to come conventional boats and 'nukes' would complement each other until a decision based upon financial concerns rather than tactical matters would see the demise of the diesel-electric boats.

Running in tandem with the advances that would lead to the nuclear reactor are advances in electronics, weapons and all those aspects that make the submarine such a formidable adversary. Those advances appear to be limitless. As the navy's Unmanned Underwater Vehicles programme develops we will doubtless be made aware of some of them.

About this Book

All naval submarines launched or, for their first commitment to water, lowered by crane or synchronised shiplift at the Barrow-in-Furness Shipyard are listed within this book. Also included are brief references to some of the submarines it was hoped would be built, commercial 'mini-subs', First and Second World War German submarines subject to the public's view or conversion/experiment and the re-activation of the Canadian Upholder Class.

Refit, modification, repair and routine maintenance work, although extensive, is not covered in this book (though they are more than worthy of inclusion). In fact those subjects (considered in the light of the immense support given by the Yard in assisting the Royal Navy's 'nukes' to maintain their sea-going capability during the Cold War) encapsulate an incredible story that perhaps one day can be told. Service history is generally kept brief as there are a number of works which are dedicated to this.

Class main characteristics generally provide the latest data available but because of in-service modifications will not, regardless of the decade, be likely to exactly reflect the as-built and accepted-by-the-customer version. BAE, the Yard's present owner, gave permission for the use of drawings, sketches, photographs and written material within their ownership and this includes the use of material produced by previous owners, in particular the Yard's most famous owner – Vickers. Where appropriate that written material has been amended and corrected.

Basic Facts and Figures

The intent of this book is to provide some basic facts and figures for every submarine launched, dunked or lowered by shiplift at Barrow. Each class has a set of main characteristics which provide details of dimensions, machinery, armament etc. The need for brevity and clarity precludes mention of each individual variation within a class.

This is not a technical book but nevertheless to prevent each chapter appearing as a catalogue of data, aspects of Shipyard history are offered and, as the company which was a long-time owner was also a long-time player on the global front, facts and figures concerning Vickers are included. Varying amounts of detail on service history are offered. Lack of such detail does not mean a boat does not have an interesting or useful life – we are again back to brevity and clarity.

Each class is illustrated by a photograph or drawing. Not every photograph is of the best standard as occasionally the originals were of inferior quality. However, we consider the reader would prefer an inferior copy rather than no picture at all. We have rejected the use of plans to illustrate classes as they do not lend themselves to this format.

During the course of our research we uncovered significant information that appears to be new to devotees of this type of book; consequently speeches, spy trials and the occasional unplanned event are mentioned. Individuals hold opinions on what is important, and what should be included; because this is a history there are few aspects that have not been touched on, albeit a very brief touch at times. We have assumed the reader will have some knowledge of submarines (which will generally be referred to as boats) and possibly the Shipyard at Barrow-in-Furness (which will generally be referred to as the Yard).

The main characteristics are taken from a number of sources. There is no general source that is totally reliable, be it the Yard records, Admiralty, Ministry of Defence (MoD), Royal Navy, or any one of the major reference books or the internet. The latter is arguably the most misleading of all.

The question of information and drawing availability is troublesome. In Cumbria both Barrow and Carlisle maintain information, the National Maritime Museum is another source and we are reliably informed that all manner of photographs are scattered throughout archives and museums the length and breadth of England.

A similar situation exists with regard to boat and ship models. Although Barrow's Dock Museum hosts many fine examples there are still many models – which should rightfully be housed at Barrow – reposing in collections around the country. Interestingly Cdr Charles W. Craven, a famous Vickers stalwart, would comment on such a situation when he opened Barrow's museum in October 1930 and noted that many fine Barrow models had found their way to museums in the south of England and should now find their way back.

All statements within this book are the responsibility of the authors and as a consequence the same responsibility will be accepted for any errors. BAE and the MoD have examined photographs, drawings and sketches contained within the work and accept that they do not transgress the company's or national security requirements.

1

The Early Submarines
(1886-1912)

Nordenfelt Submarines

2 built on behalf of Mr T. Nordenfelt

[The] hull [was] designed to withstand the pressure of water … The boiler [was] so constructed that although the fire door, ash pit, door and funnel could be hermetically closed yet it continued for a limited time to supply the engine with the steam necessary to keep it in motion … The descending apparatus consisted of an upright tube or tubes passing through the vessel and containing a screw or screws which could be driven by shafting passing through the interior of the vessel. The boat or vessel had a small amount of buoyancy and consequently rose to the surface whenever the rotation of the screws and the application of power was suspended.

Shipyard Records

Nordenfelt I	(Yard No.143)	Launched 14 April 1886
Nordenfelt II	(Yard No.149)	Launched 26 March 1887

In the 1880s Thorsten Nordenfelt, a Swedish industrialist, commissioned the building of four submarines, two of which were constructed at the Barrow Shipyard. The first of the four Nordenfelt submarines was constructed in Sweden, the second at Barrow, the third at Chertsey on the River Thames and the fourth at Barrow. The construction of the Nordenfelt I (Yard No.143) signalled the start of an era of submarine construction on the Furness peninsula which continues to the present day.

In 1886 Thorsten Nordenfelt, Swedish owner of the Nordenfelt Gun & Ammunition Co. Ltd, and co-owner with George William Garrett of the Nordenfelt Submarine Torpedo Boat Co., placed an order with the Barrow Shipbuilding Co. Ltd (BSCL) for the construction of a submarine boat, the first such to be built at the Barrow Yard. Identified on the build sheets as Yard No.143, this was the second of Nordenfelt's boats and was intended for the Turkish Navy. Nordenfelt was the financier for the boats and was also involved in the design, Garrett was the principal designer, captain for trials and demonstrations and chief instructor to intended crews; Basil Zaharoff was the salesman.

The boat was launched on 14 April 1886 and, after trials at Barrow, went to Liverpool where it was dismantled and loaded onto a steamer for freighting to Turkey. The dismantled sections (seven in total) were reassembled, not without considerable difficulty and delay, at the Tashkizak Yard in Constantinople. The Barrow Yard records indicate the boat was registered

Right: A model of *Nordenfelt I* (later the *Abdul Hamid*), the first Barrow-built submarine. *Below:* A model of *Nordenfelt II*, the second Barrow-built submarine. *(Both extracted from Barrow Museum Service CAT 2659)*

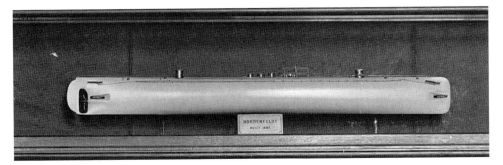

with the Board of Trade as a merchant vessel displacing 68 tons, which is somewhat at odds with the truth, but perhaps typical of the Nordenfelt/Garrett liaison. It is possible that the registering detail was done in the only way possible to insure both the trials and the transit of a new type of boat for a foreign navy. The re-assembled boat was relaunched on 6 September 1886 and later named *Abdul Hamid* after the then Sultan.

The second Nordenfelt boat built by the BSCL was identified as Yard No.149 and was launched on 26 March 1887 (Queen Victoria's Jubilee year). Immediately following the launch the boat adopted an extremely severe stern down attitude; ballasting calculations were re-addressed and the boat was eventually brought back into trim.

Following limited tests and trials at Barrow the boat sailed to Southampton (then a record journey for a submarine boat) for more rigorous trials and a series of extensive demonstrations. The demonstrations would eventually be undertaken for representatives of various foreign navies as neither the British or colonial navies were impressed by the boat's performance. In fact, not withstanding a number of dramatic and sometimes high-speed surface manoeuvres, in particular those at the Queen Victoria Golden Jubilee Naval Review, professional observers deemed the boat far too buoyant and virtually uncontrollable while submerged. These observations were correct. This boat, in common with the other Nordenfelts, had an inherent damning fault – lack of longitudinal stability when submerged – to which a number of design aspects contributed.

The Nordenfelts were propelled by steam engines powered by coal-fed boilers. For submerged operations the engines were powered by latent energy. Prior to diving, the boilers, having raised steam to set pressures, were then sealed, as were funnels, venting or air apertures.

Dependent upon the particular design, steam was then circulated through either a system of heat exchangers, reservoirs, cisterns, etc., or a boiler-to-boiler heating system, to continue to power the engines and auxiliary machinery. The latent energy was expended fairly quickly. Theoretically a speed of 5 knots for two hours was available but this was never achieved.

Shipyard workers in 1896 using electric drills (during the construction of HMS *Niobe* (Yard No.248) – a Diadem Class cruiser of 11,080 tons). Drills of this type would be used on the soon-to-be-built Holland boats.

The steam and water ballast systems dictated that a variety of water-containing vessels and tanks were in use. The slightest deviation from an even keel caused the water in the containers, particularly in the large ballast tanks, to surge to and fro. The already difficult task of keeping a submerged Nordenfelt in trim was thus compounded to a degree which placed the boat in constant extremes, ever ready to plunge to the bottom or break surface. The use of hydroplanes, ballast transfer systems and, dependent on design, the horizontally or vertically mounted screw propellers used to assist the boats to submerge were never able to compensate for the water surge. As a consequence, the second Barrow Nordenfelt failed to spark sufficient interest for a buyer to be found, but the Russian Navy was sufficiently interested to request further demonstrations provided they took place in Russian waters.

In October 1888 the Nordenfelt, escorted by Garrett's yawl *Lodestar*, left for Russia but never arrived. Due to navigation errors, both the Nordenfelt and *Lodestar* ran aground on the Horns Reef off the Jutland coast of Germany. *Lodestar* was wrecked and the Nordenfelt was eventually declared to be beyond economic repair and was bought by the company that insured the boat.

Neither the *Abdul Hamid* or the Chertsey boat were able to meet the performance requirements of the Turkish Navy, and the Nordenfelt built for the Greek Navy was equally unsuccessful. None of the three Nordenfelt boats were good or safe enough to use operationally; all would end their lives as rusting hulks.

Although the first two Barrow-built submarines were failures, blame could not be laid on the builders who constructed the boats to contract. The failure of the Nordenfelts to perform ultimately lay in their design and they were further damned by unproven claims in the specifications offered to potential buyers, claims backed up by gross exaggeration and blatant lying by Nordenfelt, Zaharoff and Garrett.

Nordenfelt, a trained engineer from a wealthy background, was successful via lucrative contracts held with British and European forces for the Nordenfelt Gun & Ammunition Co. Ltd. Nordenfelt appeared more interested in the marketing spin-off from torpedoes and mechanical components than submarines themselves. Indeed, he ensured all patents raised for the boats and their components were always in his name and not Garrett's. Nordenfelt's exaggerations were to further already successful business interests.

As for Zaharoff, all the evidence about him indicated that his lying and scheming made up the very essence of the man; he was motivated totally by wealth and power and he didn't care where or how he came by it. As the saying goes 'he could have lied for England' and probably did so. How good was Zaharoff the salesman? He was the best. His various employers, Vickers being pre-eminent, apparently involved British and French governments, the First World War allies, some thirty or so countries and several hundred assorted companies. These employers would, over a period of fifty years, award him knighthoods and titles, countless decorations and highly lucrative commissions. Zaharoff also would boast of intelligence contacts throughout the world, of setting country against country; he would be vilified by the press who named him the 'Merchant of Death' and, amongst other matters, would accuse him of starting, prolonging and ending the First World War. Zaharoff was simply amazing.

We can now turn to Zaharoff's colleague, George William Garrett. In 1875 Garrett left Trinity College, Dublin, with a BA in Experimental Sciences and a championship medal specially struck and awarded to him as a lightweight bare-knuckle boxer, having won the heavyweight championship of the college. He beat opponents weighing 70lb more than his 140lb. After several years spent teaching, he passed theological examinations to become curate at the Anglican Christ Church in the then rural village of Moss Side, near Manchester. He was ordained in 1877, but was struck from the clerical register in 1882 for reasons unknown.

Garrett's first submarine was the pedal-powered *Egg* and this was followed by the steam-powered *Resurgam* (literally meaning 'I shall rise again'), the development of which would earn him the title Father of the British Submarine. *Resurgam* was lost off the coast of north Wales in 1880. The following year Garrett commenced his partnership with Nordenfelt and by 1885 the two had produced their first submarine for Zaharoff to sell. Garrett the part-time curate was now Garrett the full-time submarine designer, commissioning engineer and crew instructor.

These developments were beyond Garrett's wildest dreams and could be bettered by only one thing, the construction of a submarine which would respond exactly as Garrett required, and this is where his dream began to fade. Garrett had always exaggerated the prowess of his boats, but it seemed his desire to build the perfect submarine blinded him to anything else. How otherwise could his conscience have permitted him to desert his Anglican pastoral duties, and to indulge in gun-running and selling warships to potential enemies of the Crown? For this is what the sale of the Swedish Nordenfelt to Greece involved. Perhaps it was Garrett's fanaticism that carried him so far but it would be used ruthlessly and cynically by Nordenfelt and Zaharoff in pursuit of their own ends. By the time Turkey had ordered two Nordenfelts and taken delivery of the first Barrow boat, Garrett was caught in an overlapping web of problems involving travel between Britain and Turkey, as he sought to apply his talents to solving the difficulties arising with design, demonstration and training.

The travelling would in itself be arduous but it was combined with a requirement for Garrett to be at sea with the Nordenfelts in their ferocious, debilitating environment of temperatures up to 60°C and a carbon monoxide-enriched atmosphere. Had Nordenfelt and Garrett been given the opportunity to step back and take time to solve their differing problems, it is probable that the boats could have achieved a reasonable degree of success. Time, however, was a luxury that was not available; even worse, Nordenfelt was having cash flow problems and, unknown to him, Zaharoff was doing deals with other companies. Consequently the grounding and wrecking of the Nordenfelt for Russia signalled the beginning of the end. There would be no more orders for Nordenfelts. Boardroom manoeu-vres would ease Nordenfelt out of armaments and shipbuilding and reduce his personal circumstances to those of an employee of his nephew, producing agricultural machinery in France. He would, however, remain a comparatively wealthy man.

It was Zaharoff who prospered, and it was Zaharoff who led the boardroom manoeuvres against Nordenfelt which would eventually bring the Vickers brothers from their River Don foundries to the Barrow Yard.

George William Garrett emigrated to America with his family and died of tuberculosis and exhaustion in New York in 1892. Penniless, he was buried in a pauper's grave without a headstone. The recovery of *Resurgam* would provide a fitting permanent memorial to a man who deserved so much more.

By 1909, the Barrow and Chertsey Nordenfelts would be documented as 'rusting hulks in a weather-beaten shed on the Golden Horn awaiting disposal instructions from the Turkish government'. They were still there in 1914 when an inspection by the German Legation declared them beyond re-activation. In 1921 the occupying Allies apparently deemed them a threat and the rusting hulks were scrapped.

Submarine construction therefore commenced in Barrow in 1886 and abruptly finished in 1887. It would be fourteen years and the twentieth century before it would recommence.

In 1990 George William Garrett's great grandson, Bill Garrett, visited Barrow to gain further insight to his great grandfather's work. In 1995 *Resurgam* was located by amateur divers off Rhyl and Mr Garrett has since had the opportunity to dive on her. During the preparation of this book, it was reported that Mr Garrett had offered funding to assist *Resurgam*'s salvage.

★ ★ ★

The following article appeared in the *Barrow Herald* just a few days following the launch of the second of the two Nordenfelt submarines.

Launch at the Shipyard

The Barrow Shipbuilding Company launched from their yard, on Saturday last, a new submarine vessel built to the order of Mr Nordenfelt, which is the largest and most complete vessel of the kind yet constructed, and is the second built by the Barrow Shipbuilding Company for the same owner. The vessel was named the Nordenfelt, and is 110 feet over all and 12 feet diameter. The midship section is a true circle tapering to a straight stem at each end, the top and bottom being exactly alike. At the after end is the main propeller for driving her through the water, also the rudder. At the fore end is the place for firing the torpedoes; this will be bored out to suit the particular kind of torpedo that may be adopted. On deck are three separate structures, the forward one being the conning tower, the others forming the entrances to the engine-room and the stoke-hole respectively. The steering wheel, together with the hand rails and side lights are all made portable. She is fitted with two funnels, which can be removed, and water-tight doors put on when under water. All the openings on deck have doors which can be readily made watertight. The engines and boilers were made by Plenty & Son, Newbury, and have been made specially to suit the very limited space. There are two high pressure cylinders 16 inches diameter, and two low pressure 26 inches diameter, all 16-stroke working on four separate cranks, arranged so that each set of engines can be worked indepen-

dent of the other. Working pressure, 150lbs per square inch, the type being the inverted compound direct-acting surface condensing. The cylinders are supported by steel columns well braced with diagonal rods; the condenser is underneath the crank shaft and forms the bedplate. The air circulating feed and bilge pumps are all worked by a separate engine. The Nordenfelt is fitted with Joy's patent valve gear. Steam is supplied by two cylindrical boilers with two furnaces in each. When the vessel is under water the furnace mouths are made perfectly tight by means of a plate bolted on. Smokebox doors are also joined so that no hot air can escape. At each end of the ship there is an opening, in which a small propeller, working horizontally, is driven by double cylinder engines, these being used solely for descending or ascending. There is a steam steering engine which can be worked from above or below. In descending, all the deck openings are made good, the ballast tanks are flooded with water until the vessel has nearly lost all her buoyancy, then the horizontal propellers are put in motion, which causes the vessel to sink to any required depth, and by simply regulating the speed of the propellers can be kept at any particular depth. (Of course if a certain depth is exceeded, the vessel would collapse from external pressure.) She can remain under water about 12 hours, if necessary. The engines develop 1,200 indicated horse-power, when running at 300 revolutions. For getting up steam rapidly there are two fan engines. The steam in the boiler is raised to 150lbs, and then everything is closed up for going under water, the various engines working with steam down to about 10lbs per square inch. The speed when above the surface is expected to be about 19 knots. The Nordenfelt proceeds to Southampton for experimental trials.

Nordenfelt I Submarine – Main Characteristics

Overall Length/ Beam/Draught	100ft x 12ft x 12ft
Displacement	160 tons surfaced (registered with the Board of Trade as 68 gross tons) / submerged displacement unknown
Power	1 x 250hp Plenty & Sons Ltd twin-cylinder compound engine driving a single screw (for both surface and submerged propulsion)
Diving Depth	100ft
Speed	Unknown
Propeller	1
Endurance	150 miles at 10 knots surfaced / 12 miles at 5 knots submerged
Armament	2 x 14in torpedo tubes
	2 x quick-firing Nordenfelt guns
Complement	5
Miscellaneous	2 x 6hp engines driving the downhall screws, depth maintenance equipment, 1 x Lamm accumulator, air and water circulating pumps
	Steam raised via one double-furnaced boiler
	3 x ballast tanks – 1 aft, 1 forward and 1 amidships which compensated for consumed fuel (coal)

Nordenfelt II Submarine – Main Characteristics

Overall Length/ Beam/Draught	125ft x 12ft x 12ft
Displacement	160 tons surfaced / 240 tons submerged
Power	2 x Plenty & Sons Ltd twin–cylinder compound engines jointly rated at 1,000hp driving a single screw (for both surface and submerged propulsion)
Diving Depth	100ft
Speed	17 knots surfaced / 5 knots submerged
Propeller	1
Endurance	1,000 miles at 8 knots surfaced (which could be doubled by using the ballast tanks as coal bunkers) / submerged endurance unknown
Armament	2 x torpedo tubes 2 x 2-pounder Nordenfelt guns (to be fitted after commissioning)
Complement	Unknown
Miscellaneous	Other auxiliary engines powering closed feed system, steering, forced draught fans, ballast bilge pumps, 2 x downhall screws and compressors 9 x ballast tanks

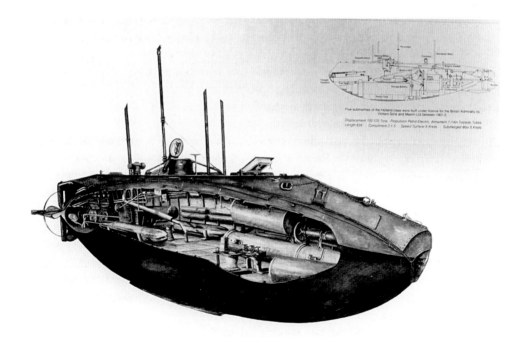

A cutaway view of a typical Holland Class submarine. This picture shows the appallingly cramped conditions that early submariners had to endure.

Holland Class Submarines

5 built on behalf of the Royal Navy

The Admiralty are not prepared to take any steps in regard to submarines because the vessel is only the weapon of the weaker nation. If, however, the vessel can be rendered practical the nations which possess it will cease to be weak and will become really powerful. More than any other nation, we should have to fear the attacks of submarines.

Mr Hugh Oakley Arnold-Forster (Parliamentary Secretary at the Admiralty), addressing the House of Commons in 1900

HMS *Holland 1*	(Yard No.280)	Launched 2 October 1901
HMS *Holland 2*	(Yard No.281)	Launched 21 January 1902
HMS *Holland 3*	(Yard No.283)	Launched 9 May 1902
HMS *Holland 4*	(Yard No.284)	Launched 23 May 1902
HMS *Holland 5*	(Yard No.282)	Launched 10 June 1902

Although popularly accepted as the Holland Class, the first submarine boats ordered by the Royal Navy are also variously referred to as HM Submarine Torpedo Boats or Holland VI Class. Although their names are generally listed as *Holland 1* through to *Holland 5*, it is not unusual to see them more simply called HM Submarine No.1 through to HM Submarine No.5. What is certain is that the Royal Navy's first order for submarines was for a total of five boats, all of which were built and launched at the Barrow-in-Furness Shipyard then owned by Vickers, Sons & Maxim Ltd. Indeed in 1902, while the Hollands were under construction, the Barrow Shipyard was exclusively contracted to build all Royal Navy submarines until 1906, an agreement which was later extended until 1912.

Up to 1900, the British Admiralty had stolidly refused to have anything to do with submarines, considering them to have a defensive role only for the weaker maritime nations, and to be a 'damned un-English weapon'. But the fact that the French were rapidly building up a submarine fleet undoubtedly helped persuade them to 'test the value of the submarine boat as a weapon in the hands of our enemies'. Accordingly, five submarines were ordered, to be built at Barrow by Vickers, Sons & Maxim, under license from the Electric Boat Co. who in 1899 purchased all the patents from John P. Holland, owner of the Holland Torpedo Boat Co. and designer of the Holland boats purchased by the USN. Holland, an Irish emigrant to America, had long had an interest in submarines seeing them as a means of demoralising, or even destroying, the English Fleet. It is ironic that these weapons were subsequently being built in England to defend the English Fleet.

By 1893, the development of the working submarine was well advanced. The United States Naval Board recognised that there was a place for the submarine in naval warfare and laid down a set of requirements for naval submarines. These requirements were met by a boat of Holland's design, and in 1895 he was awarded a contract to build a submarine for the

A view of the Barrow shipyard in 1903. The owners at this time were Vickers, Sons & Maxim Ltd. (Barrow Museum Service CAT 4607)

US government. Development proceeded rapidly from here, and the design destined to become the Royal Navy's *Holland No. 1* was, it is thought, America's *Holland No. 10* – known as the Alder Class. Overseeing construction for the Royal Navy was vested in Capt. Reginald Bacon with Lt Forster D. Arnold-Forster, his assistant and soon to be the Royal Navy's first submarine Commanding Officer. Working drawings supplied to Vickers had many discrepancies and in some particulars were obviously incorrect.

But building went on to these plans, and it was only after one boat almost turned on end during dock trials that Vickers were allowed to make modifications. The problems were due, in part, to the difficulties of communication with the Holland Boat Co. (the Electric Boat Co. bought all the Holland patents in 1899) and the fact that construction of the RN *Holland 1* was ahead of the prototype Alder Class – the drawings had not been proved. In the American design no periscope was fitted; the only way to see was to look through a scuttle in the conning tower. A periscope of British design was fitted to one of the Hollands; this was a hinged periscope, raised and lowered on a ball and socket joint on the hull. The target was only upright when ahead; when abeam it was on its side; when astern it was upside down.

During the Holland construction programme, Vickers determined to design their own submarines and this, far from severing ties with the Electric Boat Co., strengthened them. Vickers and Isaac Rice, already a director of Electric Boat and a millionaire in his own right, bought substantial holdings to help Electric Boat out of financial problems in 1904 and again in 1909. Vickers also bought licensing agreements on the Holland patents and maintained business arrangements with Electric Boat up to the 1930s. It is interesting to note that Vickers' association with the Electric Boat Co. was renewed in the 1960s with the construction of Britain's first nuclear-powered submarine HMS *Dreadnought*. The five Holland Class boats were completed by mid-1903 at a cost of £35,000 each. Although they were poor sea boats and could dive only to 100ft, they were sufficiently successful to convince the Admiralty to continue the development of the submarine.

The records of *Holland 1*, which was salvaged in 1982 (she foundered under tow to the breakers yard in 1913), indicate that she may never have dived below 58ft. If true, this was extremely fortuitous. Naval construction personnel calculated, following post-salvage inspections, that hull failure would have commenced at 60ft! *Holland 1* is now on public display at the Royal Navy Submarine Museum, Gosport. In January 2001 BAE generously topped up a lottery grant with a further sum of £150,000 to assist in the conservation of *Holland 1*. Hollands 1 to 3 were sold for scrap in 1913 (No.1 to T.W. Ward, No.2 to Pollack & Brown and No.3 to Ryadyk). *Holland 4* was deliberately sunk by gunfire experiments in October 1912 and *Holland 5* foundered under tow to the breakers in 1912.

HMS *Holland 5* in 1902. The almost 'tear-drop' hull and aft cruciform control surfaces were a fore-runner to the nuclear boats of the sixties.

HMS *Holland 1* pictured after being salvaged in 1982.

Holland Class Submarines – Main Characteristics

Overall Length/ Beam/Draught	63ft 9in x 11ft 9in x 10ft
Displacement	104 tons surfaced / 120 tons submerged (No.1)
	104 tons surfaced / 150 tons submerged (Nos 2 to 5)
Power	1 x 160bhp single-shaft petrol engine of 4 cylinders (vertical design and American make) for surface propulsion
	1 x 74bhp motor for submerged propulsion (No.1)
	1 x 250bhp single-shaft petrol engine of 4 cylinders (vertical design and American make) for surface propulsion
	1 x 74bhp motor for submerged propulsion (Nos 2 to 5)
Diving Depth	100ft
Speed	8 knots surfaced / 5 knots submerged
Propeller	1
Endurance	235 miles surfaced / 20 miles at 5 knots submerged
Armament	1 x 14in torpedo tube in bow (3 torpedoes carried)
Complement	7
Notes	• Most sources list only one set of characteristics for all five Holland Class submarines, giving those for *Holland 1*. One such source was the *Link* (VSEL in-house magazine) articles of 1983 covering the history of Barrow-built submarines which gave the overall dimensions as 63ft 10in x 11ft 10in x 11ft 10in; displacements, 113 tons/ 122 tons; speeds, 7.4 knots/6 knots; and complement (design), 8. Additionally, *Link* gave a torpedo tube size of 18in.
	• Some sources state that the Holland Class submarines were designed to be fitted with an 8in 'Dynamite' gun on the bow. The gun was apparently to have been 11ft 3in long with a range of one mile and capable of firing a 22lb projectile from a 100lb gun-cotton charge. There is no evidence that such a gun was ever fitted to these submarines.

First A Class Submarines

13 built on behalf of the Royal Navy

Around 1900 Vickers, Sons & Maxim Ltd concerned themselves with providing housing and amenities for a growing workforce. Accordingly they purchased some 341 acres on Walney Island at almost £100 an acre and had built by 1904 some 930 houses and the King Alfred Hotel (all with electric light). 19 acres were set aside for institutes, football, cricket pitches and public parks and sites were allocated for the building of churches of all denominations. The area was described as a marine garden city. Its name is Vickerstown.

Vickers – A History, by J.D. Scott

HMS A1	(Yard No.285)	Launched 9 July 1902
HMS A2	(Yard No.294)	Launched 16 April 1903
HMS A3	(Yard No.295)	Launched 9 May 1903
HMS A4	(Yard No.296)	Launched 9 June 1903
HMS A5	(Yard No.303)	Launched 3 March 1904
HMS A6	(Yard No.304)	Launched 3 March 1904
HMS A7	(Yard No.305)	Launched 23 January 1905
HMS A8	(Yard No.306)	Launched 23 January 1905
HMS A9	(Yard No.307)	Launched 8 February 1905
HMS A10	(Yard No.308)	Launched 8 February 1905
HMS A11	(Yard No.309)	Launched 8 March 1905
HMS A12	(Yard No.310)	Launched 8 March 1905
HMS A13	(Yard No.311)	Launched 18 April 1905

The A Class submarine boats were notable for being the first designed by the Admiralty and also for being the first Royal Navy submarines to be fitted with a conning tower. A total of thirteen boats were built (all at Barrow-in-Furness) although the original intention was for building fourteen A Class vessels. The fourteenth, designated as A14, was cancelled although already under construction, and was modified to become B1, the first of the B Class submarines, also built at the Barrow Yard.

As a result of the Hollands' failure to totally perform to expectations, a larger boat (A1) was ordered under the auspices of the A Class which, although based on the Holland Class, were of all-British design (Capt. Bacon, Inspecting Captain of Submarines, and Vickers, Sons & Maxim). She was 40ft longer than the Hollands and, at 207 tons, had about two-thirds more displacement. Power was also increased. Laid down in 1902, she was the first of a class of thirteen – all completed at Barrow between 1903 and 1905, except for A13 (an experimental craft, fitted with diesel engines instead of petrol engines) which was completed in 1908. The hoped-for improvements in surface performance were achieved as the class developed and further changes in power were made, but in underwater performance there was little gained over the Hollands.

During the building of A1, it was decided that greater torpedo capability was required and from A2 onwards two bow tubes were fitted, side-by-side. So many modifications were made to the boats during the building programme that the A Class could be considered as four classes: A1; A2 to A4; A5 to A12; and A13, the diesel version. But the A Class still had limitations in speed and endurance, accommodation was cramped and they were not good sea boats. The unluckiest vessel of the era was surely the submarine A1. Some of the things that happened in her have served as a warning to all submariners from that day to this. Before delivery, A1 suffered the first explosion in a submarine – this was due to a pocket of hydrogen gas. When on passage off Land's End the crew had to abandon ship when seawater entered the batteries, filling the submarine with choking chlorine gas. When she was eventually delivered to Portsmouth, A1 was berthed in a remote part of the harbour, 'so that this "dangerous craft" could do as little damage as possible if she blew up'. Interestingly, A1 was berthed next to HMS *Latona*, an Apollo Class cruiser built in Barrow in 1889 (Yard No.175) and after which Latona Street on Walney Island is named.

In the summer of 1904, during manoeuvres against the Fleet, A1 was dispatched to attack a battleship. When she neared Spithead, the ocean liner SS *Berwick Castle* made an approach. No one on watch noticed the tiny periscope jutting from the waves, nor did any of her crew feel more than a slight tremble as the massive ship ran over a small unknown object. When A1 failed to report that night, it was realised that a disaster had occurred. Eleven men lost their lives in this tragedy, which caused great concern throughout the country. Capt. Bacon's report on the A1 tragedy would contain a number of recommendations for improvements to existing and future submarines, along with views on submarine rescue and salvage. An immediate undertaking was the fitting of a second watertight hatch at the foot of the conning tower, it being Capt. Bacon's opinion that 'Although the conning tower had suffered damage the leak was so small it could easily have been stopped from inside if the crew had not been stunned.'

Another problem would arise from vapour build-up from the use of the petrol engines, add to this the class being predisposed to dive without warning and it seems almost miraculous that the submarine service was manned by volunteers.

A3 sank as a result of a collision with the aptly named HMS *Hazard* – four officers and ten ratings perishing. A3 was salvaged and, following the burial of her crew, taken to sea and sunk by gunfire by the Dreadnought HMS *St Vincent*. A4 was involved in two terrifying incidents. In the first, a steamer capsized her when the wash from the steamer flooded A4 via an open ventilation tube; the quick thinking of her CO Lt M. Nasmith saved the day. Then in the same year of 1905, A4's weights shifted during a submerged exercise making her unmanageable. The crew were able to bring A4 to the surface and escape. While being towed to a dock for examination A4 sank, was refloated later, refurbished and then continued in service until 1920.

In 1905, the hitherto unknown dangers of petrol vapour caused an explosion in A5 which killed her commander and several others. This led to the move to adopt diesel engines, which used heavy oil with a much higher flash point, and A13 was fitted with an experimental diesel engine for trials at sea. During these trials the B and C Class vessels continued to be fitted with the same sixteen-cylinder Wolseley petrol engine as in A5 to A12, but now made by Vickers

HMS A5, with members of the crew posing for the camera.

and called the Vickers engine. In C19 to C38 the number of cylinders was reduced to twelve. Another less well publicised aspect of vapour build-up was its effect as an intoxicant on the crew, sometimes accidentally and apparently sometimes deliberate. Members of some crews claimed fumes were deliberately inhaled as a means of combating tedium and poor conditions.

Although such behaviour would clearly impair judgement, it was not clear if any of the many incidents affecting the petrol-engined boats were attributable to such behaviour. A7 sank with her crew for reasons unknown on 16 January 1914 and was never recovered; the burial service was held at sea on 12 March 1914. A8 sank after being shaken by an internal explosion. Two officers, a PO and a rating, all of whom formed the bridge watch, were the only survivors. Fourteen men perished. A8 was subsequently salvaged. The Holy Trinity Church at Gosport, Hampshire, has a memorial to A1, 3, 5 and 8.

First A Class Submarines – Main Characteristics (A1 to A4)

Overall Length/ Beam/Draught	100ft x 11ft 6in x 11ft 6in
Displacement	165 tons surfaced / 180 tons submerged
Power	1 x 16-cylinder 500bhp Wolseley petrol engine (later modified to 12-cylinder) for surface propulsion
	1 x 150bhp electric motor for submerged propulsion
Diving Depth	100ft
Speed	11 knots surfaced / 7 knots submerged
Propeller	1
Endurance	310 miles surfaced / 20 miles submerged
Armament	1 x 18in torpedo tube in bow (A1)
	2 x 18in torpedo tubes in bow (A2 to A4)
Complement	11 to 14

First A Class Submarines – Main Characteristics (A5 to A13)

Overall Length/ Beam/Draught	105ft x 12ft 6in x 11ft 6in
Displacement	180 tons surfaced / 207 tons submerged
Power	1 x 550bhp petrol engine for surface propulsion
	1 x 150bhp electric motor for submerged propulsion (A5 to A12)
	1 x heavy oil engine for surface propulsion
	1 x 150bhp electric motor for submerged propulsion (A13)
Diving Depth	100ft
Speed	11.5 knots surfaced / 7 knots submerged (A5 to A12)
	10 knots surfaced / 7 knots submerged (A13)
Propeller	1
Endurance	490 miles surfaced / 20 miles at 5 knots submerged
Armament	2 x 18in torpedo tubes in bow
Complement	14

The shipyard's engine shop as it would have looked when the B Class submarines were under construction (although this photograph is from an 1896 publication describing the Barrow Shipyard).

B Class Submarines

11 built on behalf of the Royal Navy

> *As a matter of fact, till the invention of the periscope enabled it to see where it was going when submerged, the submarine was little if anything but a proper menace. The periscope altered all this.*
>
> The British Battle Fleet by Fred T. Jane

HMS B1	(Yard No.312)	Launched 25 October 1904
HMS B2	(Yard No.320)	Launched 19 August 1905
HMS B3	(Yard No.321)	Launched 1 September 1905
HMS B4	(Yard No.322)	Launched 31 October 1905
HMS B5	(Yard No.323)	Launched 14 November 1905
HMS B6	(Yard No.324)	Launched 30 November 1905
HMS B7	(Yard No.325)	Launched 30 November 1905
HMS B8	(Yard No.326)	Launched 23 January 1906
HMS B9	(Yard No.327)	Launched 26 January 1906
HMS B10	(Yard No.328)	Launched 28 March 1906
HMS B11	(Yard No.329)	Launched 24 February 1906

As with the A Class, the B Class submarine boats (eleven in total) were all built at Barrow-in-Furness. B1 had started life as A14 but was cancelled and modified to meet the requirements of the B Class, a class which was larger than the preceding A Class and with improved control, greater endurance and better habitability.

The limitations of the A Class boats were well understood: little speed underwater, poor endurance, cramped accommodation and they were not good sea boats. However, Admiral Sir John Fisher was the submarine service's champion and a successor, the B Class, was already underway prior to the completion of the A Class. Once more, in an attempt to improve on these shortcomings, a larger vessel was designed, some 40ft longer than A1, 10in more in beam, and 100 tons more displacement. This was the start of the B Class, of which eleven were built between 1903 and 1906. The B Class were the first submarines to be fitted with deck casings. Surface performance was improved over that of the A Class, but underwater performance was practically the same. As in the A Class, propulsion was via petrol engine when surfaced and batteries when submerged, but the B's fore and aft hydroplanes improved surface running and general seaworthiness. Eight months after A3 was sunk, B2 was sunk (4 October 1912) following a collision with the Hamburg-Amerika liner *Amerika*. The 23,000-ton liner was travelling at 17 knots when it was realised a collision was imminent.

With the exception of Lt Pulleyne there were no other survivors from the B2. B2 could not be raised and a funeral service was held over the sunken boat. Lt Richard Pulleyne was subsequently lost on E34 when it failed to return from a North Sea patrol in July 1918. B11, under command of Lt Holbrook, entered the Sea of Marmara and sank the Turkish battleship *Messudieh*. Holbrook was the first submariner of the First World War to be awarded the VC. B11 also captured an Austrian flying boat which had been forced to put down due to engine trouble.

Victoria Cross
HMS B11
Lieutenant Norman Douglas Holbrook

The King has been Graciously pleased to approve the grant of the Victoria Cross to Lieutenant Norman Douglas Holbrook, Royal Navy, for the conspicuous act of bravery as specified below. For most conspicuous bravery on 13th December, when in command of the submarine B11, he entered the Dardanelles, and, notwithstanding the very difficult current, dived his vessel under five rows of mines and torpedoed the Turkish battleship *Messudiyeh*, which was guarding the minefield. Lieutenant Holbrook succeeded in bringing the *B11* safely back, although assailed by gun fire and torpedo boats, having been submerged on occasion for nine hours.

22 December 1914

HMS B10 during builder's trials in 1906. Note the ventilator on the conning tower and the rudimentary canvas dodger (screen). Several dockyard staff are visible immediately fore and aft of the conning tower.

B Class Submarines – Main Characteristics

Overall Length/ Beam/Draught	142ft 2.5in x 13ft 7in x 13ft 7in
Displacement	285 tons surfaced / 313 tons submerged
Power	1 x 16-cylinder 180bhp petrol engine for surface propulsion
	1 x 180bhp electric motor for submerged propulsion
Diving Depth	100ft
Speed	12 knots surfaced / 8 knots submerged
Propeller	1 x (3 blades – 5ft diameter)
Endurance	740 miles surfaced / 23 miles at 7 knots submerged
Armament	2 x 18in torpedo tubes in bow (4 torpedoes carried)
Complement	15
Miscellaneous	Fuel capacity of 15 tons
	Two sets of hydroplanes to improve control
Notes	Pre-First World War British submarines also carried three white mice, which were entered on the pay-roll as part of the crew. Being extremely sensitive they notified the slightest escape of petrol fumes – by squeaking – or so the Admiralty mistakenly believed. The crew members felt the mice served no useful purpose other than amusement value.

C Class Submarines

32 built on behalf of the Royal Navy

In the old days there were large gas engines bolted on the walls. The shop floor was all of earth, often saturated with oil or soluble cutting mixtures which imported a rancid odour, perhaps encouraged by the practice of mending the floor with cast iron machine cuttings. Candles were in constant use, any general lighting coming from paraffin flare or the uncertain gas flames from fish tailed burners. In winter the old shops were dark, draughty and smoky. No practice existed of providing hot water for tea. Before the invention of thermos flasks tea was brought in already brewed and in cans, to be warmed up on one of the many fires.

John Wilkinson (Chief of Armament Design at Barrow)
recalling the Yard at the beginning of the twentieth century

HMS C1	(Yard No.334)	Launched 10 July 1906	(Group One)
HMS C2	(Yard No.335)	Launched 10 July 1906	(Group One)
HMS C3	(Yard No.336)	Launched 3 October 1906	(Group One)
HMS C4	(Yard No.337)	Launched 18 October 1906	(Group One)
HMS C5	(Yard No.338)	Launched 20 August 1906	(Group One)
HMS C6	(Yard No.339)	Launched 20 August 1906	(Group One)
HMS C7	(Yard No.340)	Launched 15 February 1907	(Group One)
HMS C8	(Yard No.341)	Launched 15 February 1907	(Group One)
HMS C9	(Yard No.342)	Launched 3 April 1907	(Group One)
HMS C10	(Yard No.343)	Launched 15 April 1907	(Group One)
HMS C11	(Yard No.346)	Launched 17 May 1907	(Group One)
HMS C12	(Yard No.351)	Launched 9 September 1907	(Group One)
HMS C13	(Yard No.352)	Launched 14 January 1907	(Group One)
HMS C14	(Yard No.353)	Launched 7 December 1907	(Group One)
HMS C15	(Yard No.354)	Launched 21 January 1908	(Group One)
HMS C16	(Yard No.355)	Launched 19 March 1908	(Group One)
HMS C21	(Yard No.375)	Launched 26 September 1908	(Group Two)
HMS C22	(Yard No.376)	Launched 10 October 1908	(Group Two)
HMS C23	(Yard No.377)	Launched 26 November 1908	(Group Two)
HMS C24	(Yard No.378)	Launched 26 November 1908	(Group Two)
HMS C25	(Yard No.379)	Launched 10 March 1909	(Group Two)
HMS C26	(Yard No.380)	Launched 20 March 1909	(Group Two)
HMS C27	(Yard No.381)	Launched 22 April 1909	(Group Two)
HMS C28	(Yard No.382)	Launched 22 April 1909	(Group Two)
HMS C29	(Yard No.383)	Launched 19 June 1909	(Group Two)
HMS C30	(Yard No.384)	Launched 19 July 1909	(Group Two)
HMS C31	(Yard No.387)	Launched 2 September 1909	(Group Two)
HMS C32	(Yard No.388)	Launched 29 September 1909	(Group Two)
HMS C35	(Yard No.391)	Launched 25 May 1909	(Group Two)
HMS C36	(Yard No.392	Launched 30 November 1909	(Group Two)
HMS C37	(Yard No.393)	Launched 12 January 1910	(Group Two)
HMS C38	(Yard No.394)	Launched 10 February 1910	(Group Two)

Of the thirty-eight C Class submarines ordered by the Royal Navy, no fewer than thirty-two were constructed and launched by the Barrow Yard. For the first time the Royal Navy entrusted submarine boat building to another shipyard, realising no doubt the potential problems of having a single 'expert' supplier for such machines. Numbered consecutively from C1 through to C38, those built away from the Furness peninsula were C17, C18, C19, C20, C33 and C34; all six of which were constructed and launched at HM Dockyard, Chatham.

As with the B Class, there would be improvements made to the Cs but Vickers, Sons & Maxim Ltd had to contend with the loss of their submarine-building monopoly. Barrow would build thirty-two of the thirty-eight boats while Chatham built six, but this is not registered if Barrow provided the lead yard services. Though the Admiralty deemed it wise to distribute building to other yards, Barrow's domination would never be usurped. Indeed, Vickers confidence in believing they could continue to be the major submarine constructor was evidenced in 1912 by a demand to their submarine specialists to sign five-year contracts binding them to the company. The specialists duly refused. The C Class would become the last of the petrol-engined boats, a decision which was probably greeted with relief by the submariners. Furthermore the decision to fit C12 to C16 with 'airlocks' or 'airtraps' (enclosed spaces, three on the port and one on the starboard side with four diving helmets stored in each space – one for each crew member) indicated rescue was being given more

A sixteen-cylinder petrol engine, as fitted in B Class submarines. These engines were also fitted in the A Class boats and early C Class (C1 to C18). *(Barrow Museum Service CAT 2527)*

HMS C8 with, pictured in the background, two A Class boats – A5 and A6.

consideration. The airlocks utilised the torpedo hatch as an escape route and were retrospectively fitted to all the B and C Class submarines.

C11 was the first of the C Class to meet a watery fate, and the Admiralty announced it thus: 'The Secretary to the Admiralty regrets having to communicate that Messrs Farra, Groves & Co.'s steamer *Eddystone*, bound for Hull, was in a collision with submarine C11 at 11.45 last night 4.5 miles north-west of Haisborough Light, off Cromer, and the submarine was sunk.' The incident, which occurred on the evening of 14 July 1909, would result in only three survivors – Lt C.G. Brodie (the CO), 1st Lt G. Watkins and A.B. Stripes. The *Eddystone* had created no small degree of panic amongst a flotilla of eleven C boats and eight torpedo boats which, having completed various fleet manoeuvres, were returning to base on a clear moonlit night when *Eddystone* attempted to pass through the lines of submarines. C16 and C17 collided trying to avoid the steamer, with C17 being so badly damaged that she needed to be towed by tug to Sheerness. Eyewitnesses reported that C11 had sunk within forty seconds of having been struck and the three survivors were fortunate to have been picked up by C12. Although the C Class were the first to carry 10ft Berthon boats, there would have been no time to launch the boat even assuming some crew members could have cleared the hull.

Another C boat, C14, was in collision with *Government Hopper 29* on the evening of 10 December 1914. C14's crew attempted 'valiant and disciplined efforts' to stem the flood taking the boat down by the stern. The incident took place in Plymouth Sound and, with help close at hand, the crew of C14 were saved. C14 sank, was raised eight days later and refurbished at Devonport to give eight years' more service.

Although the A, B and C Classes were intended for coastal duties, the professionalism displayed by the crews and the advocacy for further ranging duties being urged by Admiral Fisher showed that 'Fisher's Toys' as they had become known were here to stay. The C Class would be the last single-shaft conventional submarines until the Upholder Class were built in the 1980s.

The shipyard joiners' shop in the early 1900s. *(Barrow Museum Service CAT 6614)*

Victoria Cross
HMS C3
Lieutenant Richard Douglas Sandford

The King has been Graciously pleased to approve the grant of the Victoria Cross to Lieutenant Richard Douglas Sandford, Royal Navy for conspicuous gallantry. This officer was in command of Submarine C3 and most skilfully placed that vessel in between the piles of the viaduct before lighting his fuse and abandoning her. He eagerly undertook this hazardous enterprise, although well aware (as were all his crew) that if the means of rescue failed and he or any of his crew were in the water at the moment of the explosion, they could be killed outright by the force of such an explosion. Yet Lieutenant Sandford disdained the use of gyro steering, which would have enabled him and his crew to abandon the submarine at a safe distance, and preferred to make sure, as far as humanly possible, of the accomplishment of his duty.

23 July 1918

C Class Submarines – Main Characteristics

Overall Length/ Beam/Draught	143ft x 13ft 6in x 11ft 6in
Displacement	290 tons surfaced / 320 tons submerged (Group One)
	290 tons surfaced / 321 tons submerged (Group Two)
Power	1 x 600bhp petrol engine for surface propulsion
	1 x 200bhp electric motor for submerged propulsion
Diving Depth	100ft
Speed	13 knots surfaced / 8 knots submerged
Propeller	1 x (3 blades of 5ft 7in diameter)
Endurance	910 miles surfaced / 16 miles at 8 knots submerged
Armament	2 x 18in torpedo tubes (4 torpedoes carried)
Complement	16
Notes	Most sources ignore the fact that there were two groups within this class of submarines, largely because there was barely any difference between the two, save for the fact that Group Two boats were fitted with forward hydroplanes and had a slightly larger submerged displacement.

D Class Submarines

6 built on behalf of the Royal Navy

The new craft, which will presumably be the first of the group provided for in the 1907/08 Naval Estimates, was launched on Saturday last from the yard of Messrs. Vickers, Son & Maxim. She has been reared in a private and strictly guarded shed and the men who had been employed upon her are all sworn to secrecy. The ceremony of bringing forth the new submarine was confined to the departmental heads of the great Barrow firm and to several of the Officers of the cruiser Mercury which is moored off the yard. Immediately on taking the water, the mysterious submarine was hurriedly towed to a wharf, barricaded on land and rendered invisible from the sea by a huge pontoon. Here she will be darkly and furtively brought to completion.

Western Daily Mercury, 19 May 1908

HMS D1	(Yard No.350)	Launched 16 May 1908
HMS D2	(Yard No.390)	Launched 25 October 1910
HMS D3	(Yard No.403)	Launched 17 October 1910
HMS D4	(Yard No.404)	Launched 27 May 1910
HMS D5	(Yard No.405)	Launched 28 August 1911
HMS D6	(Yard No.406)	Launched 23 October 1912

The D Class submarines were notable for being the first British submarines to be fitted with diesel engines and twin propellers. Eight boats were built in this class, six of them (D1 to D6) at Barrow-in-Furness. Chatham Dockyard was responsible for the building of both D7 and D8.

Following the trials in A13, diesels were adopted for the D Class and the use of petrol engines in new designs came to an end, along with the attendant danger to crews from petrol fumes. The D Class, approved by the Admiralty Board in 1906, was designed to overcome, as far as possible, the limitations of the earlier submarine classes. Although far from perfect they were, nevertheless, a great improvement on the previous classes. Initial design work was carried out by the Admiralty for the first time on a submarine project, but with the usual procedure for other Admiralty vessels. Between 1907 and 1912, eight of the class were built – six at Barrow and two at HM Dockyard, Chatham. The class had far better endurance than previous boats, and can be regarded as being the first submarines to have a proper patrol capability.

The introduction of twin screws meant that better manoeuvring power was obtained, and the conning tower – being much larger than previously – gave the class a profile similar to that of modern-day submarines. A significant innovation was the use of saddle tanks to hold the main ballast water. The use of external tanks provided additional inboard space and improved accommodation standards. However, with the introduction of a stern torpedo tube (the first in a British submarine), an increased engine size to give greater power and an increased complement in a vessel of the same hull diameter as the C Class, and with only a 20ft increase in length, it is doubtful whether the additional space was properly utilised to improve standards of accommodation.

A major advance in the D Class was the incorporation of a wireless system for the first time, the aerial being rigged to the submarine's mast. Before the submarine could dive, the mast had to be lowered by hand and the wireless aerial stowed away along the side of the vessel. Previous submarines had been equipped with receiving sets, but the D Class was the first to have both receiving and transmitting facilities. Unfortunately, wireless signals could neither be received nor transmitted when the boat was submerged as the tip of the transmitter aerial had to be clear of the water to work; this was a problem that remained unsolved until the late 1920s. It is interesting to note that, despite the introduction of what was then considered to be 'state of the art technology', homing pigeons were still used by the crew when the boat was out of wireless range. Security during the construction of D1 was inordinately severe and for her launching at Barrow in May 1908 there was scarcely any let-up. Immediately after taking to the water she was towed to a wharf and hidden from prying eyes.

D4 was the first Royal Navy submarine to carry a gun. The 12-pounder was fitted on a disappearing mounting that had to be operated by compressed air. This mounting was slow moving and cumbersome and permanent deck-mounted guns were introduced during the Great War.

All eight D Class submarines were in commission at the start of the First World War and took up station on the East Coast of England, where their long-range potential was exploited to the full, with overseas patrols in the Heligoland Bight. During the first three months of the war, two of the class were lost in the North Sea – D5 hitting a mine off the coast of Great Yarmouth and D2 going on patrol never to be heard of again. Visitors to the historic city of

Chester may wish to note that one of the Cathedral windows is in memory of Lt Cdr F. Lewis Copplestone, lost on D2. Towards the end of the war, two more of the class were lost. D3 was accidentally sunk in the English Channel in March 1918, and three months later D6 was sunk by a U-boat off the north coast of Ireland.

Of the remainder, D1 was sunk deliberately as a target in October 1918 whilst D4, D7 and D8 survived the war, to be taken out of service in July 1919 and bringing to an end a highly successful class from which the famous E Class would be developed.

Even the local newspaper could gather only a little information about this new class of submarine and, on Tuesday 19 May 1908, was forced to speculate somewhat when reporting her launch thus:

New Type of British Submarine
Launch at Barrow

For a considerable time the Naval authorities and Messrs Vickers, Sons & Maxim, Barrow-in-Furness, have been engaged on the designs of a new and more powerful submarine vessel.

The result of their experiences was seen on Saturday, when there was launched from the Barrow Yard a submarine of an entirely new type.

This vessel really is an experiment.

She embodies all the improvements that the building and manoeuvring of over forty submarines for Britain have suggested.

All the previous boats have had only one torpedo tube forward and one propeller.

The experimental vessel is said to have four torpedo tubes – two forward and two aft – and twin screws.

She is larger in every way.

The launch into Walney Channel of HMS DI. *(Barrow Museum Service CAT 2371)*

The previous craft had much of their space taken up by trimming tanks.

The new one carries a trimming tank on each side, extending half her length, and in shape like a submarine.

Viewed from above the vessel looks like three submarines attached, the larger in the centre. She will, it is understood, have no tower.

When on the surface the whole of the vessel will be visible.

In the older vessels only about half of the vessel was above, the tapering ends being submerged.

D Class Submarines – Main Characteristics

Overall Length/ Beam/Draught	162ft x 20ft 6in x 11ft
Displacement	550 tons surfaced / 620 tons submerged
Power	1 x 1,200bhp Vickers diesel engine for surface propulsion
	1 x 550bhp electric motor for submerged propulsion
Diving Depth	100ft
Speed	14 knots surfaced / 10 knots submerged
Propeller	2 x (3 blades – 5ft 3in diameter)
Endurance	2,500 miles at 11.5 knots surfaced / 65 miles at 5 knots submerged
Armament	3 x 18in torpedo tubes (2 bow, 1 stern – 6 torpedoes carried)
	1 x 12-pounder gun (D4 only)
Complement	27
Miscellaneous	The 12-pounder gun fitted to HMS D4 (making it the first Royal Navy submarine to be so armed) was housed in the casing and brought into action by being raised via a pneumatic ram

Japanese Submarines

2 built on behalf of the Imperial Japanese Navy

In the case of the Japanese company, the initiative came even more directly from the Japanese government, which by 1907 was very much concerned about the country's lack of ordnance capacity. They accordingly invited both Armstrongs and Vickers, as well as other firms on the Continent and in America, to enter into arrangements with Japanese financiers for the founding of a large ordnance factory. Vickers and Armstrongs both accepted the invitation, and the Japanese Steel Works was founded with a capital of £1,000,000, which was increased in 1909 to £1,500,000, the shareholders then being Vickers and Armstrongs, each with £275,000, and Japanese interests for the rest.

Vickers – A History *by J.D. Scott*

No.8	(Yard No.366)	Launched 19 May 1908
No.9	(Yard No.367)	Launched 19 May 1908

The Barrow Shipyard built two submarines for the Imperial Japanese Navy in 1907/1908, although it may have been five. Some sources indicate that, in addition to the two submarines listed above, there were indeed three others built at Barrow and sold to the Japanese, though the authors of this book have been unable to either prove or disprove this theory. What is certain is that the launches of both 'known' submarines, No.8 and No.9, were low-profile affairs with no official ceremony taking place. Indeed they were reported in the local press in a most low-key way. It is therefore 'possible' that others were built but this history can only list the two boats above which are verified by official records.

Ordered by the Imperial Japanese Navy, under the auspices of the 1907 Programme, these single-hulled boats, Yard Nos 366 and 367 (Hull Nos 8 and 9), were very similar to the C Class boats of the Royal Navy but with a slightly shorter range. Both boats were renumbered in 1924 as HA-1 and HA-2, which indicated they were designated as boat No.1 and boat No.2 of the coastal class (the smallest class of submarine within the Imperial Japanese Navy).

To deliver the boats, the Yard designed and built a special vessel which they also owned. SS *Transporter* (Yard No.370) was 235ft long x 35ft 8in beam x 17ft 3in draught and had steam engines producing 650bhp and a speed of 9 knots. Her design was different to other cargo vessels of that time in that a large part of her upperworks was portable. To prepare the *Transporter* for accepting, loading and conveying the two boats, a sequence of events involving the removal and replacement of superstructure and components, dry and wet docking and the use of divers was developed. The late distinguished Barrow maritime historian James Melville, writing for the *North Western Evening Mail*, described the sequence:

The masts and dock winches were put ashore before the vessel was taken to the dry dock. Bulwarks and hatch coamings on the port side were left loose, as well as deck plating for the width of the hatches along the beams, over a length of approximately 140 feet, and these were removed. A number of bilge blocks had been fitted below the vessel about midships to take the concentrated weight due to the presence of the submarines when loaded on board. All machinery likely to be damaged by water was coated with grease and this included the windlass and steering gear. After the water had been pumped out of the dock a manhole on the bottom of the ship on each side was taken off and all sidelights, doors, skylights, manholes, sea valves, etc. were opened to allow free passage for water and escape of air. The dock was then flooded to a suitable depth above the dock to allow the first submarine to be floated above her submerged position. When this was confirmed, the dock was gradually emptied and, as the superstructure of the submarine came below the level of the main deck beams she was hauled over to the starboard side in the hold. As more water was pumped out of the dock the submarine gradually came to rest upon the blocks previously fitted on the tank top of the Transporter. A diver then placed other temporary chocks under the submarine to prevent listing. When the first submarine was adequately secured she was ballasted to make sure she would not rise when the ship was again submerged, and after the dock was again flooded the process was followed for Submarine No.2, which was lowered into position on the port side

Japanese submarine No.8 at Kure on Boxing Day 1916. No.8 was renamed HA-1 by the Japanese in 1924 and was one of two Japanese C1-type boats built at Barrow (the other being No.9 – renamed HA-2 in 1924). *(US Naval Institute)*

Japanese submarine No.13 (later renamed HA-6). This submarine was a copy of the original Vickers C1/C2 design and was built under license by Kawasaki at Kobe. *(US Naval Institute)*

Japanese submarine No.10 (later HA-3). One of three Japanese C2-type submarines which some sources claim were built at Barrow and shipped to Japan in sections – the others being No.11 (later HA-4) which is visible on the left, and No.12 (later HA-5). *(US Naval Institute)*

and secured. The dock was again pumped out and all loosework on the Transporter was fitted and the ship closed up for her long voyage to Japan, which must have taken nearly three months. After reaching her destination the following were removed from the Transporter: Masts, deck winches, all portable woodwork and furniture, bulwarks and hatch coamings on the port side, sufficient deck plating and beams to allow the submarine to be floated off, in turn, while the vessel was submerged. In fact, almost an exact reversal of the process used in Barrow when the submarines were loaded on board. Both the embarking and disembarking programmes were very carefully planned and, after being followed exactly, proved most successful. Thus the firm fulfilled their contract.

The Transporter was finally fitted out and was offered for sale to shipowners.

Under the heading 'Vessel for Carrying Submarines Launched at Barrow' the *Barrow News* reported the launch of SS *Transporter*. Following her immediate duty of carrying the two Japanese submarines, it was reported that 'Subsequently the vessel will be used by the company for carrying guns, gun mountings, etc. from Barrow to the dockyards and other shipbuilding yards where they hold contracts.'

★ ★ ★

Occasionally instances arise in which Vickers' archives and reputable reference works and histories have such a lack of commonality that there must be doubt as to which is correct. This is possibly the case in respect of Yard Nos 397, 398 and 399 and the reader may wish to pursue the matter further. Vickers' archives reference Yard Nos 397, 398 and 399 each as orders for 'The engines of an unknown Japanese submarine', though there is no reference to hulls or hull sections. However, the authoritative reference work *Warships of the Imperial Japanese Navy, 1869-1945* states that three Vickers C2 type, Nos 10, 11 and 12, were built at Barrow between 1910 and 1911 and shipped in sections, in the style of Nordenfelt, for re-assembly at Kure Dockyard. *Warships of the Imperial Japanese Navy* describes these boats as being HA-3, 4 and 5 and continues to describe a C Class variant built under licence by Kawasaki at Kobe in 1912, numbered HA-6, and a further two Vickers C types built under

A submarine oil engine as fitted in Japanese, Spanish, Polish and French submarines under licence around the mid-1920s. These engines were capable of generating 1,000bhp at 450rpm or 1,200bhp at 500rpm.

licence at Kure Dockyard (1916-1917) and designated HA-7 and HA-8. Finally, *Warships of the Imperial Japanese Navy* gives details of eighteen Vickers' L types built under licence (between 1918 and 1927), incorporating various modifications by Mitsubishi at Kobe and given the Japanese designation RO51 through to RO68.

During research for this section of the book we were in touch with the Shipbuilding and Ship Machinery department of the Japan Ship Centre who were kind enough to check back numbers of the Japanese magazine *Ships of the World*, published by the Kaijinsha Co. Ltd. Our contact translated Chapter 2, 'Development of Japanese Submarines 2 – Machinery', of special issue No.37, dated August 1993, which contained the following: 'Vickers provided two complete submarines and three sets of engines, periscopes and gyros' – a statement with which the authors of this book would agree. We believe Yard Nos 397, 398 and 399 have been construed as boats in sections by several major books and this is the reason for the anomalies contained therein.

Japanese Submarines – Main Characteristics

Overall Length/ Beam/Draught	135ft x 13ft 5in x 11ft 3in
Displacement	286 tons surfaced / 325 tons submerged
Power	1 x 600bhp diesel engine for surface propulsion
	1 x 300bhp electric motor for submerged propulsion
Diving Depth	100ft
Speed	12 knots surfaced / 8 knots submerged
Propeller	1
Endurance	600 miles at 12 knots surfaced / 60 miles at 4 knots submerged
Armament	2 x 18in torpedo tubes in bow
	1 x machine gun
Complement	21

2
First World War Submarines
(1912-1919)

E Class Submarines

18 built on behalf of the Royal Navy
2 built on behalf of the Royal Australian Navy

> *The E's proved admirable submarines – submerged; but the 'hard-lying' money, to which all submarine ratings were entitled, was still well earned.*
>
> Sir Roger Keyes (Admiral of the Fleet)

Royal Navy

HMS E3	(Yard No.415)	Launched 29 October 1912	(Group One)
HMS E4	(Yard No.416)	Launched 5 February 1912	(Group One)
HMS E5	(Yard No.417)	Launched 17 February 1912	(Group One)
HMS E6	(Yard No.418)	Launched 12 November 1912	(Group One)
HMS E9	(Yard No.430)	Launched 29 November 1913	(Group Two)
HMS E10	(Yard No.431)	Launched 29 December 1913	(Group Two)
HMS E11	(Yard No.432)	Launched 25 April 1914	(Group Two)
HMS E14	(Yard No.438)	Launched 7 July 1914	(Group Two)
HMS E15	(Yard No.439)	Launched 23 April 1914	(Group Two)
HMS E16	(Yard No.440)	Launched 23 September 1914	(Group Two)
HMS E17	(Yard No.452)	Launched 16 January 1915	(Group Two)
HMS E18	(Yard No.453)	Launched 4 March 1915	(Group Two)
HMS E19	(Yard No.470)	Launched 13 May 1915	(Group Two)
HMS E20	(Yard No.471)	Launched 12 June 1915	(Group Two)
HMS E21	(Yard No.472)	Launched 24 July 1915	(Group Two)
HMS E22	(Yard No.473)	Launched 27 August 1915	(Group Two)
HMS E23	(Yard No.474)	Launched 28 September 1915	(Group Two)
HMS E24	(Yard No.475)	Launched 9 December 1915	(Group Two)

Royal Australian Navy

HMAS AE1	(Yard No.419)	Launched 22 May 1913	(Group Two)
HMAS AE2	(Yard No.420)	Launched 18 June 1913	(Group Two)

The Royal Navy ordered a total of fifty-six E Class submarines, with all but one being constructed (E28 was cancelled in April 1915). Of the fifty-seven boats in the class which were built, no fewer than eighteen were constructed and launched from the Barrow Shipyard, with the remaining thirty-nine being built at twelve other shipyards. In addition to those supplied to the Royal Navy, the Barrow Yard built two boats of this class for the Royal Australian Navy. The boats built in this class were divided into two groups: Barrow was responsible for four from Group One and sixteen (including the Australian boats) from Group Two, though one of these, HMS E24, was slightly modified and built as a minelayer (as were five others being built at other yards). Unusually, two of the Group Two boats, E25 and E26 (Yard Nos 458 459, respectively), were completed at Barrow, though they cannot be considered true Barrow-built submarines as their hulls were constructed (and launched) by Beardmore of Dalmuir in Scotland.

The results of experience gained with D1, the prototype diesel-driven submarine, were incorporated in the design of the famous E Class submarines, which carried out such outstanding work during the First World War. The boats were considerably larger than the D Class in order to accommodate the introduction of broadside torpedo tubes, a major change in the design. Six of the later E Class boats were fitted as minelayers; this meant that the broadside torpedo tubes were omitted and twenty mines were carried in vertical tubes in the saddle tanks. The mines were released by a mechanism operated from inboard. The E Class were the first British boats to be fitted with internal watertight bulkheads.

These internal bulkheads strengthened the pressure hull and, as events during the war proved, the E Class were eventually designated as being capable of diving to a depth of 200ft. Fifty-five E Class were built between February 1911 and August 1917, only one being cancelled. Of the first twenty-four, eighteen were built and completed at Barrow between January 1913 and January 1916, two were built at Beardmore's at Dalmuir and completed by Vickers, and six were built at Chatham. The remaining thirty were divided between twelve other shipyards that were entering the field of submarine construction for the first time, including Armstrong's at Newcastle, Cammell Laird at Birkenhead and Scott's on the Clyde.

Boats ordered before the war took between twenty and thirty months to complete but E19, ordered in November 1914, was built, equipped and handed over in the record time of eight months, setting the pace for several later boats. This achievement was aided by the fact that the class were fitted with engines being built at the time by Vickers for the newly ordered G Class submarines.

As with the D Class, the E Class boats had twin screws. Their diesels developed 1,600bhp which gave a surface speed, in service, of 14 knots. The submerged speed was 9.5 knots, produced by 840bhp electric motors. The radius of action of the E Class was 3,000 miles on the surface at 10 knots and up to sixty-five miles submerged, at approximately 5 knots.

Although a large class, built over a number of years, the characteristics between the various groups within the class did not alter appreciably. Changes in form, dimensions and displacement were not sufficient to make any marked difference in speed and endurance. However, as a result of war experience, large guards were fitted around the hydroplanes – the appendages restricting the class to a surface speed of 14 knots and a submerged speed of

Guests, including the ship's sponsor, prior to the launch of HMS E3 on 29 October 1912. *(Barrow Museum Service CAT 3203)*

9 knots. With extensive superstructure, combined with a navigating bridge built over the conning tower, the class were a big advance as sea boats and were easy to navigate even in the roughest weather.

At the outbreak of the First World War nine of the new E Class submarines had been delivered and six were used in the Heligoland Bight, first for reconnaissance patrols only and subsequently with a free hand.

The first offensive success by a British submarine was scored by E9, commanded by Lt-Com. Max Horton, who had 'stood by' his boat during her construction at Barrow. On 13 September 1914, Horton sighted the German cruiser *Hela* near Heligoland, closed to 600yds and fired two torpedoes, one of which struck amidships. *Hela* sank and E9 was hunted for the remainder of the day, but successfully escaped. During her next patrol in the Bight, E9 sank the destroyer S116. It was following these exploits that Lt-Com. Horton invented the tradition of Royal Navy submarines flying the skull and crossbones on return to port following completion of a successful patrol.

These first successes were followed by many courageous exploits. Particularly important were the operations carried out in the enemy waters of the Baltic and the Sea of Marmara where British submarines operated with devastating effect during the early years of the war. They were so effective that E11's 'career of destruction' earned her commander, Lt-Com. Martin Eric Nasmith, the Victoria Cross.

E14 was captained by two VC winners. On 27 April 1915, Cdr E.C. Boyle was awarded the VC while in command of E14. Another commander of E14, Lt-Com. Geoffrey White, was also awarded (posthumously) the Victoria Cross for his bravery in the Dardanelles in January 1918.

Very rarely did British and German submarines come into direct action but, in October 1914, when U-27 and E3 met off the German coast, the latter was cut in two by a torpedo and was lost with all hands.

Throughout the war the E Class served with conspicuous success, but they also suffered very severely, more than half their number being lost. AE1 and AE2 were built at Barrow for

HMS E11 running on the surface.

the Royal Australian Navy and these sailed to the Antipodes under their own power. One of these actually accomplished 30,000 miles before a complete refit of her propelling machinery was thought to be desirable.

These boats, the first for the Royal Australian Navy, arrived in Australia in 1913. They were the first to be docked in the Cockatoo Yard, Cockatoo Island, Sydney Harbour. (Vickers-Armstrongs first held a small nominee shareholding in 1937 then took over the majority of the shares in 1947 but retained the name of Cockatoo Docks & Engineering Co. Pty Ltd.)

Around the time E17 was fitting out, the 650-ton German submarine U–21, under the command of Korvettenkapitän Otto Hersing, surfaced off Walney Island on Friday 29 January 1915 and opened fire on the airship shed at North Walney. (Many Barrovians believed the intent of the attack was to cause major disruption by aiming for the heart of Royal Navy submarine construction. Submarine U–21's armament, however, did not have the necessary range.) Fort Walney's battery engaged U–21 and, when it submerged, believed it sunk. However, U–21 escaped to create havoc in and around the Irish Sea by sinking several vessels. Some months later Hersing's U–21 would oppose the Royal Navy in the Dardanelles, opening his account by torpedoing the Barrow-built battleship HMS *Triumph* (Yard No.289, 12,000 tons) on 25 May 1915.

★ ★ ★

It is of interest to note that Barrow-in-Furness is, in addition to being the first and foremost submarine constructor, the birthplace of British naval aviation which commenced in 1908 with Vickers, Sons & Maxim winning a tender to build a rigid airship for the Admiralty.

The Inspecting Captain of Airships was Admiral Bacon who had been the navy overseer for the Holland boats. One of Vickers' Airship Department's senior assistants at this time was Cdr Charles Craven, later to become Managing Director of the Vickers-Armstrongs Works at Barrow. The last airship built at Barrow was for the Japanese government, a small non-rigid reconnaissance type which completed trials over Barrow in May 1921. The airship was dismantled and conveyed to Japan by sea.

Victoria Cross

HMS E14

Commander Edward Courtney Boyle

The King has been Graciously pleased to approve the grant of the Victoria Cross to Commander Edward Courtney Boyle, Royal Navy for the conspicuous act of bravery as specified below. For most conspicuous bravery, in command of submarine E14, when he dived his vessel under enemy minefields and entered the Sea of Marmara on the 27th April, 1915. In spite of great navigational difficulties from strong currents, of the continual neighbourhood of hostile patrols, and of hourly danger of attack from the enemy, he continued to operate in the narrow waters of the Straits and succeeded in sinking two Turkish gunboats and one large military transporter.

21 May 1915

Victoria Cross

HMS E11

Lieutenant Commander Martin Eric Nasmith

The King has been Graciously pleased to approve the grant of the Victoria Cross to Lieutenant Commander Martin Eric Nasmith, Royal Navy for the conspicuous act of bravery as specified below. For most conspicuous bravery in command of one of His Majesty's Submarines HMS E11 while operating in the Sea of Marmara. In the face of great danger he succeeded in destroying one large Turkish gunboat, one ammunition ship and three store-ships, in addition to driving one store-ship ashore. When he had safely passed the most difficult part of his homeward journey he returned again to torpedo a Turkish transport.

24 June 1915

A completed builder's model of an E Class submarine. *(Barrow Museum Service CAT 2663)*

E Class Submarines – Main Characteristics (Group One)

Overall Length/ Beam/Draught	176ft x 22ft 6in x 12ft
Displacement	660 tons surfaced / 795 tons submerged
Power	2 x 800bhp diesel engines for surface propulsion
	2 x 840bhp electric motors for submerged propulsion
Diving Depth	200ft
Speed	16 knots surfaced / 9 knots submerged
Propeller	2 x (3 blades – 5ft 7in diameter)
Endurance	3,000 nautical miles at 10 knots (or 1,500 miles at full power) surfaced / 10 miles at 9 knots (or 65 miles at 5 knots) submerged
Armament	4 x 18in torpedo tubes (2 bow; 2 beam)
	1 x 6-pounder or 4in gun
Complement	30

E Class Submarines – Main Characteristics (Group Two)

Overall Length/ Beam/Draught	181ft x 23ft 6in x 12ft 6in
Displacement	662 tons surfaced / 835 tons submerged
Power	2 x 800bhp diesel engines for surface propulsion
	2 x 840bhp electric motors for submerged propulsion
Diving Depth	200ft
Speed	16 knots surfaced / 10 knots submerged
Propeller	2 x (3 blades – 5ft 7in diameter)
Endurance	3,000 nautical miles at 10 knots (or 1,500 miles at full power) surfaced / 10 miles at 9 knots (or 65 miles at 5 knots) submerged
Armament	5 x 18in torpedo tubes (2 bow; 2 beam; 1 stern)
Complement	30
Notes	HMS E24 was slightly modified and built as a minelayer, the beam tubes being omitted so that the boat could carry 20 mines instead.

Victoria Cross

HMS E14

Lieutenant Commander Geoffrey Saxon White

On 21 January 1918 the German battle cruiser *Goeben*, which had been mined while attempting a raid against Mudros, ran aground off Nagara Point in the Dardanelles. Repeated air attacks failed to achieve any noticeable results and at dusk on 27 January HM submarine E14, under the command of Lt-Com. G.S. White left Imbros in the desperate hope of torpedoing her. Despite being caught in the anti-submarine nets, White succeeded in bringing E14 up to Nagara only to find the *Goeben* had gone during the night. There was nothing White could do except to reverse course and start back down the Straits. When off Chanak he sighted and fired at a large merchantman, but the torpedo exploded prematurely and E14 was badly damaged. For two hours the submarine continued her dived passage towards the open sea but finally she became so flooded as to be uncontrollable. White gave the order to surface in the hope of making a final dash clear, but E14 was hit by gunfire from the shore batteries. With no hope of escape White altered course towards the shore to give his crew a chance of safety, but was himself killed by shell-fire shortly before E14 sank.

24 May 1919

First V Class Submarines

4 built on behalf of the Royal Navy

Numerous other designs of controlled mines, net mines, river mines etc., are also available for special purposes.

Since the 1914-1918 war, mines of various types have been supplied to Holland, the Dutch East Indies, Greece, Italy, Argentina, Chile, Japan, Romania, Jugo-Slavia and Portugal.

The Activities of Vickers-Armstrongs Ltd (Barrow-in-Furness)

HMS V1	(Yard No.437)	Launched 23 July 1914
HMS V2	(Yard No.449)	Launched 17 February 1915
HMS V3	(Yard No.450)	Launched 1 April 1915
HMS V4	(Yard No.451)	Launched 25 November 1915

Just four V Class boats were ordered by the Royal Navy, with the entire class being constructed at the Barrow Shipyard.

Taking the identifying letter from the name of the builder, the V Class was Vickers' interpretation of a coastal-type submarine designed to meet the requirements of the 1912 Submarine Committee. Four of the class were ordered, the first being laid down in November 1912.

The principal design feature of these submarines was the hull form. Although classed as double-hulled, the V Class boats were actually partial double-hulled vessels – the double-hull being limited to the middle portion of the boat, with the outer hull fairing into the pressure hull at the forward and aft ends. Vickers carried out a number of tank experiments on several hull forms before opting for this design.

The estimated cost of the four V Class submarines was £76,100 each, but this was later amended to £75,799. The diesel engines of the V Class boats developed 450bhp at 450rev/min and were the first Vickers-built submarine engines to have steel cylinder jackets – previously these had been of cast iron.

The battery consisted of 132 Exide cells – small for the size of the boat; the A Class of less than half the displacement carried 120 cells. However, despite this, the designed submerged speed of the boats was still attained, although at the expense of endurance. Vickers claimed that the V Class could dive to 150ft as against 100ft in other submarines of the period.

Although the pressure hull sections were far from circular, this depth was possible because the strength of the hull was increased by the external framing between the inner and outer hulls. The armament of the class was two 18in bow torpedo tubes, positioned low in the vessel. Two spare torpedoes, without warheads, were stowed on the starboard side of the torpedo room, one above the other, with the warheads conveniently located nearby on the flat. The torpedo hatch was mechanically operated as in the E Class. Some records (though not the Shipyard's own archives) state that a 12-pounder gun was fitted. Presumably, if other sources are indeed accurate, this was after completion.

All four V Class submarines were taken out of service in July 1919 and were ultimately scrapped in the early 1920s (V3 and V4 in 1920 and their sister ships, V1 and V2, a year later in 1921).

V Class submarine HMS V3, which was launched at Barrow-in-Furness on 1 April 1915. (*Barrow Museum Service CAT 0001*)

The shipyard's iron foundry in the early 1900s. *(Barrow Museum Service CAT 6584)*

First V Class Submarines – Main Characteristics

Overall Length/ Beam/Draught	147ft 6in x 12ft 9in x 11ft 6in
Displacement	364 tons surfaced / 486 tons submerged
Power	2 x 8-cylinder 450bhp diesel engines for surface propulsion
	2 x 150bhp electric motors for submerged propulsion
	Also fitted with a 132 cell 260 volt battery
Diving Depth	150ft
Speed	14 knots surfaced / 9 knots submerged
Propeller	2 x (3 blades – 4ft 6in diameter)
Endurance	1,130 miles at full power surfaced / 50 miles at 5 knots submerged
Armament	2 x 18in torpedo tubes in bow (4 torpedoes carried)
	1 x 12-pounder gun
Complement	18
Notes	V1 carried 6% more fuel than the other boats in this class and therefore the endurance figures for that boat can be increased proportionately.

The Floating Dock in Devonshire Dock (c.1914). A locomotive can be seen moving a large calibre gun to the left under the 150-ton crane. *(Barrow Museum Service CAT 7285)*

Experimental Submarine – HMS *Nautilus*

1 built on behalf of the Royal Navy

> *For many years before 1914 the construction and arming of ships for the British Navy had been Vickers' main home business; it was for this that its accumulation of capital on the one hand, and skill on the other, had been built up. Thus whereas in land material the outbreak of war meant a violent interruption, uncertainty, confusion and improvisation, in naval construction and armament it meant only a change of gear.*
>
> Vickers – A History by J.D. Scott

HMS *Nautilus*   (Yard No.436)   Launched 16 December 1914

The *Nautilus* was a one-off design, an experiment, for an ocean-going submarine which was ordered by the Royal Navy in 1913. More pressing work on wartime submarine building meant that she was not completed until October 1917. *Nautilus* never became operational due to teething problems and the fact that she was slower than envisaged.

Nautilus was a bold experiment – with an increase in surface displacement and a change from the saddle tank type of construction to a double-hull. She was a twin-shaft vessel with two Vickers diesel engines, each of 1,850bhp, two main motors of 500bhp and 352 Exide cells in two battery tanks. The *Nautilus*, renamed N1 in June 1917, was designed by Vickers to have good sea-keeping qualities for extended operations in all weather conditions. Regarded by submarine officers as 'an exceedingly interesting experiment', *Nautilus* was laid down in March 1913 and, with an overall length of nearly 260ft, was twice the size of any existing submarine.

The estimated cost of building *Nautilus* is given as £203,850 but, because of the extended building time, the changes that occurred, the increase in displacement and additions such as hydroplane guards, this figure was undoubtedly exceeded.

Although the designed surface speed is given as 17 knots, it is doubtful whether any reliable 'in service' figures for speed and endurance were obtained since she was not completed until October 1917 and had little, if any, service as an operational submarine. Her designed diving depth is given as 200ft and compared with that achieved by previous classes this would seem to be reasonable. Her armament consisted of two 18in bow torpedo tubes, four 18in beam tubes and two 18in stern tubes (with sixteen torpedoes carried). A 3in High Angle (HA) gun was fitted on the superstructure just forward of the bridge and this was raised and lowered on a vertical ram. It is said that *Nautilus* was a failure. This may be true; she had little real service experience, being used mainly as a depot ship for instructional purposes and supplying power

Experimental submarine *Nautilus* (later renamed N1) in Devonshire Dock with the Corn Mill in the background.

to other submarines. However, *Nautilus* was significant because the step from small to large-size submarines, with greatly increased engine power, had been taken, and this provided considerable experience and confidence for building later classes.

Experimental Submarine HMS *Nautilus* – Main Characteristics

Overall Length/ Beam/Draught	258ft 5in x 26ft x 18ft
Displacement	1,441 tons surfaced / 2,000 tons submerged
Power	2 x 1,850bhp diesel engines for surface propulsion
	2 x 500bhp electric motors for submerged propulsion
Diving Depth	200ft
Speed	17 knots surfaced / 9 knots submerged
Propeller	2 x (3 blades – 6ft 3in diameter)
Endurance	4,400 miles at maximum of 5 knots surfaced / submerged endurance unknown but designed to be 72 miles maximum
Armament	8 x 18in torpedo tubes (2 bow, 4 beam, 2 stern)
	16 torpedoes carried
	1 x 3in HA gun
Complement	42
Notes	Some sources claim that the boat was equipped with a 12-pounder gun.

G Class Submarines

6 built on behalf of the Royal Navy

> *It was in submarines also that Canadian Vickers made their main contribution. Construction began in January 1915, and by early 1916 six submarines were delivered to the British Isles and another four to the Dardanelles. In 1917 eight submarines were delivered to the Italian government and six built for the Russian government. There had been some planning in Canada for the building of destroyers, but in the end it was decided that cargo vessels would be more useful. All told, the yard at Montreal built twenty-four submarines, 214 armed motor boats and seven cargo vessels in addition to trawlers and drifters, and the works produced one and a half million shells and projectiles.*
>
> *Vickers – A History* by J.D. Scott

HMS G8	(Yard No.463)	Launched 1 May 1916
HMS G9	(Yard No.464)	Launched 15 June 1916
HMS G10	(Yard No.465)	Launched 11 January 1916
HMS G11	(Yard No.466)	Launched 22 February 1916
HMS G12	(Yard No.467)	Launched 24 March 1916
HMS G13	(Yard No.468)	Launched 18 July 1916

The Royal Navy ordered a total of fifteen G Class submarines, though ultimately only fourteen were built, G15 being cancelled in April 1915 after being ordered some six months earlier from White's of Cowes. Barrow built six of the fourteen boats in this class with the remainder being supplied by HM Dockyard, Chatham (five – G1 to G5), Armstrong Whitworth (two – G6 and G7) and Scott's of Greenock (one – G14). Based on the Italian Laurenti double-hulled submarines, the G Class were the first Royal Navy submarines to be armed with 21in torpedoes.

In December 1913, after discussing the German submarine programme, the Admiralty decided that they should prepare a design for an overseas patrol boat of about E Class surface displacement, of partial double-hull construction and with single 21in torpedo tubes forward and aft and two 18in beam tubes. This would be the G Class. In June 1914, five G Class submarines, G1 to G5, were ordered from Chatham Dockyard in London and one month later G6 and G7 were ordered from Armstrong Whitworth.

Vickers engines of the E Class type were fitted in all seven boats, although it was originally intended to fit G6 and G7 with Nuremberg (MAN) and Sultzer engines. (Difficulties in obtaining the Sultzer engine and the impracticability of a MAN design prevented this.) In November 1914, Vickers were given orders for six more boats, G8 to G13, and to build the engines for four of the class being built at Chatham. G14 was ordered from Scott's on the Clyde. Costing an estimated £125,000, the G Class were twin-shafted vessels, with two eight-cylinder diesels that together generated 1,600bhp, giving a surface speed of 14 knots. Two single armature motors, each of 420bhp, gave a submerged speed of 9 knots. The class carried 200 cells in two battery tanks, which gave a submerged endurance of ninety-five miles at 3 knots. Early war experience gained by other classes led to the proposed G Class armament being changed to two 18in bow tubes, two 18in beam tubes and one 21in stern tube. This signalled the beginning of the 21in torpedo in Royal Navy submarines, although the experimental submarine *Swordfish* – ordered from Scott's a year earlier, but launched after G1 – was also fitted with 21in tubes. The class also carried one 3in Quick Fire High Angle (QF HA) gun which was fitted just forward of the bridge and a portable 2-pounder which could be fixed to a pedestal at the after end of the bridge. Living conditions were considered by crew members to be good – because the G boats boasted such luxuries as an electric oven! Although the designed diving depth of the G Class was given as 200ft, the operational depth was probably 100ft.

HMS G10, one of the six G Class submarines built at Barrow.

However, it was noted that in 'an exceptional circumstance one G boat dived to 170ft when chased by mistake by British destroyers.' During the First World War G7, G8 and G11 were lost on active service through unknown causes and in September 1917 G9 was sunk in error by HMS *Petard* off the Norwegian coast. Of those that survived, four were taken out of service at the end of the war and the remaining six were withdrawn from service in January 1921.

G Class Submarines – Main Characteristics

Overall Length/ Beam/Draught	187ft x 22ft 7in x 16ft 7in
Displacement	700 tons surfaced / 985 tons submerged
Power	2 x 800bhp Vickers diesel engines for surface propulsion
	2 x 420bhp electric motors for submerged propulsion
Diving Depth	200ft
Speed	14 knots surfaced / 9 knots submerged
Propeller	2 x (3 blades – 5ft 8in diameter)
Endurance	1,650 miles at full power surfaced / 95 miles at 3 knots submerged
Armament	4 x 18in torpedo tubes (2 bow; 2 beam)
	1 x 21in stern torpedo tube
	1 x 3in QF HA gun
	1 x 2-pounder gun
Complement	31

K Class and K26 Submarines

7 built on behalf of the Royal Navy

> *The method taught by the boilermakers to the builders of the early iron ships, for joining plates to one another, was the familiar process of rivetting – punching or drilling holes along the edges of the plates and stitching them together by hammering hot metal plugs into the holes. For extra strength more rows of holes and rivets [were made] – a somewhat crude but nevertheless effective joint, made watertight by burring the overlapping edges of the plate with a special caulking tool. The methods of those early days continued with little change other than the inevitable growth of mechanisation, until quite recent times. Indeed, in some less progressive shipyards they still prevail.*
>
> *Ships* by J.S. Redshaw

HMS K3	(Yard No.480)	Launched 29 May 1916
HMS K4	(Yard No.481)	Launched 15 July 1916
HMS K8	(Yard No.482)	Launched 18 October 1916
HMS K9	(Yard No.483)	Launched 8 November 1916
HMS K10	(Yard No.484)	Launched 27 December 1916
HMS K17	(Yard No.492)	Launched 10 April 1917
HMS K26	(Yard No.564)	Launched 26 August 1919

The original intention by the Royal Navy was for the building of no less than twenty-one K Class submarines but, ultimately, just seventeen were constructed. The keels of the four cancelled boats (K18 through to K21) were used to build four of the later M Class submarines (see pages 70-73). The Barrow Yard was responsible for building six of the K Class submarines with the others being built by HM Dockyard, Portsmouth (three – K1, K2 and K5,), HM Dockyard, Devonport (two – K6 and K7), Armstrong's (two – K11, K12), Fairfield's (two – K13, K14), Scott's of Greenock (one – K15) and Beardmore's (one – K16). K13, built by Fairfield's, was later refitted and recommissioned as K22, following an incident in which thirty-one men lost their lives. Never again was the number thirteen allocated to a Royal Navy submarine.

K26 was one of six submarines (K23 to K28) ordered as follow-ons to the K Class. In the event only K26 was completed. The Barrow Shipyard had been earmarked to build K26 to K28, while K23 to K25 were to have been built by Armstrong's. Interestingly, although K26 was built and launched at Barrow, it was subsequently towed to Chatham Dockyard for completion work.

K Class submarines were the most bizarre and ill-fated submarines of the First World War period. Their conception, in the spring of 1915, arose from the demand for a submarine that could accompany the Grand Fleet at speeds of up to 24 knots. A 1913 Admiralty design was adopted and, given the outline particulars, Vickers were requested to proceed with the detailed drawings. The first-of-class K3 was laid down by His Majesty the King in May 1915 and was completed at Vickers within fifteen months of being ordered. As a result of her trials, additional fans were fitted in the turbine room to combat the very high temperature generated by the steam turbines. Of the seventeen of the class, six were built at Vickers, each at an estimated cost of £340,000. Originally twenty-eight K Class submarines were ordered, but of these several were later cancelled.

K18 to K21 were redesigned and became the M Class – K26 was used as an experimental submarine, built in an attempt to overcome the defects of the earlier K boats. At the time they were built, the K Class were not only the largest submarines in the world, but also the fastest – their phenomenal speed being attained from 10,500bhp oil-fired steam turbines. In addition to the steam turbines, the class had an auxiliary diesel generator for charging the batteries and powering the electric motors.

The pioneer vessels of the K Class had a flush deck with a slight sheer forward but, because of a tendency to dive into head seas, later boats were redesigned to overcome this alarming habit and were fitted with large clipper bows and buoyancy tanks. In order to allow this change, the armament and torpedo tubes were rearranged – the guns were removed to the superstructure and, where fitted, twin 18in deck tubes for use on the surface at night were removed. The outline of the K boats was broken by two small funnels which were hinged to fold down into a watertight well. The large air-intakes for the two oil-fired boilers also required watertight seals.

In the concise words of a contemporary submariner, the K Class had 'too many damned holes' and a minor obstruction or wire rope was sufficient to jam a vent open just as the submarine was ready to dive. An added disadvantage was that the highly ingenious design of the class was so complex that it was vulnerable to small defects. K Class submarines could

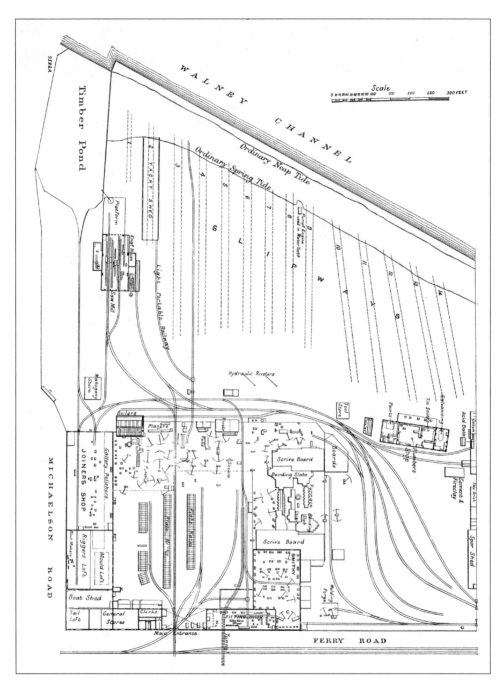

A plan showing the layout of the Barrow-in-Furness Shipyard at the end of the nineteenth century.

A model of a K Class submarine. *(Barrow Museum Service CAT 2659)*

submerge faster than any previous steam submarine, but the delay was still impossibly long. Although the specified time to close down and secure the boiler room, funnel, etc. was only thirty seconds, the class still took about five minutes to dive. Once submerged the class could dive to a depth of 200ft.

The K Class boats, being high-speed Fleet submarines, were fitted with a deckhouse built over and around the conning tower forming, in fact, a fully-enclosed bridge and giving, for the first time in the history of Royal Navy submarines, protection other than by canvas screens (dodgers) to bridge personnel.

K Class submarines began to enter service in 1916, but because of their role with the Fleet they were unduly exposed to the risk of collision, and a chapter of accidents befell the class. The worst accident occurred on the night of 31 January 1918 when ten K Class boats were operating with battle cruisers on a night exercise off May Island.

During the night, the helm in K14 jammed to starboard and she swung round and collided with K22, which was actually the K13 renamed after she had drowned most of her crew on her maiden voyage. The two boats locked together and in a series of collisions K4 was sunk by K6 (losing all hands) and K7 was sunk by HMS *Fearless* (also losing all hands). Four other submarines were damaged. This incident added further to the suspicion of a hoodoo on the K Class; just two months earlier K1 had been sunk by the gunfire of HMS *Blonde* off the Danish coast. These disasters finally sealed the fate of the K Class submarines and most were taken out of service at the end of the war. The class never had an opportunity to prove themselves as Fleet submarines – only six of the seventeen boats built were in commission for six years or more, and the maximum time in service was nine years.

However, experience gained from the K Class led to the building of the experimental submarine K26, which was laid down in June 1918 and launched at Vickers fourteen months later. In 1920 she was towed to Chatham and was completed in June 1923. Based on the K Class design, K26 was intended to eliminate or at least reduce the known defects of that class.

Although the general layout in K26 was practically the same as the boats in the K Class, the introduction of six 21in bow torpedo tubes in lieu of four 18in bow tubes was responsible for an overall increase in length of 12ft. The main machinery of K26 was the same as that fitted in the K Class, but her design surface speed of 23.5 knots was 0.5 knot slower. At the same time the loss of speed was blamed on the repositioned 'after hydroplanes being in the wake of the propellers and the increased draught'. The increased displacement was the reason. K26 had a displacement of 2,140 tons with 300 tons of oil fuel. The 24 knots for the K Class was achieved at 1,980 tons displacement carrying the normal load of 197 tons of fuel oil.

A great advance was made in K26 by the introduction of battery compartments – which became standard in the designs of the 1920s. K26 could submerge more rapidly than previous steam submarines, and her diving depth was increased to 250ft – although there is no apparent

HMS K26 – the follow-up to the earlier, unfortunate, K Class boats. This improved boat had a longer hull and increased armament but retained the same machinery, with a decreased performance as a result.

reason for the 50ft increase over that of the K Class. In 1926 K26 began a world voyage which excited considerable attention. She proceeded via Gibraltar, Malta and the Red Sea, to Colombo and Singapore and, after a short stay there, voyaged back again. K26 was taken out of service in April 1931.

The most embarrassing of all the mishaps which befell the ill-fated K Class submarines occurred on K3, a boat which tended to bury her bows in the water when steaming on the surface. When the future King George VI of England (then Prince George) was on board for a visit she decided to bury her bows in the mud of Stokes bay though she freed herself and resurfaced after twenty minutes. This incident probably happened in 1916 or 1917 when the prince was twenty-one years old.

K Class Submarines – Main Characteristics

Overall Length/ Beam/Draught	339ft x 26ft 7in x 21ft
Displacement	1,883 tons surfaced / 2,600 tons submerged
Power	2 steam turbines producing 10,500bhp for surface propulsion
	1 x 800bhp diesel engine to assist diving and surfacing
	2 x 1,400hp electric motors for submerged propulsion
Diving Depth	200ft
Speed	24 knots surfaced / 10 knots submerged
Propeller	2 x (3 blades of 7ft 6in diameter)
Endurance	800 miles at full power surfaced (when using normal stowage of oil fuel) / 12,500 miles at 10 knots surfaced (when using diesel engine only)
	8 miles at 8 knots submerged or 30 miles at 4 knots submerged
Armament	8 x 18in torpedo tubes (4 bow; 4 beam – 16 torpedoes carried)
	2 x 4in guns
	1 x 3in gun
Complement	55
Notes	Twin 18in deck tubes, for use on the surface at night, were included in the K Class design, but were subsequently removed where fitted.

K26 Submarine – Main Characteristics

Overall Length/ Beam/Draught	351ft 3in x 28ft x 21ft 9in
Displacement	2,140 tons surfaced / 2,770 tons submerged
Power	2 steam turbines producing 10,500bhp for surface propulsion
	2 x 1,400hp electric motor for submerged propulsion
Diving Depth	250ft
Speed	23.5 knots surfaced / 9 knots submerged
Propeller	2 x (3 blades of 7ft 6in diameter)
Endurance	1,200 miles at full power surfaced or 12,670 miles at 10 knots surfaced (when using diesel engine only)
	8 miles at 8 knots or 30 miles at 4 knots submerged
Armament	6 x 21in torpedo tubes in bow
	4 x 18in torpedo tubes in beam (20 torpedoes carried in total)
	3 x 4in guns (with a range of 9,000yds)
Complement	59

L Class Submarines

19 built on behalf of the Royal Navy

This, then, was the position during 1919 – Sheffield turning over to railway material, forgings and stampings; Barrow to merchant shipbuilding and the production of locomotives, boilers, turbines, reciprocating steam engines; Erith to matchmaking machinery, machine tools, cardboard box-making machinery and gas meters; Crayford to sporting guns, sewing machines and motor car parts; Dartford to furniture, wooden toys, washing machines and so forth. Wolseley were planning the production of mass-produced cars, but high-class mass-produced cars costing £800, such that 'no American car could compete with'.

Vickers – A History by J.D. Scott

HMS L1	(Yard No.489)	Launched 10 May 1917	(Group One)
HMS L2	(Yard No.490)	Launched 6 July 1917	(Group One)
HMS L3	(Yard No.495)	Launched 1 September 1917	(Group One)
HMS L4	(Yard No.496)	Launched 17 November 1917	(Group One)
HMS L11	(Yard No.510)	Launched 26 February 1918	(Group Two)
HMS L12	(Yard No.511)	Launched 16 March 1918	(Group Two)
HMS L17	(Yard No.512)	Launched 13 May 1918	(Group Two)
HMS L14	(Yard No.513)	Launched 19 June 1918	(Group Two)
HMS L18	(Yard No.533)	Launched 21 November 1918	(Group Two)
HMS L19	(Yard No.534)	Launched 4 February 1919	(Group Two)
HMS L20	(Yard No.535)	Launched 23 September 1918	(Group Two)
HMS L21	(Yard No.536)	Launched 11 October 1919	(Group Two)
HMS L22	(Yard No.537)	Launched 25 October 1919	(Group Two)

HMS L23	(Yard No.538)	Launched 1 July 1919	(Group Two)
HMS L24	(Yard No.539)	Launched 13 February 1919	(Group Two)
HMS L25	(Yard No.540)	Launched 19 February 1919	(Group Two)
HMS L26	(Yard No.541)	Launched 29 May 1919	(Group Two)
HMS L27	(Yard No.542)	Launched 14 July 1919	(Group Two)
HMS L32	(Yard No.547)	Launched 23 August 1919	(Group Two)

The Barrow Shipyard was responsible for building no less than nineteen L Class submarines (though L32 was cancelled prior to being completed) and, in addition to those listed above, was originally intended to construct four others (L28 to L31) before these boats were cancelled. In total a wide variety of shipyards delivered a total of thirty-four L Class submarines to the Royal Navy, though at least as many again (including the five earmarked for Barrow) were cancelled. Four of the Barrow-built boats (L23, L25, L26 and L27) were launched at the Barrow Shipyard but then towed away to other yards to be completed. L Class submarines fell into three distinct groups but, although they built over half of the class, the Barrow Shipyard only constructed submarines in Groups One and Two.

Delighted with the success of the E Class submarines, in 1916 the Admiralty decided to revert to the saddle tank-type of construction, incorporating the lessons learned from war experience. Two submarines to a new Admiralty design were ordered from Vickers in February 1916 and, being practically elongated Es, they were called E57 and E58. However, overall improvements so distinguished the design that a new class title was adopted, the L Class, and the two boats were later renamed L1 and L2. By December 1916, a total of thirty-four L Class submarines had been ordered, but of these only twenty-seven were commissioned – L28 to L32 were broken up after commencement and L34 and L35 were cancelled. Submarine L13 was never ordered, presumably for 'superstitious' reasons (memories of the K13 perhaps?) Eighteen of the class were built at Vickers and three were completed in other yards.

L Class submarines can be divided into three groups: L1 to L8 with 18in bow and beam tubes; L14, L17 and L24 to L27, which were fitted as minelayers with 21in bow tubes; and L9 to L33 (excluding the minelayers) which had 21in bow tubes and 18in beam tubes. In addition to the torpedo armament, the class carried a gun mounted on the superstructure forward of the bridge. Although the earlier boats (L1 to L8) carried a 3in HA gun, all the class were eventually fitted with a 4in gun of various descriptions – for a three-man increase in the complement. This increase meant that the L boats had a thirty-eight-man crew, but even so, they carried only one 12ft 6in collapsible lifeboat. The L Class were the first submarines to carry some of the normal fuel stowage in external tanks. Although only about 20 tons of fuel was carried in two lightly-constructed tanks, this started the practice, which was developed in the 1920s, of carrying a large amount of fuel externally.

The main engines of the class were two 12-cylinder diesels, giving a total of 1,200bhp at 380rev/min. Some authorities quote 2,600bhp, but this was the bench test power of the engines. L Class submarines carried 336 cells in three battery tanks, grouped to allow working at 220 volts in series and 110 volts in parallel, producing submerged power for four

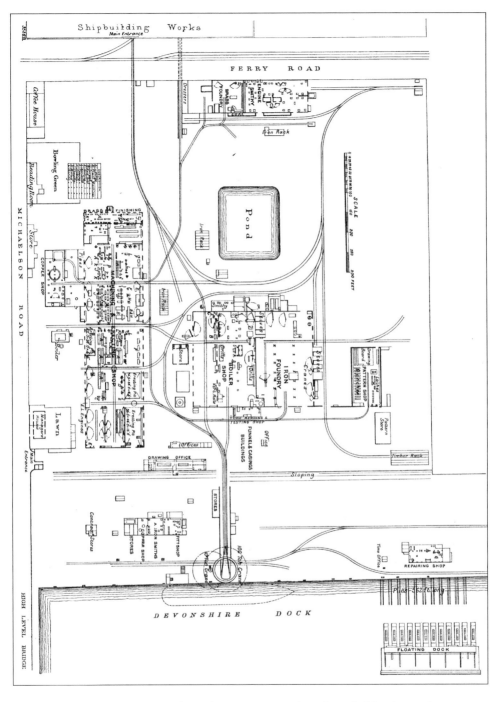

A plan of the Barrow-in-Furness Shipyard's Engineering Works at the end of the nineteenth century.

main motors of the open shunt wound double-armature type, developing a total of 1,600bhp at 300rev/min for 1½ hours. Also, an auxiliary drive consisting of a 20bhp motor, driving the starboard shaft through a worm drive, could give a slow-running submerged speed of 1.75 knots.

A surface speed in excess of 17 knots was hoped for in the L Class and, even when carrying additional fuel in the external tanks, there is no doubt that this speed was attained. The first boat on trials, L1, actually obtained 17.2 knots and in 1930 17.6 knots was given as the design surface speed for the class. Although a design submerged speed of 11 knots was anticipated in L1, the fitting of a 5ft 6in-high fixed bridge screen reduced this to 10.5 knots. Although it has been stated that the designed diving depth of the L Class was 250ft, the officially used maximum diving depth, in 1925, was 150ft – based on such criteria as the age of the boats and their wartime construction. However, depths in service of more than 250ft have been recorded and, on one occasion, L2 accidentally submerged to 300ft and, except for minor faults, withstood the pressure.

Of the L Class, only one was lost during the war – L10 in the North Sea. In August 1923, L9 foundered in Hong Kong harbour in a typhoon and was later salvaged, but was not refitted. In January 1924, L24 was accidentally rammed and sunk off Portland by the battleship HMS *Resolution*. At the time, prolonged efforts were made to salvage her, and a team of German divers, with a new type of diving suit which enabled them to work in deeper waters, was brought over. Unfortunately, the strong underwater currents proved too difficult and the L24 still lies where she sank. On 10 July 1929, during a transit of St George's Channel off the Pembroke coast of Wales, L12 was in collision with H47 which sank with only three of her twenty-four-man crew surviving. L12 lost three of her crew.

Devonshire Dock in 1918. This photograph shows three different classes of submarine built at Barrow-in-Furness. On the left of the three is L12, an overseas 'saddle tank' boat. In the centre is H28, a single-hull coastal boat. On the far right, almost hidden, is R7, one of the famous 'hunter-killer' class. All three boats were commissioned on 29 June 1918.

A twelve-cylinder starboard diesel engine as fitted in L Class submarines. *(Barrow Museum Service CAT 3004)*

In October 1947, L27 was the last L boat to be taken out of service – twenty-eight years after she was laid down – thus reflecting the success of the class. The building of the L boats led to the construction of the L50 Class, which was the L Class modified to give increased armament. Although none were built at the Vickers Yard at Barrow-in-Furness, a total of twenty-five L50 submarines were ordered from seven yards, but of these only seven were completed.

L Class Submarines – Main Characteristics (Group One)

Overall Length/ Beam/Draught	231ft x 23ft 6in x 14ft
Displacement	890 tons surfaced / 1,070 tons submerged
Power	2 x 1,200bhp diesel engines for surface propulsion
	2 x 800bhp electric motors for submerged propulsion
Diving Depth	150ft
Speed	17.5 knots surfaced / 10.5 knots submerged
Propeller	2 x (3 blades – 5ft 7in diameter)
Endurance	2,850 miles at full power surfaced / 14 miles at full power submerged
Armament	6 x 18in torpedo tubes (4 bow, 2 beam)
	10 torpedoes carried
	1 x 3in or 4in gun
	Carried 16 to 18 mines
Complement	35
Notes	Group One L Class submarines were designed to have two 3in D/HA guns but were only fitted with one. All had 3in guns except L4 which had a 4in gun.

HMS L27. *(Campbell McCutcheon)*

L Class Submarines – Main Characteristics (Group Two)

Overall Length/ Beam/Draught	238ft 6in x 23ft 6in x 14ft
Displacement	890 tons surfaced / 1,075 tons submerged
Power	2 x 1,200bhp diesel engines for surface propulsion
	2 x 800bhp electric motors for submerged propulsion
Diving Depth	150ft
Speed	17.5 knots surfaced / 10.5 knots submerged
Propeller	2 x (3 blades – 5ft 7in diameter)
Endurance	2,850 miles at full power surfaced / 14 miles at full power submerged
Armament	2 x 21in torpedo tubes in bow
	2 x 18in torpedo tubes in stern
	10 torpedoes carried
Complement	38
Notes	Some Group Two boats had four 21in bow tubes and carried fourteen mines. L14 had no deck gun. L12, L14, L17 and L18 had a 4in gun.

M Class Submarines

2 built on behalf of the Royal Navy

The R.9 left Barrow in April 1917, and was used successfully for the training programme for which she had been built. Meanwhile both Armstrongs and Beardmores had been brought in on the building of an improved R.9 type, the designs and working drawings being prepared by

Vickers. These airships – they were the R.23 class – were now wanted in a hurry. As much as possible of the design of the R.9 class was adopted, while once again the ships were to be extra strong for use by inexperienced crews. They had 900,000 cubic feet capacity, a length of 535 feet, and a speed of 55 miles an hour with over 18 hours endurance. Two ships of this class, the R.23 and the R.26, were built at Barrow and were delivered, one in October 1917 and the other in March 1918.

Vickers – *A History* by J.D. Scott

HMS M1   (Yard No.491)   Launched 9 July 1917
HMS M2   (Yard No.494)   Launched 15 April 1919

The M Class submarines were effectively submersible battleships, an idea first mooted by Lord Fisher in 1915 after his resignation. His idea was to mount a 12in (60-ton) gun from a battleship in front of the conning tower of a submarine. The idea was put into action in early 1916 with the ordering of four M Class boats, the guns to come from King Edward VII Class battleships, and the keels of the new boats to be those from the cancelled K Class submarines (18 to 21). Although four boats were ordered – two from Barrow and two from Armstrong Whitworth's – only three were completed with M4 being cancelled prior to completion and sold back to the builders (Armstrong Whitworth's) as scrap.

Inspired by the news of German U-cruisers with 5.9in guns, the Committee on Submarine Development decided to construct submarine monitors – the M Class – with 12in guns. Four K Class submarines (K18 to K21) had been ordered in February 1916 but, when Vickers received an order to build a boat to the new design, K18 was remodelled and became M1. M2 (ex K19) was ordered from Vickers in May 1916 and two more, M3 (ex K20) and M4 (ex K21), from Armstrong Whitworth in August 1916. Of the three M Class submarines built (M4 was scrapped before completion) only M1 was completed before the end of the war, although she was never used in action because it was thought that if she was copied by the enemy Britain was likely to suffer more from the use of the 12in gun than Germany. Why this was never thought of before construction remains a mystery. M2 and M3 were completed in 1920.

The fact that the M Class design got further than the conference table is a reflection of the failure by the Admiralty to recognise the proper nature of submarine operations. Although their 12in guns were ideally suited for bombarding coastal defences, their method of attack at sea was rather primitive. The attack procedure was to cruise at periscope depth until the target was 'lined up'. The submarine was then brought up until about 6ft of the gun barrel protruded from the water. A round (weighing 850lb) was fired and the submarine would then make a rapid dive – unable to fire again as the gun could not be reloaded under water. Known as the 'dip-chick' method, this attack procedure took about thirty seconds to complete. The M Class were partially double-hulled submarines with the double-hull extending for about 65% of the length of the boat.

A surface speed of 15 knots was attained from two Vickers 12-cylinder diesel engines, each of 1200bhp. Underwater, four double-armature-type main motors, generating 400bhp each,

A model of an M Class submarine. *(Barrow Museum Service CAT 2660)*

gave a submerged speed of 9 knots. Power for submerged operations was supplied from three battery tanks containing a total of 336 Exide cells. The guns used by the M boats came from the King Edward VII Class battleships – the gun and mounting weighing about 120 tons and the forty rounds of ammunition 29 tons. At the end of the war, the question of future employment arose as 'there were no targets and the enemy had not initiated anything bold in submarine policy'. Consequently, during the 1920s, the three M Class submarines led contrasting lives.

On 12 October 1925 M1 was attempting to resurface, having failed to establish satisfactory trim during dived manoeuvres, when she was struck by the Swedish vessel SS *Vidal*. *Vidal*'s bow tore the gun muzzle and housing out of M1's hull which, unable to blow tanks because she had exhausted high-pressure air during the attempted resurfacing, plunged to the seabed. M1's crew perished. M2 and M3 had their large 12in guns removed in the late 1920s to conform with the Washington Disarmament Treaty, which stated that no submarine should have larger than 8in calibre guns.

M2 was refitted with a seaplane hangar forward of the conning tower and a catapult to launch a small Parnall Peto seaplane. This conversion was seemingly a success, and M2 could surface from periscope depth, open the hangar door and catapult the plane, close the door and dive again within five minutes. However, M2 was subsequently lost during exercises in the English Channel in 1932 when undertaking this operation. Because M2 was a large boat it actually required fifteen minutes to blow all the main tanks fully clear of water, following which the seaplane would be brought out of the hangar, assembled and launched. Under battle conditions the boat would be extremely vulnerable during that period. Because of that and a Newcastle collier skipper witnessing M2's apparent last dive as stern first, many submariners believe a shortened procedure evolved thus:

When the boat's superstructure cleared the surface, the hydroplanes were used to maintain the boat on the surface. Even though the ballast tanks were not completely empty, the pressure hull access hatch to the hangar, and then the hangar door, were opened and the seaplane prepared. On that fateful day on 26 January 1932 it is considered the hydroplanes, for whatever reason, suffered a failure and M2 slid stern first into the sea, the open hangar door and hatch hastening her doom. In 1927, M3 was converted to an experimental minelayer, stowing her 100 mines on rails inside a large free-flooding casing outside the hull. The mines were laid over her stern by means of a chain conveyor belt. M3 was finally taken out of service in April 1932 and scrapped in 1933. Although the M Class may be considered unsuccessful because their big guns were never used for the purpose intended, they were popular with their crews and were claimed to be handy underwater, quick to dive and easy to handle.

M Class Submarines – Main Characteristics

Overall Length/ Beam/Draught	296ft x 24ft 6in x 16ft
Displacement	1,650 tons surfaced / 1,950 tons submerged
Power	2 x 1,200bhp diesel engines for surface propulsion
	4 x 400bhp electric motors for submerged propulsion
Diving Depth	200ft
Speed	15.5 knots surfaced / 9.5 knots submerged
Propeller	2 x (3 blades of 5ft 10in diameter)
Endurance	2,000 miles at full power or 4,500 miles (maximum) surfaced /
	9 miles at 8+ knots submerged
Armament	4 x 18in torpedo tubes in bow (M1, M2 and M3)
	4 x 21in torpedo tubes in bow (M3)
	8 torpedoes carried on all boats
	1 x 12in gun
	1 x 3in AA gun
Complement	60 to 70
Notes	The four 21in torpedo tubes which were fitted to M3 increased the boat length by 10ft.

H Class Submarines

12 built on behalf of the Royal Navy

In the entrance hall of the Company's Works at Barrow there hangs a small brass plaque bearing the name 'Barrow Shipbuilding Co.' and the date 1872; a link with the almost forgotten days when from still-existing slipways came the City of Rome *for the Inman Line,* Orizoba *and* Oroya *to sail the far Pacific, early ventures into Naval Construction for the Admiralty, and many fine ships in great variety.*

Ships *by J.S. Redshaw*

HMS H21	(Yard No.499)	Launched 20 October 1917	(Group Two)
HMS H22	(Yard No.500)	Launched 7 September 1918	(Group Two)
HMS H23	(Yard No.501)	Launched 29 January 1918	(Group Two)
HMS H24	(Yard No.502)	Launched 14 November 1917	(Group Two)
HMS H25	(Yard No.503)	Launched 27 April 1918	(Group Two)
HMS H26	(Yard No.504)	Launched 15 November 1917	(Group Two)
HMS H27	(Yard No.527)	Launched 25 September 1918	(Group Two)
HMS H28	(Yard No.528)	Launched 12 March 1918	(Group Two)
HMS H29	(Yard No.529)	Launched 8 July 1918	(Group Two)
HMS H30	(Yard No.530)	Launched 9 May 1918	(Group Two)
HMS H31	(Yard No.531)	Launched 16 November 1918	(Group Two)
HMS H32	(Yard No.532)	Launched 19 November 1918	(Group Two)

The H Class submarines fell into two groups, twenty submarines being ordered from Group One and thirty-four from Group Two. All the Group One boats were ordered from Bethlehem Corp. in the USA, with the orders for the Group Two boats being placed with British shipbuilders. In the event, ten of the proposed British-built boats were cancelled, though Barrow – with an initial order of twelve Group Two boats – did not suffer any cancellations at all. Barrow built the first of the Group Two class, H21, and for this reason these boats are often referred to as H21 Class submarines to differentiate them from the first twenty ordered from the USA.

While L Class submarines were under construction, Vickers received an order, in January 1917, to build twelve boats to the American H Class design. Twenty boats of this class had been contracted from the Bethlehem Steel Works, USA, in November 1914 for the Royal Navy. Fourteen were delivered (H1 to H12, H14 and H15) – the other six were forfeited to Chile as compensation for warships seized in 1914. H14 and H15 were transferred to the Royal Canadian Navy in April 1919. The British H boats, known as the H21 Class, were a modification of the American design, and accommodated a heavier torpedo armament (21in bow tubes replacing 18in tubes) which increased the overall length of the class by over 21ft.

Engines, main motors and other fittings obtained from America speeded up construction, and the Vickers-built first-of-class H21 was completed in January 1918 – eleven months after being laid down. In June 1917, further orders were given to five other yards for twenty-two additional H21 submarines (H33 to H54) with their engines and motors being made in England to the American H Class design. Ten of these boats were subsequently cancelled when it was decided, in October 1917, to construct twelve new R Class submarines.

The H21 Class were the first Royal Navy twin-shafted single-hulled submarines, and their American-designed eight-cylinder vertical single armature diesel engines produced a total of 480bhp. Their main motors, also of American design, were powered by 120 battery cells, produced 620bhp for one hour and had a continuous rating of 320bhp.

As the H21 Class employed the same engines and main motors as the American H boats, but had an increase in displacement of over 70 tons, quoting the American design speeds – 13 knots surfaced and 10.5 knots submerged – was obviously optimistic. In service, speeds of 11.5 knots surfaced and 9 knots submerged were recorded.

Although built for service in the First World War, the only H21 Class submarines to be lost on active service were, ironically, during the Second World War – over twenty years later.

Of the Barrow-built H Class submarines H21, H22, H23, H25, H26, H27 and H30 were all eventually sold in the late 1920s and early 1930s. H32 also survived its service life, being scrapped in 1944. H24, launched in 1917, was rammed by HMS *Vancouver* while submerged (in July 1922) but although her conning tower was badly damaged in the incident she was duly repaired. She continued to give service until 1934 when she was sold. H28 would eventually be scrapped at Troon in August 1944, but not before she had managed to collide with a steamer in the Bruges Canal in May 1929. The career of H29 was rather more tragic. On 9 August 1926, she sank in Devonport Dockyard while trimming down with her hatches open, an incident which claimed the lives of five civilians and one ERA. H29 was later raised (in 1927) and sold. The most successful Barrow-built H Class boat on active service was H31: she was responsible for sinking UJ-126 in the North Sea in July 1940 and, in November of

HMS H28, one of the twelve H Class submarines built at the Shipyard at Barrow.

the following year, assisted in preventing the *Scharnhorst* from breaking out of Brest. Tragically H31 was lost, assumed mined, in the Bay of Biscay on Boxing Day 1941 (though some sources state Christmas Eve 1941).

H Class Submarines – Main Characteristics (Group Two)

Overall Length/ Beam/Draught	171ft x 15ft 6in x 14ft
Displacement	440 tons surfaced / 510 tons submerged
Power	2 x 240bhp diesel engines for surface propulsion
	2 x 160bhp electric motors for submerged propulsion
Diving Depth	150ft
Speed	13 knots surfaced / 10 knots submerged
Propeller	2
Endurance	1,100 miles at full power or 1,600 miles at 10 knots surfaced /
	9 miles at 8 knots or 34 miles at 3.5 knots submerged
Armament	4 x 21in torpedo tubes in bow (6 torpedoes carried)
	1 x 12-pounder gun (some boats only)
Complement	22
Fuel capacity	16 tons

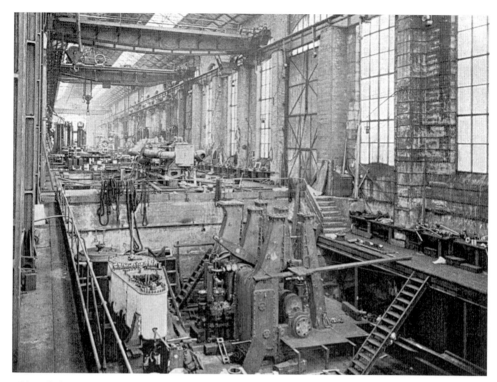

Although this picture of the Engine Fitting Shop at the Shipyard dates from c.1896, it will still have looked much like this when the H Class submarines were being constructed at Barrow.

First R Class Submarines

2 built on behalf of the Royal Navy

> *There were other acquisitions in 1917 and 1918, but these were made, not with a view to gaining a further control over wartime products, but with a view to entering post-war markets, in a peace which, in the spring of 1918, seemed a long way off.*
>
> Vickers – A History by J.D. Scott

HMS R7	(Yard No.549)	Launched 14 May 1918
HMS R8	(Yard No.550)	Launched 28 June 1918

The Barrow Shipyard built just two of the first R Class submarines ordered by the Royal Navy, these being the first submarines designed specifically to attack enemy U-boats. In total ten boats were built in this class, four by HM Dockyard Chatham, two by Cammell Laird, two by Armstrong-Whitworth's and of course the two Barrow-built boats. The original intention had been for twelve boats in this class but R5 and R6 were cancelled.

R Class submarines, the forerunners of the modern-day hunter-killers, were built on the premise that a submarine with an exceptionally high submerged speed and with the ability to launch a number of torpedoes might be able to overtake and sink the enemy.

In October 1917, twelve R Class boats were ordered from five yards. R7 was the first to be completed at Vickers, in June 1918, within nine months of order. Vickers also constructed R8. R5 and R6, two boats that were to be built at Pembroke Dockyard, were cancelled before launch.

The R Class boats' surface speed of 9.5 knots was attained from one 240bhp engine of the H Class type and their high submerged speed of 15 knots from two main motors, driven by 220 battery cells, generating 1,200bhp.

The fact that the class could reach a submerged speed of 15 knots, which remained a record until the closing stages of the Second World War, was partly due to their lightened superstructure, which was cut to a bare minimum, and a streamlined fish-shaped hull. From war experience, designers became rather optimistic in their assessment of diving depths and the designed diving depth of the R Class was given as 250ft, but the operational diving depth would have been fixed at 150ft.

The R Class were the first Royal Navy submarines to be fitted with six 18in torpedo tubes, which was a powerful torpedo armament for the size of the boat. One spare torpedo was allowed for in the design, but during the war six spares were stowed at the expense of one Senior Rating's accommodation.

Originally it was intended to fit a 4in gun forward of the bridge, but this was never adopted as it would have had an adverse effect on submerged speed, which was the main characteristic of the design. Having a greater submerged radius than most submarines of the period, the R Class boats used five hydrophones to detect submerged enemy vessels – had they been fitted with a better detection device the development of the modern submarine may have gone ahead more quickly. An R Class boat is credited with torpedoing a U-boat in October 1918 – had the torpedo exploded the R Class boats may have earned more respect instead of being thought of as curiosities.

HMS R7. One of the two R Class submarines built at Barrow.

First R Class Submarines – Main Characteristics

Overall Length/ Beam/Draught	163ft x 15ft 9in x 11ft 6in
Displacement	410 tons surfaced / 500 tons submerged
Power	1 x 240bhp diesel engine for surface propulsion
	2 x 600bhp electric motors for submerged propulsion
Diving Depth	150ft
Speed	9.5 knots surfaced / 15 knots submerged
Propeller	1
Endurance	2,400 miles at full power surfaced / 15 miles at full power or 150 miles at 1.5 knots submerged
Armament	6 x 18in torpedo tubes in bow (7 torpedoes carried)
Complement	22

3
Submarines between the Wars
(1926 to 1936)

O Class Submarines

2 built on behalf of the Royal Australian Navy
3 built on behalf of the Royal Navy
3 built on behalf of the Chilean Navy

At Barrow, in the spring, 'the birds were nesting in the cranes'. Never before, and never since, had times been so hard as they were in 1922 and 1923; at the end of every day the men still in work were met at the gates by barefoot children calling out: 'any bread left?'

Vickers – A History by J.D. Scott

Royal Australian Navy

HMAS *Oxley*	(Yard No.621)	Launched 29 June 1926	(Group One)
HMAS *Otway*	(Yard No.622)	Launched 7 September 1926	(Group One)

Royal Navy

HMS *Osiris*	(Yard No.633)	Launched 19 May 1928	(Group Two)
HMS *Oswald*	(Yard No.634)	Launched 19 June 1928	(Group Two)
HMS *Otus*	(Yard No.635)	Launched 31 August 1928	(Group Two)

Chilean Navy

Capitan O'Brien	(Yard No.645)	Launched 2 October 1928	(Group Two)
Capitan Thompson	(Yard No.646)	Launched 15 January 1929	(Group Two)
Almirante Simpson	(Yard No.647)	Launched 15 January 1929	(Group Two)

There were two groups within the O Class submarines, and the Barrow Shipyard built boats from both. Three Group One submarines were built, though just one – the first-of-class *Oberon* (built at Chatham) – was for the Royal Navy. The other two, the Barrow-built boats, were for the Royal Australian Navy and although almost identical to *Oberon* (and classified as Group One boats) they were in fact some 5ft longer with slightly higher displacements. The Royal Navy ordered six of the Group Two O Class submarines, three of which were constructed at Barrow. In addition the Barrow Shipyard supplied the Chilean Navy with three of the Group Two boats.

The first submarines to be designed after the First World War were the O Class – a post-war concept of an Overseas Patrol Submarine. With this class it appears that the Admiralty finally decided that the submarine deserved the dignity of a name; thus, the pioneer of the class was called *Oberon* (built at Chatham). The L50 Class submarines were chosen as a model for the *Oberon* design, but the new class had much greater endurance, increased diving depth, improved torpedo armament and increased wireless range. However, a 75% increase in displacement led to a loss of both surface and submerged speed. During the building of *Oberon*, the unforeseen growth in topside fittings had a devastating effect on submerged speed and, although modifications were made after her completion in August 1927, a quoted underwater speed of 9 knots, attained from two twin-armature motors developing 1,300bhp, seems impossible. The two Admiralty-designed six-cylinder diesels in *Oberon* developed 2,700bhp and, giving a quoted surface speed of 13.5 knots, were made at HM Dockyard at Chatham.

Laid down after *Oberon*, *Oxley* and *Otway* were built by Vickers for the Royal Australian Navy and had their engines redesigned, an increase in the bore and stroke of the cylinders giving 3,000bhp, which resulted in an increase in surface speed of approximately 1.5 knots. *Oberon* was the first submarine to carry ASDIC – a device originally designed under the auspices of the Allied Submarine Detection Investigation Committee to detect submarines. However, ASDIC, the forerunner of SONAR, was put to good use by submariners against surface targets and took over from the hydrophone which was unable to measure, with any accuracy, the speed, course or distance of an enemy vessel. On their delivery voyage to Australia in 1928, *Oxley* and *Otway* encountered very severe weather in the Bay of Biscay which badly strained their engine columns, forcing them to remain in Malta for several months whilst British experts repaired the damage. After giving useful service in the Royal Australian Navy, the two vessels were transferred to the Royal Navy in April 1931.

In 1925, the need for a new programme of Overseas Patrol Submarine construction resulted in the Odin Class. This class was 13ft longer than the Oberons, owing primarily to

HMS *Oswald*, built at Barrow-in-Furness for the Royal Navy. *(Barrow Museum Service CAT 0007)*

A model of an O Class submarine. *(Barrow Museum Service CAT 3210)*

a 7ft 6in increase in the engine room length. *Odin* was approved by the Board in August 1926 and was the first of a class of six: the others being *Oswald*, *Osiris*, *Otus*, *Olympus* and *Orpheus*. The Odin Class was fitted with four-cycle blast-injection eight-cylinder diesels, accommodated in the larger engine room, and designed to develop a total of 4,400bhp. In each case the main engines were made by the building yard. By the late 1920s the ability to dive quickly had become a major consideration, but it was believed that a submarine could not submerge faster than about 2ft per second. The minimum time to dive from full buoyancy to periscope depth appeared to be in the order of one minute.

The range of seawater density in which submarines of the period were designed to dive was quite limited, and it wasn't until late in the building of the Odin Class that a requirement to be able to dive in fresh water was introduced – resulting in changes to the compensating water tanks. The ability to dive in waters with a specific gravity of 1.00 to 1.30 remained for all submarines until the Second World War, after which it decreased to 1.015 to 1.03. The Oberon, Odin, Parthian and Rainbow Classes were designed to dive to a depth of 500ft. The Oberons were tested to 200ft and in the three later classes the deep diving trials were to 300ft, although it is known that some boats went deeper. Rear-Admiral (Submarines) (RA(S)) laid down 300ft as the test diving depth of boats designed to withstand depth pressure at 500ft.

It is interesting to review the policy regarding deep diving. In 1928, the Director of Tactical Division (DTD) stated: 'The ability to dive to 500ft was introduced principally in order that pressure hulls of these submarines should be more capable of withstanding the effect of the explosion of a depth charge. Submarine officers do not visualise any intentional diving to such depths as 500ft though the ability to do so is an asset in the event of any involuntary deep dive which might cause the submarine to go much deeper than ever was intended.'

When on patrol, the daily fuel consumption for all classes, allowing twelve hours diving, twelve hours steaming at slow speed and eight hours charging, was given as 2.1 tons per day, except in *Orpheus* (the only vessel in the Odin Class to be fitted with a Vulcan clutch) where the consumption was 2.6 tons per day. In the Overseas Patrol Submarines, practically the whole of the fuel was carried in external tanks. The tanks were riveted and tested to 20psi, but they leaked to such an extent that they could be considered a failure.

Various reasons, such as defective plating, manhole covers and bad equalising arrangements, were blamed for the leaks, and many fruitless attempts were made to overcome the faults. In fact the trouble throughout had been caused by the rivets and, in an era when welded ship construction was in its infancy, the externals were ultimately successfully rebuilt in welded construction. Of the nineteen Overseas Patrol Submarines built, eighteen served in the

Second World War; twelve of these were lost on active service. The last submarine of this type to be taken out of service was the Vickers–built *Otus*, in April 1946. Of the three Chilean boats the first, *Capitan O'Brien*, was the 150th submarine to be launched at Barrow. To support their boats, the Chilean government ordered from the Barrow Shipyard the submarine depot ship *Araucano* (Yard No.652).

★ ★ ★

HMS *Oxley* was the first submarine launched at Barrow for eight years. So bad was the situation during the 1920s that in 1922 the *Jervis Bay* (a Commonwealth steamer) was the only boat being built at the Shipyard and in 1926 there was a national general strike. The *Jervis Bay* (Yard No.575) was later sunk in a running battle with the German pocket battle-ship *Admiral Scheer* whilst defending a convoy on 5 November 1940; her commander was later awarded the Victoria Cross.

In July 1922 Poor Law administrators in Barrow faced bankruptcy as the cost of poor relief soared. Twenty thousand men were out of work – the highest total in any town in the North West, apart from the great cities of Liverpool and Manchester. On 5 July the Board of Guardians cut relief rates. The new maximum for a married couple was 25s (£1.25) a week, for a single man it was 10s (50p). Average rent and rates bills in Barrow were 11s (55p) a week. Labourers at Vickers were making 29s (£1.45) a week, wages having fallen over the previous three years. Board chairman Joseph Morrall was threatened and his business blacked; however, the Board owed £70,000 and the bank refused to lend more money. One Board member commented, 'You can see the flesh dropping off people's bones.' There were tense meetings between the Guardians and the unemployed and it was claimed that men kept their overcoats on even though it was July because they had no money to buy clothes to wear underneath. The men would go rummaging on scrap heaps, and sometimes, if one was better off than another, he would perhaps give him half a crown (12½p). One man named Oliver Chalker at the Salvation Army used to go down to the Labour Exchange and fight for the mens' money through use of the Means Test. On 29 July Vickers issued an official denial of a town rumour that the Shipyard was to close entirely. This rumour was sparked when a total of 500 men were paid off at the completion of the tanker *Scottish Musician* (Yard No.583). This left a workforce of less than 4,000 (engaged mostly on repair work) on the Vickers payroll, compared with 36,000 during the First World War.

In 1926 fewer than 4,000 men were still at work in the Yard.

O Class Submarines – Main Characteristics (Group One)

Overall Length/ Beam/Draught	275ft x 27ft 9in x 15ft
Displacement	1,350 tons surfaced / 1,870 tons submerged
Power	2 x 1,500bhp diesel engines for surface propulsion
	2 x 650bhp electric motors for submerged propulsion
Diving Depth	500ft
Speed	15.5 knots surfaced / 9 knots submerged
Propeller	2
Endurance	8,500 miles at 10 knots surfaced / 16 miles at 9 knots submerged

Armament	8 x 21in torpedo tubes (6 bow, 2 stern – 16 torpedoes carried)
	1 x 4in gun
Complement	54

O Class Submarines – Main Characteristics (Group Two)

Overall Length/ Beam/Draught	283ft x 29ft 9in x 16ft
Displacement	1,475 tons surfaced / 2,030 tons submerged
Power	2 x 2,200bhp diesel engines for surface propulsion
	2 x 1,325bhp electric motors for submerged propulsion
Diving Depth	500ft
Speed	17 knots surfaced / 9 knots submerged
Propeller	2 x (3 blades of 6ft 5in diameter)
Endurance	11,400 miles at 8 knots surfaced / 52 miles at 4 knots submerged
Armament	8 x 21in torpedo tubes (6 bow, 2 stern – 14 torpedoes carried)
	1 x 4in gun
Complement	53

P Class Submarines

4 built on behalf of the Royal Navy

Thus, although during the year 1927 Vickers-Armstrongs had signed only one contract for a British naval vessel, during 1928 orders were received for four submarines and a destroyer. All these were launched in the early summer of 1929 and delivered in the early summer of 1930. As Barrow was the supreme specialist submarine yard in Britain, the submarine orders were vital to keep a unique industrial capacity in being…

Vickers – A History by J.D. Scott

HMS *Perseus*	(Yard No.638)	Launched 22 May 1929
HMS *Poseidon*	(Yard No.639)	Launched 21 June 1929
HMS *Proteus*	(Yard No.640)	Launched 23 July 1929
HMS *Pandora*	(Yard No.641)	Launched 22 August 1929

Six P Class submarines were ordered by the Royal Navy, with Barrow building no fewer than four of these. The remaining boats, *Parthian* and *Phoenix* were built at HM Dockyard Chatham and Cammell Laird, respectively. These boats are often referred to as Parthian Class submarines as that boat was the first of the class. These submarines were similar to the O Class though larger to accommodate more powerful machinery. They were designed for use in the Far East and were fitted with external long-range fuel tanks.

The launch of HMS *Perseus* into Walney Channel on 22 May 1929. *(Barrow Museum Service CAT 2375)*

In the 1927 programme, six Parthian Class submarines were ordered (*Parthian*, *Perseus*, *Poseidon*, *Proteus*, *Pandora* and *Phoenix*). Although slightly larger than the O Class boats, the main particulars of these two classes were practically the same. The Parthian Class were all fitted with four-cycle blast-injection eight-cylinder diesels, accommodated in the larger engine room and designed to develop a total of 4,640bhp. In each case the main engines were made by the building yard.

During the preparation of this work, in June 2000 the *North West Evening Mail* carried a moving account of the tribute paid to the crew of HMS *Perseus* by relatives. *Perseus* was mined and sank in December 1941 off the coast of Italian-occupied Cephalonia. Greek divers located the boat, which lay tilted to starboard in 171ft of water, in 1998.

Incredibly there was one escapee, Leading Stoker John Capes, who managed to swim ashore to be hidden by the islanders from Axis forces for eighteen months before being smuggled to Turkey. An account of the mining and the escape is given in *British Submarines at War 1939-1945* by Alistair Mars.

A view of the Barrow-in-Furness Shipyard in the 1920s. This view is taken from a painting by Barrow artist and draughtsman William McDowell. *(Barrow Museum Service CAT 6549)*

P Class Submarines – Main Characteristics

Overall Length/ Beam/Draught	289ft x 28ft x 15ft
Displacement	1,760 tons surfaced / 2,040 tons submerged
Power	2 x 2,320bhp Admiralty diesel engines for surface propulsion
	2 x 1,635bhp electric motors for submerged propulsion
Diving Depth	500ft
Speed	17.5 knots surfaced / 8.5 knots submerged
Propeller	2 x (3 blades – 6ft 5in diameter)
Endurance	10,750 miles at 8 knots surfaced / 8.5 miles at 8.5 knots or
	70 miles at 4 knots submerged
Armament	8 x 21in torpedo tubes (6 bow, 2 stern) – 16 torpedoes carried
	1 x 4in gun
Complement	56
Miscellaneous	Fitted with long-range fuel tanks

Second R Class Submarines

3 built on behalf of the Royal Navy

During the years 1928 to 1934 the benefits which the company was deriving from the holdings in foreign companies – in Spain and in Japan, in Italy, Roumania, Yugoslavia and elsewhere – were declining. These benefits had never in reality been nearly so important to the company as they were in the legend of the 'international armaments business', a legend which itself was growing markedly during this period. And now, even such as it had been, this international armaments business was, so far as Vickers was concerned, coming to an end. Economic

nationalism in Japan, Italy and Spain, the effects of the world-wide economic depression, the
distortion of international exchanges – these were among the main reasons.

Vickers – A History by J.D. Scott

HMS *Regent*	(Yard No.653)	Launched 11 June 1930
HMS *Regulus*	(Yard No.654)	Launched 11 June 1930
HMS *Rover*	(Yard No.655)	Launched 11 June 1930

The Second R Class submarines are sometimes referred to as the Rainbow Class, as the HM Dockyard Chatham-built first of class also bore this name. Only four boats in total were built in this class (from an original order of six), the other three all being built at the Barrow Shipyard. The two cancelled boats were to have been built at Beardmore's (*Royalist*) and Cammell Laird (*Rupert*).

The following year (1928), six Rainbow Class submarines (*Rainbow, Regent, Regulus, Rover, Rupert* and *Royalist*) were ordered. Of these *Rupert* and *Royalist* were subsequently cancelled in 1929. Although slightly larger than the O Class boats, the main particulars of these two classes were practically the same. However, in an attempt to make living conditions more pleasant on long surface passages to the Far East, the Rainbow Class were fitted with a galley on the upper deck and a shower in the conning tower. This was the first class to include

HMS *Rover*, one of three Second R Class submarines constructed at Barrow. *(Barrow Museum Service CAT 0009)*

wardroom heads but the fresh water capacity was not increased. The Rainbow Class were all fitted with four-cycle blast-injection eight-cylinder diesel engines, accommodated in the larger engine room and designed to develop a total of 4,640bhp. In each case the main engines were made by the building yard.

The Rainbow Class was designed to dive to a depth of 500ft. The deep diving trials were to 300ft, although it is known that some boats went deeper. Rear-Admiral (Submarines) (RA(S)) laid down 300ft as the test diving depth of boats designed to withstand depth pressure at 500ft.

Second R Class Submarines – Main Characteristics

Overall Length/ Beam/Draught	287ft x 30ft x 16ft
Displacement	1,763 tons surfaced / 2,030 tons submerged
Power	2 x 2,320bhp diesel engines for surface propulsion
	2 x 1,670bhp electric motors for submerged propulsion
Diving Depth	500ft
Speed	18 knots surfaced / 9 knots submerged
Propeller	2 x (3 blades of 6ft 9in diameter)
Endurance	10,900 miles at 8 knots surfaced / 8.8 miles at 8.8 knots or
	60 miles at 4 knots submerged
Armament	8 x 21in torpedo tubes (6 bow, 2 stern) – 14 torpedoes carried
	1 x 4in gun
Complement	51
Notes	These boats were originally designed with a 4.7in gun, later replaced with the 4in version.

This photograph shows the Shipyard's Mould Loft (c.1930). *(Barrow Museum Service CAT 3007)*

Vickers-MAN two-stroke eight-cylinder diesel engine as fitted in HMS *Medway* (Yard No.629) – a submarine depot ship. *(Barrow Museum Service CAT 3157)*

First Porpoise Class Submarines

3 built on behalf of the Royal Navy

> *In both labour and capacity Vickers were, at the beginning of rearmament, a good deal better off than most other firms. They had, as Craven wrote later: 'always maintained a steady flow of indentured apprentices under training, even through the difficulty preceding 1935, so that as regards manpower, we felt also we could deal with the situation satisfactorily'. They had also spent a good deal of money on maintaining their unused berths, and comparatively a great deal of money on keeping their plant and equipment up to date.*
>
> *Vickers – A History* by J.D. Scott

HMS *Porpoise*	(Yard No.679)	Launched 30 August 1932
HMS *Narwhal*	(Yard No.701)	Launched 29 August 1935
HMS *Rorqual*	(Yard No.708)	Launched 21 July 1936

The first Porpoise Class submarines (so named because they were the first-of-class boats) totalled six in number, with the Barrow Shipyard building exactly half of them. Of the other three HM Dockyards, Chatham built two (*Grampus* and *Seal*) while the remaining boat (*Cachelot*) was constructed at Scott's of Greenock. Because these submarines carried a payload of fifty mines, the periscope standards were offset to starboard to allow a clear run for the mine-carrying 'railway' which ran the full length of the boat.

The history of Royal Navy minelayers began when six of the E Class submarines ordered in 1914 were built to carry twenty mines in mine tubes in the saddle tanks. E24, the first Royal Navy minelayer, was completed on 9 January 1916, and later that year it was ordered that six submarines of the L Class be fitted with mine tubes in the external tanks. In July 1920 the Naval Staff investigated the need and requirements for submarine minelayers – the main bone of contention being whether the mines should be carried internally or externally. As an experiment, M3 was converted in 1927 to carry mines externally. The satisfactory performance of M3 led to the design of a new submarine minelayer, the famous Porpoise Class. Specifically designed for the task of minelaying, six of the class were ordered in the 1930 Programme – the first-of-class *Porpoise*, *Narwhal* and *Rorqual* from Vickers, *Grampus* and *Seal* from Chatham and *Cachelot* from Scott's. Slightly slimmer than the Overseas Patrol Submarine, but with greater displacement, the new class had a capacity to carry fifty standard Mk XVI mines in a full-length deck outside the pressure hull.

During the trials of M3 it was found that whilst the minelaying gear and compensating arrangements to maintain trim were satisfactory, the jigger-type mine-launching equipment required excessive upkeep to ensure its efficiency. Therefore this equipment was changed in the Porpoise Class to a chain and rack system fitted outside the hull in the superstructure casing. The mines and minelaying gear weighed approximately 54 tons. The conversion of M3 also had an adverse effect on its diving qualities – the time taken to flood the mine casing meant that it took about five minutes to dive in calm weather and thirteen minutes or more in rough weather. Only by careful design arrangements was this reduced in Porpoise – she could dive, with mines on board, to periscope depth from full buoyancy in 1 minute 32 seconds and, using Q tank, in 1 minute 14 seconds.

The hull form of *Porpoise* was very similar to that of the Overseas Patrol Submarine, *Parthian*, but the effect of carrying fifty mines meant that the stern torpedo tubes were deleted and the main engine horse-power was reduced by 25% – resulting in a loss of surface speed. The design diving depth was also reduced to 300ft. Although the external tanks were of 'non-leaking' welded construction, as in the Thames Class, it was thought that if exposed to depth charge attacks leaks would occur and give away the submarine's position. Therefore, the hull-form of the Chatham-built *Grampus* was radically changed so that fuel oil, which was carried externally in *Porpoise*, could be carried in internal tanks. (The changes included extension of the saddle tanks, alteration of the pressure hull, and a revised internal design.) This change of the hull-form also increased the main ballast water carried by *Grampus* by about 100 tons, and at the same time improved the stability and reserve buoyancy of the submarine.

All the vessels of the class had balloon tanks, i.e. pressure-tight tanks, in the forward super-structure to balance the buoyancy of the mines aft and prevent the submarine diving stern first. Built between 1930 and 1938, the six boats of the Porpoise Class were fitted with two Admiralty-designed vertical four-stroke blast-injected six-cylinder diesels that together generated 3,300bhp, giving a surface speed, in service, of 16 knots. Tandem sets of motors on each shaft developed a total of 1,630bhp, giving a submerged service speed of 8.9 knots. Carrying 336 cells in three battery tanks weighing a total of 139 tons, the class had a submerged endurance of sixty-six miles at 4 knots. In addition to the fifty mines, the armament of the class consisted of six 21in bow tubes (with twelve torpedoes carried) and a 4in gun (a 4.7in gun was originally fitted in *Porpoise*) with 120 rounds of ammunition – this being chosen as the standard gun to be fitted in Royal Navy submarines. When the gun of *Porpoise* was changed to the standard calibre, a weight saving of about 7 tons was achieved.

When the Royal Navy produced a mine which could be laid from a 21in torpedo tube, the need for specialised submarine minelayers disappeared. Surprisingly, the introduction of this newly-designed mine did not lead to the redundancy of existing minelayers, and these purpose-built vessels proved extremely successful in the Second World War when used as supply submarines, running precious cargoes to Malta in 1941 and 1942. Their spacious mine-decks were filled with such diverse items as machine-gun ammunition, glycol coolant for Spitfires, and food. Five of the six submarine minelayers were lost during the war, and the history of the class produces an unhappy diary of events.

On 5 May 1940 HMS *Seal*, the last of the class to be constructed, was captured as a near-wreck in the Kattegat and recommissioned as a German U-boat. She was finally scrapped in 1941 while, on 24 June 1940, HMS *Grampus* was lost on active service in the Mediterranean – cause unknown. On 1 August 1940 *Narwhal* was lost on active service off Norway – cause unknown. In October 1941 *Cachalot* was lost on active service – further details unknown. The first-of-class *Porpoise* was lost on active service, on approximately 19 January 1945, in the Malacca Strait – probably sunk by an aircraft.

The era of the minelaying submarine came to an end when the only surviving member of the Porpoise Class, the Barrow-built *Rorqual*, was taken out of service in April 1946.

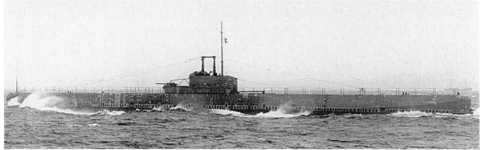

The three Porpoise Class submarines built for the Royal Navy in the 1930s. Pictured from top: HMS *Porpoise*; HMS *Narwhal*; and HMS *Rorqual*.

First Porpoise Class Submarines – Main Characteristics

Overall Length/ Beam/Draught	289ft x 29ft 10in x 16ft 9in
Displacement	1,500 tons surfaced / 2,053 tons submerged
Power	2 x 1,650bhp diesel engines for surface propulsion
	2 x 815bhp electric motors for submerged propulsion
Diving Depth	300ft
Speed	16 knots surfaced / 9 knots submerged
Propeller	2
Endurance	3,860 miles at full power or 11,500 miles at 8 knots surfaced /
	8 miles at 9 knots or 66 miles at 4 knots submerged
Armament	6 x 21in torpedo tubes in bow (12 torpedoes carried)
	1 x 4in gun
	Carried 50 Mk XVI mines
Complement	59

Thames Class Submarines

3 built on behalf of the Royal Navy

> *By all the main measures Vickers were getting busier on naval work during 1934. The number of men employed at Barrow was going up: it reached 9,000 and then 10,000, during the year, until, in the spring of 1935, 11,000 men and women were moving into the yards and the shops and the offices every day.*
>
> *Vickers – A History* by J.D. Scott

HMS *Thames*	(Yard No.672)	Launched 26 January 1932
HMS *Severn*	(Yard No.683)	Launched 16 January 1934
HMS *Clyde*	(Yard No.684)	Launched 15 March 1934

Sometimes referred to as River Class submarines, the entire Thames Class was built at Barrow. The original projection was for a class of some twenty boats but the Royal Navy drew the line at three due to the expense incurred (each boat costing some £500,000). The first-of-class HMS *Thames* reached a speed of 22.5 knots at 405 revolutions, thus becoming the first diesel submarine to exceed 21 knots.

Even though marine diesel engines of the period were incapable of propelling submarines as fast as surface craft, the Admiralty still wished, perhaps misguidedly, to build Fleet Submarines, and continued to discuss at length the functions and requirements of such vessels.

In 1928, the culmination of the removal from service of the K Class submarines and the demand by the Rear-Admiral (Submarines) for 'submarines which, in an ocean war, should be capable of operating with the Fleet' led to the development of the Thames Class Submarine.

The reader should note that these boats are actually River Class but the colloquial Vickers' Thames Class is preferred by the authors. Submitted to the Board in June 1929, the Thames Class were conventional submarines, in that they were long, well streamlined and without any large guns or other unusual features. All three vessels of the class were built at Barrow – the first-of-class HMS *Thames* was completed in September 1932, with her slightly larger sister ships, *Severn* and *Clyde*, being completed in 1935.

The original intention was to construct twenty Thames Class submarines for the Royal Navy, but a change of policy in 1933 prevented this. Built at a cost of over £500,000 each, the large and comfortable Thames Class were partial double-hull boats with a pressure hull of 'keyhole' section. In an attempt to keep down weight so as to obtain the required speed, the design diving depth was reduced from the 500ft of the Odin Class to 300ft, with the result that the pressure hull plating was reduced to 25psi as opposed to 35psi in Odin. To propel the Thames Class at the unusually high surface speed of 22.5 knots (a record at the time), and at the expense of the stern torpedo tubes, two vertical four-stroke blast-injection ten-cylinder diesels, developing a total power of 8,000bhp at 400rev/min were installed. Using two auxiliary generators, driven by two Ricardo sleeve-valve engines, these engines could be supercharged to give a total of 10,000bhp.

The machinery was of Admiralty design and, when built, weighed 347 tons – 33 tons less than allowed for in the legend weights. Without this saving the Thames Class might have had serious stability problems. When first constructed, HMS *Thames*, when surfacing, experienced heavy listing due to a water build-up in the main tanks on one side. The position of the flooding holes was modified to remedy this problem. In addition her large superstructure meant that *Thames* rolled heavily when surfacing 'beam on' in heavy seas, and it became the practice to surface 'head-to-sea' in rough weather whenever possible. As with the Overseas Patrol Submarines, the Thames Class carried fuel oil in external tanks, but whereas the Overseas boats were fitted with troublesome riveted tanks, the tanks of the Thames Class were of welded construction and were very satisfactory, though leaks occasionally occurred inboard – through rivets in the thick pressure hull plating.

With the abolition of the stern tubes, the torpedo armament of the class consisted of six 21in bow tubes (with twelve torpedoes carried). A 4.7in gun was originally fitted but, in keeping with submarine policy of the period, was changed after completion to a 4in QF gun with 120 rounds of ammunition. All three Thames Class submarines served in the Second World War and, although misemployed in the North Sea and Mediterranean, were certainly successful, but no more so than any other British submarines of the period that cost half as much to build and operate. Oddly, these submarines were never used with the surface fleet, as was intended, and perhaps the highlight of their war career was the vital cargo mission to Malta in September 1941 by *Clyde*, carrying no less than 1,200 tons of desperately needed stores. Although the Thames Class design proved successful in service it was soon realised that the concept was wrong, and with its passing it became apparent that, with surface ships being capable of 30 knots, it was imperative that underwater speed be a principal design feature in future submarine designs.

A typical view of the pattern shop in the Shipyard during the 1930s.

In conjunction with the Fleet Submarines, twelve Small Patrol Submarines were ordered in February 1929 (eight from Chatham, three from Cammell Laird and one from Scott's) and they were the forerunners of the famous S Class submarines that served so effectively in the Second World War. Called the Swordfish and Shark Classes, they were based on the saddle tank construction of the L Class submarines, the majority of which were built by Vickers ten years earlier. The Barrow-built *Thames* held the record surface speed for the period – 22.5 knots. The *Severn* and the *Clyde* were taken out of service whilst on duty in the Far East – in April 1945 and October 1945 respectively.

Thames Class Submarines – Main Characteristics

Overall Length/ Beam/Draught	345ft x 28ft x 18ft 6in
Displacement	2,165 tons surfaced / 2,680 tons submerged
Power	2 x 5,000bhp diesel engines for surface propulsion
	2 x 2,500bhp electric motors for submerged propulsion

HMS *Severn* and HMS *Clyde*. This is a view from the (now demolished) giant hammer-head crane. Immediately adjacent to the dockside is HMS *Clyde*. To the left of *Clyde* is the Portuguese submarine *Delfim*. Behind *Delfim* is HMS *Severn*. Adjacent to the floating dock is *Golfino*, another of the Portuguese boats. Finally, in the floating dock itself is the third of the Portuguese boats, the *Espadarte*. A point worth noting on this photograph is the temporary walkway running from the dockside to *Delfim's* casing and then from there onto the floating dock. Immediately behind the floating dock is the 'low level' bridge and the graving dock. The graving dock has now become the Dock Museum, a major Cumbrian tourist attraction.

Diving Depth	300ft
Speed	22.5 knots surfaced / 10 knots submerged
Propeller	2
Endurance	16,100 miles (maximum) surfaced / 13 miles at 10 knots or 118 miles at 4 knots submerged
Armament	6 x torpedo tubes in bow (12 torpedoes carried) 1 x 4in QF gun
Complement	61
Notes	HMS *Thames* was at first fitted with a 4.7in gun which was later replaced with a 4in gun.

Portuguese Submarines

3 built on behalf of the Portuguese Navy

Here also inventive minds wrestled with the fascinating problem of the submarine and evolved the first Nordenfelt in 1896, the forerunner of what in later days became a specialised activity.

Ships by J.S. Redshaw

Delfim	(Yard No.685)	Launched 5 May 1934
Espadarte	(Yard No.686)	Launched 30 May 1934
Golfino	(Yard No.687)	Launched 30 May 1934

These submarines were built on behalf of the Portuguese Navy to a Vickers design.

The Barrow-in-Furness Shipyard built three submarines for the Portuguese Navy in the 1930s. The first, *Delfim*, was launched on 5 May 1934 while the other two, *Espardarte* and *Golfino* both 'went into the water' on 30 May 1934. That launch was reported in the following day's *North West Evening Mail* as follows:

Brighter Outlook for Barrow
Vickers Armstrongs to Employ Considerably More Men
Way to Preserve Peace
Tributes to Firm and Employees' Loyalty

The outlook for Barrow was certainly positive at the launches of *Espardarte* and *Golfino* on 30 May at the Royal Naval Construction Works of Vickers-Armstrong Ltd. The afternoon luncheon that followed was well attended by a large and distinguished number of guests, including officers of the Brazilian Navy. The Portuguese dignitaries were: Ambassador and Madame Ruy Ennes Ulrich; senior naval officers Commanders Almeida Henriques and Nuno de Brion, and Madame de Brion; and General Peixoto de Cunha, Head of the Portuguese Military Commission. The British Admiralty was represented by Rear Admiral

C.P. Talbot, CB, DSO. Congratulatory toasts, extolling the virtues of the maritime mations of Great Britain and Portugal, were made by Sir Hebert Lawrence (chairman of Vickers-Armstrong), Commander Charles Craven (managing director), Ambassador Ulrich and Rear Admiral Talbot. Special thanks were given to Mesdames Ulrich and de Brion, who graciously performed the cermony of launching the ships, and they received souvenirs of the occasion.

In his speech, Sir Lawrence was particularly proud that these two ships were 'respectively the 165th and 166th submarines which this company has constructed and placed in the water … an achievement which has not been equalled by any company in the world'. He also emphasised 'that our relations with Portugal have been of the friendliest and warmest description' and that since the 1920s 'thanks to the sturdy independence of her people, thanks to the patriotism of her President, and thanks not last or least to the genius of the Prime Minister, Senhor Salazar, Portugal has emerged from her financial and economic difficulties in a way which has won the admiration of the whole world. She has set us an example.'

It must not be forgotten that this was also the period of the Great Depression and thus it is particularly important to note the number of men that the Yard employed. Sir Lawrence provided hope for the future of the company and for the economic rehabilitation of British industry itself:

> In March of this year we had about 8,700 men employed here. Today we have 9,500 and I can say to my friend, the Mayor … that as far as I can see, the prospects for the coming winter are that we shall find employment for quite a considerably larger number of men. I know how heavily the dread spectre of unemployment hangs over the head of everyone in this country, particularly over the heads of those who are in positions of responsibility like the Mayor, and, therefore, I think it may be some encouragement to tell him that during the winter to come I hope his anxieties will be relieved to quite a considerable degree. As for the future, of course it is impossible for us to see far ahead, but this I do very strongly believe, that we can overcome the difficulties which I think are now fairly generally recognised as being the causes of the economic disturbance of the world, and to which I referred when I last spoke to you – the policy of economic isolation which has been a habit contracted of late years by so many people – now that it is recognised, I believe seriously that a new spirit is arising and I think that when the new spirit is recognised to the full, we shall come through our difficulties with pain, with trouble no doubt, but still victors in the end.

The following speech was given by Ambassador Ulrich, in which he gave his thanks to Vickers-Armstrong, 'which has contributed in full or in part to the armament of all our new ships [and is] so well known throughout the world for its magnitude as well as for its efficiency and fair dealing.' Like Sir Lawrence, he expressed hope for the future of his country:

> The acquisition of new ships is the clear demonstration of the progress of my country, which at the same time is achieving a large programme of material internal improvements and creating new military forces. …

> I still believe that the cheapest and most efficient way of preserving peace is for all countries to maintain their military forces in a good standing. And I consider the fleet not only as an instrument of war, but as a useful school of moral energy, of disciplinary training, fulfilling in peace time an important function as a link between countries, and also between a colonial power and

its dependencies. It has been held that military organization is parallel to the political. And so it was said that the feudal system was due to the predominance of the knights of the medieval battles; that permanent armies were contemporary with the hereditary and aristocratic regimes; that with general conscription and popular armies comes the democratic government; that now with the dominating influence of scientific material in present or future wars the corresponding form of government must be constituted by a small body of technical men.

I shall not venture to give you my opinion on this interesting theory but I must recognise that the material progress of our navy has followed the political change in Portugal and the substitution of a democratic and irregular government by the capable efficient rule of a few men, with more scientific knowledge than political training.

In retrospect, there is a sense of pathos as Ambassador Ulrich notes that:

We are not threatened by any war and we foresee no political troubles with any country in the world. ... The contract for the building of these new ships was signed on the 9th of March, 1933, exactly 17 years after the day in which we entered the last Great War as old and faithful allies of the great British Empire. I hope that such dreadful days will never come again, but in any case I am sure that our armies and navies, British and Portuguese, will always fight shoulder to shoulder, in the most profound and sincere friendship.

The Second World War, in six years' time, would be the next test of strength for the allied nations of Europe. However, in the climate of the Great Depression and the rehabilitation following the First World War, Ambassador Ulrich gave a statement of optimism that would have offered hope and confidence to his audience:

Ladies and gentlemen, a French philosopher, Renan, said that to live men must trust in the future, and I think the same is true of nations; they, too, should have confidence in the future, and expect a brighter and higher one. That is the present state of mind in Portugal, nothing can strengthen it more than an event such as you have witnessed today.

Rear Admiral Talbot spoke very highly of the Portuguese nations and especially of the company of Vickers-Armstrong, not only for their success as submarine builders, but also for the high level of workmanship that they inspired:

The Admiralty are naturally very glad that their oldest allies are again building up their navy and that they placed orders for warships in this country, and I should like to congratulate the officers and men who will man these two submarines that their vessels have been built by Messrs. Vickers-Armstrongs.

Sir Herbert Lawrence mentioned that these were the 165th and 166th submarines they have built. A hundred and fifty-three of these, I believe, have been built for the British Admiralty out of a total of about three hundred that have been produced. They started to build submarines for the British Admiralty with the very first submarine that we had and they have continued to build them ever since. Every submarine they have built has been entirely satisfactory. I can speak with a certain knowledge of this. I have served as first lieutenant in some of them. I have commanded five Vickers-built submarines, and later I had several Vickers-built submarines in the flotillas of which I was in command. What struck me when I was here super-

intending the building of submarines was the keen pride and interest that everybody concerned took in his work, whether official, foreman or workman, and what struck me still more when I came up during the war ... was to find the extreme personal interest that all men who had anything to do with her building had taken in the doings of the previous submarine. That was most impressive, and I believe that if that spirit prevails, as it does prevail, you cannot have bad workmanship. ...

These submarines, with the workmanship that has been put in by this distinguished firm, and with the courage, determination and seamanlike skill that the officers and men will display, will I think most worthily maintain those very high traditions.

The final speech was given by Commander C.W. Craven. He too commended the workmanship of his firm, paying tribute to the loyalty of his employees, and he joined his colleague Sir Lawrence in expressing hope for the future of Vickers-Armstrong and for the country:

We all know that money can buy plant, machine tools and brains, but certainly money cannot buy loyalty. In this company we are taught loyalty to the firm and I feel that as long as that spirit prevails we can look forward to a future, not of great prosperity, perhaps, but a useful future in the service of a great industry and, possibly, in the service of our country.

★ ★ ★

The launch of the first of the three Portuguese submarines was reported locally in *The Barrow News* on Saturday 5 May 1934. An extract is reproduced below:

The first of the three Portuguese submarines building at the Naval Construction works, Barrow, was successfully launched on Tuesday. The other two will be released on the 30th inst. This submarine has been named the Delfim *and the lunchtime ceremony was performed by Madame Samar de Amarat, wife of the principal member of the Portuguese Inspection Commission station at Newcastle-on-Tyne. A bouquet of red roses and maiden-hair fern was presented to the lady who launched the ship, and was subsequently hoisted to the top of the flagpole at the bow of the ship in accordance with Portuguese custom. As the ship slid down to the Walney Channel, cheers were raised, and after she was safely afloat the Shipyard Band struck up the Portuguese National Anthem followed by 'God Save the King'. It will be remembered that these submarines were originally ordered in Italy, but later, owing to financial considerations, they were transferred to Vickers-Armstrong Ltd, who had already secured the contract for the whole of the armament for the new Portuguese naval programme. The* Delfim *is the 164th submarine to be launched from the Barrow works, and is specially designed to meet the requirements of the Portuguese Navy.*

The three Portuguese submarines built at Barrow – one moored against the dockside and the other two in the floating dock.

Portuguese Submarines – Main Characteristics

Overall Length/ Beam/Draught	227ft 2in x 21ft 4in x 12ft 8in
Displacement	800 tons surfaced / 1,092 tons submerged
Power	2-shaft Vickers diesel engines
	2 x electric motors (2,300bhp/1,000shp)
Diving Depth	200ft
Speed	16 knots surfaced / 9 knots submerged
Propeller	2
Endurance	5,000 miles at 10 knots surfaced / 110 miles at 4 knots submerged
Armament	6 x 21in torpedo tubes (4 bow, 2 stern)
	12 torpedoes carried
	1 x 4in gun (in fully enclosed shield)
	2 x machine guns
Complement	36
Notes	These were the first submarines built at Barrow in which welding was employed to any great degree.

Estonian Submarines

2 built on behalf of the Estonian Navy

> *The use of Soviet naval crews for fighting ashore — a task which they undertook with great*
> *gallantry — resulted not only in heavy losses, but also in additional lack of sea training, which*
> *was already in general on a low level.*
>
> *Soviet Warships of the Second World War* by Jurg Meister

Kalev	(Yard No.705)	Launched 7 July 1936
Lembit	(Yard No.706)	Launched 7 July 1936

Built for the Estonian Navy for minelaying, these boats were a significant departure from the usual formula of inter-war exports, being based on existing Royal Navy designs. Their design was unique to Vickers although similar to First World War Royal Navy E and L Classes, with their mines carried in chutes in the saddle tanks. The Admiralty clearly had confidence in Vickers' design and asked them to quote for installing the *Lembit/Kalev* minelaying system on early T Class boats. When Estonia was occupied during the Second World War, both boats were commandeered by the Soviet Navy in June 1940. *Kalev* was mined and lost in Autumn 1941 while carrying out transport duties between Kronshtadt and Hangö. (Some records state *Kalev* was scuttled.) *Lembit* survived the war and was, with a number of Soviet submarines, awarded the Order of the Red Banner and re-numbered U-1, then in 1949 re-designated S-85 and used in naval experiments prior to becoming a museum/memorial ship in 1978.

On 7 July 1936 the two submarines, *Kalev* and *Lembit*, built at Barrow-in-Furness on behalf of the Estonian Navy, were launched into Walney Channel. The following day, the *North West Daily Mail* carried an article entitled:

Part of a Great Machine
Sir Charles Craven and Vickers-Armstrongs Activities
Estonian Minister and British Associations Friendship

A large company attended the luncheon that followed the launches of *Kalev* and *Lembit*. Commander Sir Charles Craven, chairman of Vickers-Armstrongs Ltd, presided and the company included representatives from several other nations for whom contracts were being carried out at Barrow (such as Romania, Argentina and Portugal), the Mayor and Mayoress of the Borough (Alderman and Mrs Longstaffe), the deputy Mayor and Mayoress (Alderman and Mrs Morton), Sir Jonah Walker-Smith MP and Lady Walker-Smith, together with shipyard officials and leaders of local industries. Also present were the Estonian Minister August Schmidt and Admiral Sir Percy Addison, the Admiralty Director of Dockyards. Mesdames Schmidt and Strobel had the honour of launching the ships and they received souvenirs for perfroming this duty.

The *Lembit* and *Kalev* were the first defence units of the new Estonian Navy. In his speech, Sir Craven commended these ships because they:

> ... *incorporated in them the experience of the officers of the Estonian Navy, many of whom have had considerable service in submarines, and also of the members of the staff of the company, several of whom were serving with us when the first submarines for the British Navy were laid down at the end of the last century.*

To further demonstrate British support for Estonia, he added:

> ... *the first two units of the Estonian Navy, after the country secured her independence, were two British destroyers, which were handed over by our Government some eighteen years ago and which I am informed rendered good service to the country. ... It has been the policy of the Admiralty to render all assistance, including the training of crews where necessary, to friendly foreign navies who are building their ships in this country.*

Estonian Minister August Schmidt thanked the British Admiralty for its support throughout the years and emphasised the importance of these two acquisitions to the Estonian Navy:

> *Of the three Baltic States, Estonia perhaps has the closest connections with the sea. Our Northern and Western frontiers are entirely bound by the waters of the Baltic. During centuries the sea has been our main gateway, sometimes our only gateway, to the West. ... In more recent times, during the war for our independence, the sea was our only means of communication with the outside world.*

In a similar sentiment to the Portugeuse Ambassador at the launch of *Espardarte* and *Golfino*, Herr Schmidt expressed a wish for peace and believed that it was still important to remain conscious of the country's defences:

> *Our most sincere wish is to live in peace with our neighbours, great and small alike. We are happy in having established friendly relations with all of them, and I sincerely hope that these relations may endure. But every Government conscious of its responsibilities must think of its defences. The two submarines we have just launched will form one link in the defensive forces of Estonia. I am sure that these ships will prove excellent in service. ... I also trust that the officers and men of our navy, when their services are required, will be animated by the same spirit as they were during the war for our independence, the spirit that calls up the great traditions of the powerful and glorious British Navy. I mean the sense of duty, the sense of sacrifice, and the firm determination to brave calmly and unflinchingly whatever dangers may face them.*

It had been two years since the launch of the Portugeuse ships and Sir Lawrence's confidence that employment would rise in the Shipyard proved to come true. Sir Craven was happy to announce the remarkable increase in the number of people employed by Vickers-Armstrong Ltd: 'today we have 12,742 at work', which was an increase of over 3,000 men. They were all part of a great machine that was doing something to help the great industries of this country.

Lembit immediately prior to launch in 1936.

In the depression-stricken days of the 1930s, the Yard had a desperate need of contracts and following construction there could be a follow-up opportunity to supply spares and possibly munitions. Additionally, Estonia had declared an interest in the purchase of a new, or refurbished, cruiser of around 3,000 tons, although the British government would eventually refuse the supply of this. Contract negotiations commenced in 1930 and took several years to finalise, the major problem being how Estonia would finance the deal. Financing was eventually settled through Estonia's sale of two of their old destroyers to Peru and an agreement by Vickers to accept payment in instalments.

The negotiations were possibly made more difficult by Estonia's refusal to allow Vickers' local agent to take any part in the proceedings. This was due to information from neighbouring Latvian officials advising of the agent's very obvious attempts to influence matters concerning that country's submarine procurement programme via financial incentives. However, before too much criticism is directed at this matter, it should be noted that this was a fairly standard approach to 'doing business' and had the agent been more discreet then possibly Latvia and Estonia would have adopted a different stance. Estonia's negotiations with Vickers were conducted through the British Consul and the contract allowed for the training of Estonian crew members in boat operations by the Royal Navy. *Kalev* and *Lembit* were subsequently delivered in 1937.

Estonian Submarines – Main Characteristics

Overall Length/ Beam/Draught	190ft 9in x 24ft x 11ft
Displacement	600 tons surfaced / 820 tons submerged
Power	2 x 1,200bhp Vickers diesel engines for surface propulsion
	2 x 450bhp electric motors for submerged propulsion
Diving Depth	240ft
Speed	13.5 knots surfaced / 8.5 knots submerged
Propeller	2
Endurance	2,000 miles at 10 knots surfaced / submerged endurance unknown
Armament	4 x 21in torpedo tubes
	1 x 40mm AA gun
	1 x 20mm AA gun
	20 mines carried
Complement	38

4

Second World War Submarines (1937-1946)

T Class Submarines

28 built on behalf of the Royal Navy

> *With the impetus in new naval construction the company was pressing hard against the limiting factors – not only gun mountings, but labour. At Barrow there were not enough riveters, shipwrights or fitters, and 'it is not now possible to import any efficient men of these trades into the district'. Nor could the company find any more apprentices in Barrow; to get boys they now had to go to the West Cumberland distressed areas.*
>
> Vickers – A History by J.D. Scott

HMS *Triton*	(Yard No.716)	Launched 5 October 1937	(Group One)
HMS *Triumph*	(Yard No.731)	Launched 16 February 1938	(Group One)
HMS *Thistle*	(Yard No.736)	Launched 25 October 1938	(Group One)
HMS *Triad*	(Yard No.739)	Launched 5 May 1939	(Group One)
HMS *Truant*	(Yard No.740)	Launched 5 May 1939	(Group One)
HMS *Tetrarch*	(Yard No.745)	Launched 14 November 1939	(Group One)
HMS *Trusty*	(Yard No.770)	Launched 14 March 1941	(Group Two)
HMS *Turbulent*	(Yard No.771)	Launched 12 May 1941	(Group Two)

The launch into Walney Channel of HMS *Triton* on 5 October 1937. *(Barrow Museum Service CAT 2398)*

HMS *P311*	(Yard No.811)	Launched 5 March 1942	(Group Three)
HMS *Trespasser*	(Yard No.812)	Launched 29 May 1942	(Group Three)
HMS *Taurus*	(Yard No.813)	Launched 27 June 1942	(Group Three)
HMS *Tactician*	(Yard No.814)	Launched 29 July 1942	(Group Three)
HMS *Truculent*	(Yard No.815)	Launched 12 September 1942	(Group Three)
HMS *Templar*	(Yard No.816)	Launched 26 October 1942	(Group Three)
HMS *Tally-Ho*	(Yard No.817)	Launched 23 December 1942	(Group Three)
HMS *Tantalus*	(Yard No.818)	Launched 24 February 1943	(Group Three)
HMS *Tantivy*	(Yard No.819)	Launched 6 April 1943	(Group Three)
HMS *Telemachus*	(Yard No.842)	Launched 19 June 1943	(Group Three)
HMS *Talent*	(Yard No.843)	Launched 17 July 1943	(Group Three)
HMS *Terrapin*	(Yard No.844)	Launched 31 August 1943	(Group Three)
HMS *Thorough*	(Yard No.845)	Launched 30 October 1943	(Group Three)
HMS *Tiptoe*	(Yard No.868)	Launched 25 February 1944	(Group Three)
HMS *Trump*	(Yard No.869)	Launched 25 March 1944	(Group Three)
HMS *Taciturn*	(Yard No.870)	Launched 7 June 1944	(Group Three)
HMS *Tapir*	(Yard No.871)	Launched 21 August 1944	(Group Three)
HMS *Tarn*	(Yard No.872)	Launched 29 November 1944	(Group Three)
HMS *Tasman*	(Yard No.873)	Launched 13 February 1945	(Group Three)
HMS *Teredo*	(Yard No.874)	Launched 27 April 1945	(Group Three)

Most reference sources list only two groups of T Class submarines, some list only one, whereas in fact there were three distinct groups. This class is further confused by the fact that the T Class boats were subject to many, and often radical, modifications through the years. Indeed, so significant were these modifications that, in the early to mid-1950s there developed three further sub-groups made up of some of the existing submarines, namely Tabard Group, Streamlined T Group and Full Conversion Ts. However for this history we are only concerned with the original three groups which define the characteristics of the boats when constructed. The Group One T Class submarines were launched between 1937 and 1942, with the Barrow Shipyard building six of the fifteen which found their way into service for the Royal Navy. There were just seven Group Two T Class boats constructed (between 1940 and 1942) with Barrow being responsible for just two of these. Thirty-one Group Three Ts were built between 1942 and 1946, with the Barrow Shipyard responsible for twenty of these boats. So, in total, fifty-three T Class boats were constructed on behalf of the Royal Navy (with a further planned six being cancelled), twenty-eight of them at Barrow.

During the 1930s the construction of overseas patrol boats waned considerably, and so the Admiralty decided, in 1934/1935, to build a new ocean-going boat to replace the Oberon, Parthian and Rainbow Classes – which had not lived up to expectations. Requirements for the new class (defined as Patrol Submarines) demanded that they have a strong armament and a patrol duration of at least forty-two days. Restricted by the limitations imposed by the London Naval Treaty, which allowed only 16,500 tons of new-construction submarines, the

HMS *Triad* (Group One T Class) at the dockside at Barrow under the jib of the 250-ton hammerhead crane.

class was designed to have a displacement of about 1,000 tons so that a sufficient number could be built. The first-of-class, approved in the 1935 Programme, was built at Vickers and entered service in December 1938 under the name of *Triton*.

Fifty-three T Class submarines were eventually constructed, making it the largest class of ocean-going submarines ever built for the Royal Navy. The original order for the class was made under the growing threat of war, which forced the Admiralty to open its purse strings.

Displacing more than 400 tons less than the O, P and R Classes, the first group of twenty-two T Class submarines were noted for their simplicity of construction. They were superior to the O, P and Rs in that they had greater submerged speed, better surface and underwater handling and more torpedo tubes. However, because the displacement limitations restricted the size and power of the engines to 2,500hp surfaced (1,450hp submerged), the maximum surface speed was lower. The first T Class submarines were 274ft long and displaced 1,325 tons surfaced. Their 'surface' armament included one 4in gun and three .303in machine-guns, which were later replaced by, or supplemented by, one 20mm Oerlikon cannon. They were the last Royal Navy submarines designed for overseas patrol to have insufficient range for the Pacific.

One of the most distinguishing features of the Group One T Class boats was their high number of torpedo tubes: six bow tubes, which were reloadable from inside the pressure hull; two external bow tubes, contained in a bulbous bow casing; and two external tubes situated amidships, and so arranged as to fire ahead. This gave the class the phenomenal bow salvo of ten torpedo tubes which, the Royal Navy believed, would compensate for the inevitable errors that accompanied long-range attacks. As an alternative to this armament, a load of eighteen mines could be carried. *Tetrarch*, a Group One boat, was configured for minelaying as per the *Kalev/Lembit* boats (see Estonian Submarines, pages 100-103) but the minelaying equipment proved constantly faulty and the mine wells were eventually welded over.

Perhaps the most famous of the early T Class submarines was the ill-fated Cammell Laird-built *Thetis*. Sailing, prior to handover, in Liverpool bay on the morning of 1 June 1939, *Thetis* had on board her fifty-three-man crew and fifty passengers (Shipyard and Admiralty men concerned with the trials). For her trial dive, *Thetis* was reluctant to submerge, and so her six bow tubes were checked. When Nos 1 to 4 were correctly found empty, numbers 5 and 6 were tested to confirm each contained seawater. The test cock of No.6 tube squirted water but, strangely, the test cock of No.5 did not, and so was apparently empty. As there was only one way to be sure, the door was opened – and the sea roared in. Jammed by one of its clips, the watertight door couldn't be closed and, as two compartments flooded, *Thetis* nose-dived to the seabed 160ft below. With her stern protruding from the waves, *Thetis* remained undiscovered for a whole day and, although four men managed to escape, she became a tomb for the ninety-nine men on board – despite the efforts of rescuers. When *Thetis* was raised in November 1939, an investigation into the cause of this tragic accident revealed an incorrectly-wired bow cap indicator – showing the bow cap to be shut when it was open – and that the vital test cock was blocked with paint. To avoid any suggestion of a jinx on the boat, the Admiralty refitted her and commissioned her, in November 1940, as *Thunderbolt* and, as an epitaph to her 'previous life', she entered service with a diagonal rusty line on her hull that could not be hidden.

Under the 1940 War Programme came the decision to build nine slightly modified T Class submarines. These modifications were made in the light of experience gained with the first group of T Class boats and the main changes were in the number and disposition of torpedo tubes, the outer hull shape and the use, in most of the modified vessels, of an electrically welded, rather than a riveted, construction. The latter change assisted deeper diving, improved the resistance to depth charge attack, and also enabled the shipbuilder to adopt the new technique of prefabricating the hull in sections in the shops and assembling large units at the building berth. Notwithstanding welding and fabrication improvements, Vickers were not producing the T Class boats as quickly as agreed with the Admiralty (see Second V Class Submarines, pages 133-34, for Admiralty attitudes to welding). The Yard had based its predictions on 1939 estimates of sixteen boats a year.

Neither the Yard nor the Admiralty were able to foresee the huge increase in work the war would bring by 1941. Simultaneously under construction were several classes of submarine, along with destroyers, transports and a cruiser. Additionally, refits and repairs were continuing on warships and merchant vessels as well as a captured German U-boat, U-570 (see Appendix III). The average build time for a Barrow T Class was fifteen months (*Tantalus* – Yard No.818 – took fifty weeks) but as the workload increased so did the T Class build time, to seventeen months. Much of the increase was due to modifications and equipment demanded by combat experience and a portion could be attributed to contradictory Admiralty instructions. Nevertheless the Admiralty distributed a number of T Class boats to other yards with the result that build times increased by three months and to twenty months in the worst case.

To return to the record, this modified group of submarines was fitted, at the extreme stern, with an additional external torpedo tube, whilst the two tubes amidships were repositioned aft of the conning tower, angled to fire astern. These changes altered the shape and silhouette of the class, as did the removal of the bulbous bow casing. The bow casing had created a noticeable bow wave when running at periscope depth, hampering visibility and the correct trim of the boat. As a result of these alterations, the second group of boats were more stream-lined and the openings for the two external tubes were more clearly visible. In addition to their eleven 21in torpedo tubes, Group Two T Class submarines were fitted with a 4in gun, a 20mm Oerlikon cannon on a platform aft of the periscopes and three .303in machine-guns on removable mountings. Additional orders in the 1941 and 1942 programmes meant that a total of thirty-one modified T Class submarines entered service between 1942 and 1946, twenty-one of which were laid down at Vickers, although a number of these were completed at other yards. Of the twenty-two Group One submarines constructed, eight were built exclusively at Barrow. Along with other British submarines, the T Class boats ordered in the 1941 and 1942 Programmes were fitted with surface and air search radar sets.

During the Second World War, T Class submarines operated successfully in all theatres in which the Royal Navy was committed and many of the Group Two boats were further modified for employment in the Far East – several ballast tanks were changed into fuel tanks, thereby increasing the fuel load from 132 to 230 tons and surface range from 8,000 to 11,000 miles at 10 knots. In a theatre where it took up to a week to sail from base to the operational area, this increase in range, together with increased stores capacity, enabled long patrols to be carried out – the record being fifty-six days by the Barrow-built *Tantalus*, forty days of which were spent in the patrol area. Although the T Class obtained satisfactory results, the fact that they were one of the classes which bore the brunt of Second World War submarine operations meant that they were subjected to the highest loss rate. For example, thirteen boats were lost in the Mediterranean, despite the fact that large enemy vessels were very vulnerable in that sea.

Nevertheless, the T Class were particularly successful against submarines, and thirteen boats (six of which were Barrow-built) sank thirteen enemy submarines: six Italian, four German and three Japanese. In January 1943, *Thunderbolt* (ex *Thetis*) transported 'chariot'-type assault craft which penetrated the harbour of Palermo and sank the hull of the Italian light cruiser *Ulpio Traiano*, which was being fitted out. Other major successes included the sinking of two cruisers – the 5,700-ton *Kuma* and the 13,000-ton *Ashigara* – by the Barrovian *Tally-Ho* and (Chatham-built) *Trenchant* respectively, whilst in August 1941, another Vickers boat, *Triumph*, managed to seriously damage the 12,000-ton cruiser *Bolzano*.

HMS *Tasman* (completed as HMS *Talent*) in Walney Channel in 1945. *(Barrow Museum Service CAT 0082)*

At the end of the war, most T Class submarines were placed in reserve, taken out of service or ceded to other countries. Most of the early T Class, with riveted hulls, could not be fully modernised, but five – *Tireless, Token* and the Barrow-built *Tapir, Talent* and *Teredo* – were streamlined and completely refitted with six bow tubes, modern sonar and a fin-shaped conning tower. In 1951-1956, eight of the welded-hull boats were completely rebuilt in a manner similar to the American 'Guppy' programme (i.e. given greater underwater propulsive power). The eight converted were: *Tabard, Truncheon, Thermopylae, Totem, Turpin* and the Vickers-built *Trump, Tiptoe* and *Taciturn*.

Their hulls were cut in two and new sections added to their length, they were streamlined and their underwater propulsion capacity was increased enormously to give twice the previous submerged speed, and increased endurance. At the same time, sensing and detection equipment was updated. Although in later years their speed of 15.25 knots surfaced and 9 knots submerged was judged to be inadequate, a proof of their high reputation for reliability is demonstrated by the T Class submarines which, after many refits, were still in active service with a foreign navy in the early 1970s.

Some confusion can arise in this Class with regard to HMS *Talent*. The original *Talent* (Yard No.817) was sold to the Netherlands in 1944 and HMS *Tasman* (Yard No.873) was renamed *Talent* upon completion. To further complicate matters, there were plans for a third HMS *Talent* in this Class (Yard No.877) but that contract was subsequently cancelled (see Appendix II).

Victoria Cross
HMS *Turbulent*
Commander John Wallace Linton

The King has been Graciously pleased to approve the grant of the Victoria Cross for great valour in command of His Majesty's Submarines to Commander John Wallace Linton, DSO, DSC, Royal Navy. From the outbreak of war until HMS *Turbulent's* last patrol, Commander Linton was constantly in command of submarines, and during that time inflicted great damage on the enemy. He sank one cruiser, one destroyer, one U-boat, twenty-eight supply ships, some 100,000 tons in all, and destroyed three trains by gunfire. In his last year he spent two hundred and fifty-four days at sea, submerged for nearly half the time, and his ship was hunted thirteen times and had two hundred and fifty depth-charges aimed at her. His many and brilliant successes were due to his constant activity and skill, and the daring which never failed him when there was an enemy to be attacked. On one occasion, for instance, in HMS *Turbulent*, he sighted a convoy of two merchantmen and two destroyers in mist and moonlight. He worked round ahead of the convoy and dived to attack it as it passed through the moon's rays. On bringing his sights to bear he found himself right ahead of a destroyer. Yet he held his course till the destroyer was almost on top of him, and when his sights came on the convoy, he fired. His great courage and determination were rewarded. He sank one merchantman and one destroyer outright, and set the other Merchantman on fire so that she blew up.

25 May 1943

HMS *Teredo* entering Walney Channel immediately after launch on 27 April 1945. *(Barrow Museum Service CAT 2359)*

T Class Submarines – Main Characteristics (Groups One and Two)

Overall Length/ Beam/Draught	274ft x 26ft 6in x 16ft 3in
Displacement	1,325 tons surfaced / 1,580 tons submerged
Power	2 x 2,500bhp diesel engines for surface propulsion
	2 x 1,450bhp electric motors for submerged propulsion (Group One)
	2 x diesel engines for surface propulsion
	2 x electric motors for submerged propulsion (Group Two)
Diving Depth	300ft
Speed	15.25 knots surfaced / 9 knots submerged
Propeller	2
Endurance	8,000 miles at 10 knots surfaced / 80 miles at 4 knots submerged
Armament	10 x torpedo tubes (6 internal, 2 external bow, 2 beam)
	1 x 4in gun
	3 x .303in machine guns (later replaced or supplemented by
	1 x 20mm Oerlikon cannon)
	16 torpedoes carried (as an alternative load, these boats could carry
	18 mines)
Complement	59

T Class Submarines – Main Characteristics (Group Three)

Overall Length/ Beam/Draught	273ft 6in x 26ft 6in x 16ft 4in
Displacement	1,325 tons surfaced / 1,571 tons submerged
Power	2 x Admiralty (or Vickers) diesel engines for surface propulsion
	2 x Laurence Scott electric motors for submerged propulsion
Diving Depth	300ft riveted or 350ft welded
Speed	15.25 knots surfaced / 8.75 knots submerged
Propeller	2
Endurance	8,000 miles at 10 knots surfaced / 80 miles at 4 knots submerged
Armament	11 x torpedo tubes (6 internal, 2 external bow, 2 beam, 1 stern)
	1 x 4in gun
	1 x 20mm Oerlikon cannon
	3 x .303in machine guns
	17 torpedoes carried
Complement	65

U-570/HMS *Graph*

U-570 was caught on the surface in the North Atlantic on 27 August 1941, depth-charged and damaged by a Lockheed Hudson of Coastal Command. U-570 surrendered and was eventually towed to Barrow and berthed in Buccleuch Dock in mid-September 1941 where she was subjected to intense examination by a team of experts. However, before the examination could take place there was an urgent need to make safe and remove the electric torpedoes (in themselves a major prize) and this required the removal of hull plating distorted and damaged during the depth charging. A naval engineer and a young Yard burner bravely volunteered for, and successfully completed, the task. U-570's secrets were ready for the taking. Amongst the surprises were the all-welded hull providing greater strength and saving material and weight compared to riveting, her keel block was concrete thus saving more material and her diving depth was beyond the range of depth charges. A surface speed of 17 knots enabled U-570 to catch most merchantmen and outrun a lot of navy vessels, and listening gear helped to locate or evade other ships. Amongst her charts were a number providing German coastal minefield positions. Eventually, with the type VIIC U-boat's name changed to HMS *Graph* and a Royal Navy crew installed, she was sent against her own kind. On 21 October 1942 (Trafalgar Day), *Graph* ambushed U-333, which was returning to a French port after being rammed and badly damaged by the corvette HMS *Crocus*. U-333 evaded the torpedoes fired by *Graph* and her already badly damaged bows and superstructure made such noise underwater as to convince *Graph* that her victim was finished and break off the attack. Near the end of the war *Graph* was taken out of service (after suffering accidental damage in a naval dockyard), stripped of useful equipment and material and, in March 1944, sent to the breakers yard. On her way her tow cable snapped and she ran aground on the Isle of Islay where some remnants of her hull remain.

U Class Submarines

39 built on behalf of the Royal Navy

A young naval officer who came to collect a submarine from Barrow in 1941 wrote a descrip-
tion of the Yard: 'Vickers' yard at Barrow is a private city of noise and steel; a fevered fantasy
in a surrealistic nightmare. On the vast slipways the grinning near-skeletons of every type of
war vessel, from 8,000-ton cruisers to pathetic rat-like submarines … And, above everything,
permeating everything, the noise: the screams, groans, howls, and agonies of labour.' This officer
was Alastair Mars; the boat he was there to accept (to use the formal terminology) was
Unbroken, *and under his command she was to sink 30,000 tons of shipping and cripple two*
cruisers.

Vickers – A History *by J.D. Scott*

HMS *Undine*	(Yard No.728)	Launched 5 October 1937	(Group One)
HMS *Unity*	(Yard No.729)	Launched 16 February 1937	(Group One)
HMS *Ursula*	(Yard No.730)	Launched 16 February 1938	(Group One)
HMS *Utmost*	(Yard No.757)	Launched 20 April 1940	(Group One)
HMS *Upright*	(Yard No.758)	Launched 21 April 1940	(Group One)
HMS *Unique*	(Yard No.759)	Launched 6 June 1940	(Group One)
HMS *Usk*	(Yard No.760)	Launched 7 June 1940	(Group One)
HMS *Upholder*	(Yard No.761)	Launched 8 July 1940	(Group One)
HMS *Unbeaten*	(Yard No.762)	Launched 9 July 1940	(Group One)
HMS *Urge*	(Yard No.763)	Launched 19 August 1940	(Group One)
HMS *Undaunted*	(Yard No.764)	Launched 20 August 1940	(Group One)
HMS *Urchin*	(Yard No.765)	Launched 30 September 1940	(Group One)
HMS *Union*	(Yard No.766)	Launched 1 October 1940	(Group One)
HMS *Ullswater*	(Yard No.775)	Launched 27 November 1940	(Group Two)
HMS P32	(Yard No.776)	Launched 15 December 1940	(Group Two)
HMS P33	(Yard No.777)	Launched 28 January 1941	(Group Two)
HMS *Ultimatum*	(Yard No.778)	Launched 11 February 1941	(Group Two)
HMS *Umbra*	(Yard No.779)	Launched 15 March 1941	(Group Two)
HMS P36	(Yard No.780)	Launched 28 April 1941	(Group Two)
HMS P37/*Unbending*	(Yard No.781)	Launched 12 May 1941	(Group Two)
HMS P38	(Yard No.782)	Launched 9 July 1941	(Group Two)
HMS P39	(Yard No.783)	Launched 23 August 1941	(Group Two)
HMS P41/*Uredd*	(Yard No.784)	Launched 24 August 1941	(Group Two)
HMS *Unbroken*	(Yard No.797)	Launched 4 November 1941	(Group Two)
HMS *Unison*	(Yard No.798)	Launched 5 November 1941	(Group Two)
HMS *United*	(Yard No.799)	Launched 18 December 1941	(Group Two)
HMS *Unruffled*	(Yard No.800)	Launched 19 December 1941	(Group Two)
HMS *Unrivalled*	(Yard No.801)	Launched 16 February 1942	(Group Two)
HMS *Unshaken*	(Yard No.802)	Launched 17 February 1942	(Group Two)
HMS P48	(Yard No.803)	Launched 15 April 1942	(Group Two)
HMS *Unseen*	(Yard No.804)	Launched 16 April 1942	(Group Two)

HMS P47/*Dolfijn*	(Yard No.805)	Launched 27 July 1942	(Group Two)
HMS *Unruly*	(Yard No.806)	Launched 28 July 1942	(Group Two)
HMS P52/*Dzik*	(Yard No.807)	Launched 11 October 1942	(Group Two)
HMS *Ultor*	(Yard No.808)	Launched 12 October 1942	(Group Two)
HMS *Vandal*	(Yard No.837)	Launched 23 November 1942	(Group Two)
HMS *Upstart*	(Yard No.838)	Launched 24 November 1942	(Group Two)
HMS *Varne*	(Yard No.839)	Launched 22 January 1943	(Group Two)
HMS *Vox*	(Yard No.840)	Launched 23 January 1943	(Group Two)

The U Class submarines were ordered by the Royal Navy to replace the H Class boats. Some forty-nine boats in total were ordered, a high figure caused no doubt by the outbreak of war just two years after the first-of-class HMS *Undine* was launched at Barrow. There were two groups within the U Class, the Barrow Shipyard building all but two of the first group and all but eight of the second group. In total thirty-nine U Class submarines went down the slipways into Walney Channel in a period of just over five years. Strangely, all but three of the boats in this class (*Undine*, *Unity* and *Ursula*) had their names changed to numbers and then later back to their original names. This causes some confusion to the historian and accounts for the mixture of names and/or numbers listed above. Similarly, the fact that several boats were ceded to foreign navies accounts for some of the names listed. (See Appendix I for more specific details on each submarine.) To add further confusion, HMS *Ullswater* (built at Barrow) had her name changed to HMS *Uproar* after being commissioned.

The first three U Class submarines were ordered in 1936 to serve as unarmed targets for anti-submarine vessels. However, in a change of policy (perhaps with a foreboding of war) *Undine*, *Unity* and *Ursula*, laid down at Vickers in February 1937, were modified during construction to accommodate six bow tubes (four internal and two external) so that they could undertake short offensive missions. To allow the installation of a small deck gun, the hull forward of the conning tower was reinforced. From their first sea trials, the three U Class boats demonstrated excellent handling and manoeuvrability which, combined with ease of production and low cost, made the design particularly successful. In 1939, a realization of the inevitability of war and that the small size of the U Class boats made them particularly suitable for North Sea and Mediterranean operations, prompted the Admiralty to put the class into quantity production.

Twelve identical vessels were ordered, but of these only four were eventually fitted with six bow tubes. The two external tubes, and the bulbous bow they formed, were removed from the remaining boats because the notable bow wave the bulge created when running at periscope depth made it difficult to keep the boat trimmed longitudinally. Under the 1940 and 1941 War Programmes, a further forty-one U Class boats were ordered but only thirty-four were completed. This second group of U Class submarines did not differ substantially from the first, but an approximate increase of 5ft in the stern gave them a more streamlined shape and improved the flow of water over the propellers. In addition to their four 21in bow tubes and three .303in portable machine-guns, the U Class boats were fitted with a 3in gun forward of the conning tower. However, as this was an afterthought to the original design, no separate hatch was fitted for the gun crew or ammunition.

This resulted in the conning tower becoming extremely crowded before and after gun action and, if the gun crew were employed, rapid crash-diving was impossible. The limited offensive potential of individual U Class boats was compensated for by the considerable number that were commissioned in a short period of time, and these small and nimble vessels became one of the most important operational classes in the Second World War, with a record that can fairly be described as heroic. The wartime submarine fleet relied almost entirely on the S, T and U Classes. This policy was very different to that of the First World War (when some twelve new classes were developed) and was pursued so as to cause the minimum interference with the shipbuilders' production programme.

Of the forty-nine commissioned U Class boats, thirty-nine were built at Barrow and served with the Second Flotilla based at Malta. They achieved notable successes against warships and merchantmen. Two U Class boats, stationed in the Sicilian Channel, sank several major Italian merchant ships which were transporting troops and supplies to Africa. Like other British boats, the U Class were particularly successful against submarines – in the Mediterranean alone, five Barrow-built boats (*Upholder*, *Ultimatum*, *Unbeaten*, *Unruly* and *United*) sank a total of eight: six Italian and two German. During the war, nineteen boats of the class were lost on active service – thirteen in the Mediterranean and six in the Atlantic and North Sea. Another submarine, *Untamed*, sank in May 1943, but was salvaged two months later and returned to service as HMS *Vitality*. From 1941, numerous boats were ceded to Poland, the USSR, Holland, Norway and Free France, and of these several were lost in action. One U Class submarine that is famous for the part it played during the Second World War is the Vickers-built *Upholder*, which probably had the finest fighting record of any Allied submarine of the period. Commissioned in August 1940, and under the command of Lt-Com. Malcolm David Wanklyn VC, HMS *Upholder* sailed to her Maltese base on 10 December.

The launch of HMS *Undine*, one of the thirty-nine U Class submarines built at Barrow.

The Shipyard Laboratory shown here in the 1930s around the time that construction began on the U Class submarines. *(Barrow Museum Service CAT 6125)*

During this passage, Lt-Com. Wanklyn demonstrated that he was a man of many talents when a bulkhead door almost severed the tops of three fingers of Chief Engine Room Artificer Baker. With infinite patience and a very delicate touch, Wanklyn sorted out the mangled fingers and strapped them up. For the next four days Wanklyn painstakingly dressed the injured fingers of his patient until he could be transferred to a military hospital in Gibraltar. Due to Wanklyn's skill and patience, Baker regained the full use of his hand. Upholder eventually arrived at Malta on 10 January 1941. Upholder's first four patrols yielded no successes and doubts were raised as to Wanklyn's competence. However, on her fifth patrol off Cape Bon, *Upholder* compensated for her earlier misses with a vengeance – sinking three enemy convoy vessels and 'finishing off' an abandoned supply ship.

Following *Upholder's* seventh patrol, her commander was awarded the Victoria Cross. The failure of *Upholder's* ASDIC set had robbed Wanklyn not only of a means of detecting the enemy but also of a valuable aid in taking avoiding action during a counter-attack. Despite this handicap, *Upholder* continued to destroy enemy shipping, and it was the sinking, on 25 May 1941, of the heavily-escorted troopship *Conte Rosse* with over 1,000 members of the Afrika Corps on board, that earned Wanklyn his VC. Following this daring success, enemy destroyers counter-attacked and, during the next twenty minutes, dropped thirty-seven depth charges near *Upholder*. The citation for Wanklyn's VC stated: 'The failure of his listening device made it much harder for him to get away, but with the greatest courage, coolness and skill he brought *Upholder* clear of the enemy and safe back to harbour.' During the sixteen months that *Upholder* operated in the Mediterranean, she completed twenty-four patrols and sank 119,000 tons of German and Italian shipping – three U-boats, one destroyer, one armed trawler, fifteen transport and supply ships, and probably another cruiser and another destroyer – before she herself failed to return from a patrol in April 1942.

Remembering that the navy lost not only an outstanding submarine commander but also a very highly-trained and experienced team of officers and ratings, the Admiralty took the unprecedented step of publishing a special communiqué – praising *Upholder* and all her crew for their long and arduous duty in the Mediterranean – which ended with the words: 'The ship and her company are gone, but the example of the inspiration remain.' After the war, many of the surviving U Class submarines were put into reserve or lent or sold to other countries. Some boats were later returned by foreign navies to be scrapped, and the last of the Royal Navy U Class boats were broken up in 1950. *Uredd* was built as P41 for the Royal Navy who transferred her to the Norwegian Navy in 1941. She was named *Uredd* in 1943 shortly before she was lost.

Victoria Cross
HMS *Upholder*
Lieutenant Commander Malcolm David Wanklyn

The King has been Graciously pleased to approve the grant of the Victoria Cross for great valour and resolution in command of His Majesty's Submarine *Upholder* to Lieutenant Commander Malcolm David Wanklyn, DSO, Royal Navy. On the evening of 24th May 1941, whilst on patrol off the coast of Sicily, Lieutenant Commander Wanklyn, in command of His Majesty's Submarine *Upholder*, sighted a south-bound enemy troop convoy, strongly escorted by destroyers. The failing light was such that observation by periscope could not be relied on but a surface attack would have been easily seen. *Upholder's* listening gear was out of action. In spite of these severe handicaps Lieutenant Commander Wanklyn decided to press home his attack at short range. He quickly steered his craft into a favourable position and closed in so as to make sure of his target. By this time the position of the escorting destroyers could not be made out. Lieutenant Commander Wanklyn, while fully aware of the risks of being rammed by one of the escorts, continued to press on towards the enemy troopships. As he was about to fire, one of the enemy destroyers suddenly appeared out of the darkness at high speed, and he only just avoided being rammed. As soon as he was clear, he brought his periscope sights on and fired torpedoes, which sank a large troopship. The enemy destroyers at once made a strong counter-attack and during the next twenty minutes dropped thirty seven depth charges near *Upholder*. The failure of his listening devices made it much harder for him to get away, but with the greatest courage, coolness and skill he brought *Upholder* clear of the enemy and safe back to harbour. Before this outstanding attack, and since being appointed a Companion of the Distinguished Service Order, Lieutenant Commander Wanklyn had torpedoed a tanker and a merchant vessel. He has continued to show the utmost bravery in the presence of the enemy. He has carried out his attacks on the enemy with skill and relentless determination, he has also sunk one destroyer, one U-boat, two troop transports of 19,500 tons each, one tanker and three supply ships. He has besides probably destroyed by torpedoes one cruiser and one destroyer, and possibly hit another cruiser.

16 December 1941

U Class Submarines – Main Characteristics (Group One)

Overall Length/ Beam/Draught	190ft 9in x 16ft x 12ft 9in
Displacement	530 tons surfaced / 740 tons submerged
Power	2 x 615bhp diesel engines for surface propulsion
	2 x 825bhp electric motors for submerged propulsion
Diving Depth	200ft
Speed	11.75 knots surfaced / 9 knots submerged
Propeller	2
Endurance	4,050 miles at 10 knots surfaced / 23 miles at 8 knots submerged
Armament	4 x internal bow torpedo tubes (8 torpedoes carried)
	1 x 3in gun
	3 x .303in machine guns
Complement	33
Notes	The length of *Undine, Unique, Unity, Upholder, Upright, Ursula* and *Utmost* was 191ft 6in and the complement 27+ (to a maximum of 31). *Undine, Unique, Unity, Upholder, Upright, Ursula* and *Utmost* were also fitted with 2 x external bow torpedo tubes, while *Undine* and *Unity* were not fitted with the 3in gun.

U Class Submarines – Main Characteristics (Group Two)

Overall Length/ Beam/Draught	197ft x 16ft x 12ft 9in
Displacement	545 tons surfaced / 740 tons submerged
Power	2 x 615bhp diesel engines for surface propulsion
	2 x 825bhp electric motors for submerged propulsion
Diving Depth	200ft
Speed	12 knots surfaced / 9 knots submerged
Propeller	2
Endurance	4,050 miles at 10 knots surfaced / 23 miles at 8 knots submerged
Armament	4 x internal bow torpedo tubes (8 torpedoes carried)
	1 x 3in gun
	3 x .303in machine guns
Complement	33

Turkish Submarines

4 built on behalf of the Turkish Navy

For wherever the battleships might be built, their gun mountings must still come from Barrow or Elswick; at Barrow the 14-inch mountings for the King George V's were to be followed by the 16-inch mountings for the Lions, although by 1940 work on those had not gone very far.

Barrow in particular, with its prodigious programme of ships of all kinds, of gun mountings, control towers and ammunition hoists; of turbines, gearing and boilers; its mines, paravanes and depth charges; its steel, iron and brass foundries – Barrow was a microcosm not only of the British industry, but of its ancillary engineering; a gigantic organisation employing some 17,500 people, a unitary organisation, all under a single management, devoted very largely, although not exclusively, to supplying the navy.

Vickers – A History by J.D. Scott

Oruc Reis	(Yard No.751)	Launched 19 July 1940
Murat Reis	(Yard No.752)	Launched 20 July 1940
Burak Reis	(Yard No.753)	Launched 19 October 1940
Uluc-Ali Reis	(Yard No.754)	Launched 1 November 1940

Following the outbreak of war, in addition to vessels to be built for the Royal Navy, Vickers were contracted to build four submarines for the Turkish Navy (some fifty-five years after Nordenfelt's contract). These four boats, similar to the S Class but with weaker armament (see S Class Submarines, pages 120-24, for comparisons) were requisitioned by the Admiralty with the intent to commission them into the Royal Navy. However, it was recognised that Turkey had an urgent need of at least two of the boats to strengthen her defences. Consequently, P611 (ex *Oruc Reis* – *Reis* means Admiral) and P612 (ex *Murat Reis*) were dispatched to Turkey fully armed with instructions to defend themselves if necessary but not to seek trouble. Following their arrival at Turkey the boats were handed over to the Turkish Navy and the crews returned to Great Britain.

P614 (ex *Burak Reis*) and P615 (ex *Uluc-Ali Reis*) formed part of a large, heavily armed escort for the ill-fated convoy PQ17 which sailed from Britain in June 1942 bound for Russia. This escort was ultimately neutralised, frustrated and possibly misled. The escort comprised P614 and P615, six destroyers, corvettes and mine-sweeping anti-submarine vessels, armed trawlers, rescue ships, two anti-aircraft ships and a CAM ship. There was also a covering force of nine submarines. P614 and P615 joined the convoy on 30 June, and from 1 to 4 July this convoy was subjected to a pattern of shadowing, feints and heavy attacks by German torpedo-carrying aircraft with the result that at least four of the merchant vessels were lost.

However, there was even worse to come with the news that a German navy squadron, including the boat *Winston Churchill* christened 'The Beast' and the awesome 15in gun *Tirpitz*, was on a converging course with the convoy. The Admiralty instructed the convoy to scatter and gave varying orders to the differing elements of the escort. P614 and P615 were instructed to act independently 'and endeavour to attack the enemy', but this was easier said than done as German aircraft were paying particular attention to keeping both boats submerged. In the meantime the six destroyers from the escort joined a covering force cruiser and went to meet 'The Beast' and accompanying ships in a suicidal attempt to delay the attack on the disbanded convoy. Eventually, P614 and P615 were given instructions to

Above: Turkish submarine *Oruc Reis* under construction on the slipway. *(Barrow Museum Service CAT6973)*

Right: Turkish submarine *Burak Reis* (P614).

join what had been the covering force of submarines in forming a piquet line in the hope of gaining an opportunity to attack the German squadron. Too far away to be able to take any action, the squadron was sighted by the most easterly boat in the piquet line. This boat reported that 'The Beast' was accompanied by the *Hipper* and the squadron had a screening force of at least six destroyers and eight aircraft.

Even more importantly, it was clear that 'The Beast' and her cohort were now on a course taking them back to their base. The German admiral apparently believed the British force to be far stronger than it actually was! For the ships of the convoy it was to be a tragic story because, despite the instructions to scatter, they formed a series of small groups bonding together in a hopeless but understandable attempt to obtain mutual protection. Consequently the merchantmen suffered terrible losses. Of the thirty-five merchant ships, some twenty-four had been sunk, the bombers having accounted for fourteen of the vessels and U-boats sinking the other ten. P614 and P615 were eventually to be used for training purposes in South Africa where, 120 miles south of Freetown, Sierra Leone, P615 was torpedoed by U-123 on 18 April 1943. P614 was returned to the Turkish Navy in 1945 – reverting to her original name of *Burak Reis*.

Turkish Submarines – Main Characteristics

Overall Length/ Beam/Draught	201ft 6in x 22ft 3in x 10ft 6in
Displacement	683 tons surfaced / 856 tons submerged
Power	2 x 1,550bhp diesel engines for surface propulsion
	2 x 1,300bhp electric motors for submerged propulsion
Diving Depth	250ft
Speed	13.75 knots surfaced / 10 knots submerged
Propeller	2
Endurance	3,750 nautical miles at 10 knots surfaced
Armament	5 x 21in torpedo tubes (4 bow, 1 stern)
	1 x 3in gun
	1 x .303in machine gun
Complement	34

S Class Submarines

3 built on behalf of the Royal Navy

The big ships gave way to smaller ones, to U Class submarines, S Class submarines, Hunt Class destroyers and cargo ships. By the beginning of 1941 the ships on the slipways at Barrow consisted almost entirely of submarines and destroyers; the cruiser Spartan was there, but in suspense. And just like the ships on the slipways, those on order but not yet laid down were mainly cargo ships, submarines and destroyers.

Vickers – A History by J.D. Scott

HMS P72/P222	(Yard No.789)	Launched 20 September 1941
HMS P69/P219/*Seraph*	(Yard No.790)	Launched 25 October 1940
HMS P71/P221/*Shakespeare*	(Yard No.791)	Launched 8 December 1941

The S Class of submarines was enormous in number, with no fewer than sixty-two boats being built in total and a number of others being cancelled or planned but never ordered. There were three groups within this class. Surprisingly the Barrow Shipyard was only responsible for building three S Class submarines, all being Group Three boats. The boats in this group were all welded, whereas Group Two boats were only partially welded. None of the Group One boats were welded. The three boats built at Barrow all underwent name changes during their period under construction (two of them twice) – a fact which can lead to some confusion for the historian.

Two boats in this class were built and launched at Scott's of Greenock and transferred to be completed at Barrow. These were *Sea Rover* (Yard No.901) and *Sirdar* (Yard No.902).

HMS *Seraph*, an S Class submarine constructed at Barrow-in-Furness.

During the modernization of the submarine force in the early 1930s, the Royal Navy became aware of the need for smaller boats, suitable for employment in the North Sea and restricted waters such as the Mediterranean. In response to this requirement, orders were placed for medium-sized patrol submarines, from which the Swordfish and Shark Classes were evolved. Based on the saddle tank construction of the L Class submarines, which they were designed to replace, the twelve vessels of these two classes proved so useful that an improved version was put into mass production during the Second World War.

With a length of 217ft and displacing 814 tons (surfaced), the improved S Class boats gave outstanding war service under the most difficult conditions, and there is some justification for describing them as the most important of all the Royal Navy's submarines in the pre-missile era. Fifty improved S Class submarines were launched between 1940 and 1945, making the S Class the largest single group of submarines built for the Royal Navy: A total of sixty-two were constructed over a period of fifteen years. In one respect, the S Class boats were unique in that they were the only class to remain in production throughout the war period – which is a fair measure of their success. As can be imagined, there were considerable variations in a design which spanned fifteen years, and modifications as a result of war experience could only be incorporated depending on the stage of construction reached.

Although not in themselves above average, the combination of the S Class boats' qualities, together with the reliability of their equipment and the great ease of operation and maintenance, made them very effective and safe. No modifications were made to the first five vessels of the War Programme (*Safari, Sahib, Saracen, Satyr* and *Sceptre*) but an external stern torpedo tube was added to the group of boats that followed, bringing the number of tubes up to seven and the number of available torpedoes to thirteen. This change was indicative of the varied armament of S Class submarines. Many boats were fitted with a 20mm Oerlikon cannon, mounted on a platform aft of the periscopes and which replaced or supplemented three portable .303in machine-guns. Eighteen vessels, built towards the end of the war and intended to operate in the Far East, had their standard 3in gun replaced by a 4in gun, mounted inside a low breastwork, forward of the conning tower.

In addition, the boats fitted with the 4in gun had their stern torpedo tube removed – from weight considerations. To extend their radius of action, submarines operating in the Far East during the war had some of their main ballast tanks converted to oil fuel tanks, increasing the fuel load from 72 tons to a maximum of 98 tons. All boats stationed in this theatre proceeded on patrol carrying as many additional stores as possible – particularly food and ammunition – stowed in all manner of unlikely spaces (an ammunition locker was placed under the Wardroom table, and shells were even stored in the engine room). Naturally this practice became a matter of some concern and, although strict regulations were imposed on the stowage of ammunition (particularly regarding temperature requirements), the rules were never completely adhered to.

By these measures, the S Class boats managed to achieve long patrol times in operational areas; the record of forty-nine days was set by *Sirdar*. During 1941 and 1942, S Class submarines were fitted with the first radar sets for surface as well as air search and, during the first stages of the war, S Class boats were very active in the North Sea and the Mediterranean. As a result, losses were rather heavy and in 1940 six of the class were lost in the North Sea alone. As the war progressed, however, the class became more adept, and they were particularly successful against other submarines. Of the sixty-two S Class submarines built, seventeen were lost during the war; nine in the North Sea and Atlantic, six in the Mediterranean and two in the Pacific and Indian Oceans. It is reputed that an S Class submarine, HMS *Statesman*, fired the last torpedo of the Second World War, when she sank a Japanese derelict.

The ability of the submarine to operate stealthily made the S Class ideal for secretive missions, and the clandestine operations of the Vickers-built *Seraph* provided one of the most fascinating stories of the Second World War, and earned her the nickname 'HMS Cloak and Dagger'.

Commissioned in 1942, and under the command of Lt N.L.A. 'Jimmy' Jewell, *Seraph's* first special operation was a surveillance of the North Africa coast as preparation for Operation Torch (code name for the invasion of North Africa). This was followed by the secretive landing and recovery of an American delegation who were to meet with Vichy French

A diesel engine for an S Class submarine, photographed here in the Shipyard's Engine Shop. *(Barrow Museum Service CAT 0213)*

commanders near Algiers. A strong friendship and mutual respect grew between *Seraph*'s crew and the American passengers, which led to *Seraph* masquerading as a United States' submarine under the nominal command of Capt. Wright, United States Navy. Before the Allied invasion of North Africa, it was necessary to unite all the French forces in the various garrisons under the leadership of General Giraud. As the General did not trust the British and refused to co-operate with anyone but the Americans, *Seraph* sailed under the Stars and Stripes flag – with her crew adopting a much-practiced Anglo-American slang in order to appear as American as possible to her valuable passenger.

In the autumn of 1942, a decision was tentatively made to invade Sicily. As the Germans were bound to anticipate that Sicily would be a likely target, the question arose of how to fool them into deploying their forces elsewhere. As British officers were continually being flown around the coast of Spain to North Africa, a plan was devised to plant a body, carrying false papers, in the sea off Spain – as if coming from a crashed plane. In order to convince a post-mortem that the 'officer' had indeed drowned, the body of a man who had just died from pneumonia – in which form of death there is liquid in the lungs – was found. On the understanding that his true identity would always remain secret, consent was obtained from the dead man's relatives and, from that time forward, he became 'Major William Martin, Royal Marines', and his body was placed in cold storage as a plan was devised.

The body of 'Major Martin' was to carry two letters for delivery to Africa, one from Lt-Gen. Sir Archibald Nye, Vice-Chief of the Imperial General Staff, and the other from none other than Lord Louis Mountbatten, both of which intimated that Sardinia was the target of the assault. In addition to his identity card, the 'Major' was assumed to be a brilliant, but nevertheless extravagant, man and in his pocket was a letter from Lloyds Bank Head Office, calling on him to pay off an overdraft of nearly £80. Assuming that every young officer had some romantic attachment, 'Major Martin' carried a photograph of, and two letters from, his 'girlfriend' 'Pam'. These letters were folded and unfolded continually to look as though they had been read and re-read. Probably his engagement was the cause of his overdraft for he also had, in his pocket, a bill for £53 for an engagement ring.

With the addition of the usual paraphernalia – old bus tickets, keys, theatre tickets, scraps of paper, etc. – 'Major Martin' was ready for his mission. With the Prime Minister's approval, *Seraph* sailed at 6.00 p.m. on 19 April 1943 – with 'Major William Martin' safely stored in a 6ft metal canister packed with dry ice. For ten days *Seraph* surfaced only at night. On the morning of 30 April, 1,600yds off Huelva, Spain, *Seraph* surfaced and 'Major Martin' was slid out of his canister into the sea. He was sighted by a Spanish fisherman later that morning and recovered by the authorities. A post-mortem revealed that death was caused by 'asphyxiation through immersion in the sea'. The German agent in Huelva 'played his part' and his superiors were alerted to the existence of the documents. To complete the plot, 'Pam' sent a wreath to the 'Major's' funeral in Spain, and his name was inserted in the casualty list which appeared in *The Times* of 4 June 1943.

The success of 'Major Martin's' mission can be measured from remarks in Field-Marshal Rommel's personal papers, which reveal that when the Allies invaded Sicily the German defence was led astray: 'as a result of a diplomatic courier's body being washed up off Spain'. These missions were vital to the Supreme Allied Commander, General Dwight Eisenhower, and *Seraph*'s exploits saved thousands of Allied lives. General Patton himself praised the *Seraph*'s conduct during the invasion of Sicily, and Lt Jewell subsequently received the Legion of Merit – the highest American honour that can be bestowed on a foreigner. When she was scrapped in 1965, a *Seraph* Memorial was erected in Citadel campus at the Military College of South Carolina, and includes *Seraph*'s periscope, fore-hatch, plane wheel, Jolly Roger flag, steering wheel, ship's bell and badge and other items requested by General Mark Clark (then president of the Military College).

Seraph played cloak and dagger to the very end. On the way to the breakers yard she slipped her tow and was adrift for twenty-four hours before 'recapture'.

S Class Submarines – Main Characteristics (Group Three)

Overall Length/ Beam/Draught	217ft x 24ft x 13ft 3in
Displacement	814 tons surfaced / 990 tons submerged
Power	2 x 1,550bhp 8-cylinder diesel engines for surface propulsion
	2 x 1,300bhp electric motors for submerged propulsion
Diving Depth	350ft
Speed	14 knots surfaced / 10 knots submerged
Propeller	2
Endurance	6,000 miles at 10 knots surfaced
Armament	7 x 21in torpedo tubes (6 bow, 1 stern) (13 torpedoes carried)
	1 x 3in or 4in gun
	3 x .303in machine guns
	1 x 20mm Oerlikon cannon
Complement	48

X Craft Submarines

6 built on behalf of the Royal Navy

In that section of Armaments dealing with under-water warfare the Company are in the unique position of possessing the World Patent Rights of all the useful modern developments in connection with Submarine Mines, Depth Charges and Paravanes.

By virtue of this position, and of having a specialist technical staff dealing solely with this form of Armament, it is possible to satisfy every requirement for standard or special weapons to meet the needs of any country in connection with submarine mining, anti-submarine warfare, and anti-mining equipment.

The Activities of Vickers-Armstrongs Limited (Barrow-in-Furness)

X5	(Yard No.883)	Commissioned 29 December 1942
X6	(Yard No.883)	Commissioned 21 January 1943
X7	(Yard No.883)	Commissioned 14 January 1943
X8	(Yard No.883)	Commissioned 28 January 1943
X9	(Yard No.883)	Commissioned 29 January 1943
X10	(Yard No.883)	Commissioned 8 February 1943

Sometimes known as the X5 Class boats, but more commonly X Craft, no less than six of these midget submarines were built at the Barrow Yard, with eight others (including two prototypes built in sections as described in the text below) being constructed elsewhere. The sometimes-used class name of X5 comes from the fact that X5 was actually the first of class (X3 and X4 being prototypes, X1 an experimental fleet submarine built in 1925 and X2 a captured Italian submarine).

The history of Barrow-built submersibles reached another dimension with the development and production of Royal Navy midget submarines. Notwithstanding the fact that Britain was one of the last countries to be involved with midget submarine construction and tactical application, the Royal Navy would nevertheless make the most impressive use of this type of vessel. There are a number of books dealing with the initial development of the prototype X Craft and all, in one respect or another, are at variance with the Yard's outlook on the matter.

The Yard's version is extracted from a speech given on the occasion when the last of the X Class boats, X54 – *Minnow*, first became water-borne in May 1955.

Work commenced on a design of the prototype in the autumn of 1940 at Varley Engineering Company of Acton, London. After some progress had been made, the works were bombed and completely burnt out. The mock-up and most of the drawings were destroyed. A new site was found at Bursledon on the Hamble River and work was re-commenced. Two craft were ordered as prototypes – the centre portions being built by Vickers-Armstrongs (Barrow), the after ends by Brigham and Cowan (Hull) and the fore ends by Thorneycrofts (Southampton). The first three sections were transported to Bursledon, assembled and launched into the Hamble River where extensive trials were carried out. The second set of sections were assembled at Portsmouth Dockyard. These two craft were known as X.3 and X.4. They were used for training personnel in Loch Striven whilst the production models were being built. A new design for the production model was prepared to embody the lessons learnt from the prototypes and an order was placed with Vickers-Armstrongs, Barrow, for six craft in July 1942.

In December 1942, Vickers began to build six X Craft (X5 to X10) for employment in European waters. Their primary operation was to attack the German battleship *Tirpitz*, which was 'holed-up' in Alten Fjord, Norway. By September 1943, the six midget submarines and their hand-picked, highly-trained crews were ready to undertake a mission that was to write a chapter in the history of submarine warfare. With engines that generated 42hp (surfaced) and only 30hp (submerged), the X Craft were too small to undertake long passages and were, therefore, always towed to their target areas by full-sized submarines, at maximum speeds of 10.5 knots (surfaced) and 12 knots (submerged).

As can be expected, towing midgets reduced the endurance of submarines – the S Class, for example, had a 30% reduction in endurance, and the comparable figure for the largest T Class was 5.5%. The *Tirpitz* mission began in an undistinguished manner when, on the outward passage to Norway (which was an eight-day journey covering 1,000 miles), X9 sank and X8 had to be scuttled. Fifty miles from their target, the four remaining X Craft were cast loose to proceed under their own power, through winding, shallow fjords, mine-

A model of an X Craft Midget Submarine. The arrows indicate the approximate positions of the internally flanged joints which fastened the fore and aft sections to the centre section on the operational craft. The all-welded sections were very strong and post-war tests showed that the craft were capable of surviving depths of up to 600ft. *(Barrow Museum Service CAT 2642)*

fields and anti-submarine nets to the anchorage of *Tirpitz*. X10 penetrated the inner fjord, but had to abandon her attack because of mechanical defects. Harassed by vigorous enemy patrols, her captain valiantly stayed hidden with his small boat for five days until, finally, he could return to the 'towing ship'. X10 was scuttled on the return journey to England. On 22 September 1943, X6 (Lt Donald Cameron, RNR) and X7 (Lt Basil Place) followed an old freighter through the final set of nets and arrived at their objective within minutes of each other.

An alert guard, spotting one of the craft, raised the alarm but, although under a heavy counter-attack, X6 managed to get beneath the massive ship and drop two separate explosives – following which she became entangled in underwater nets and had to surrender. X7 also released two charges beneath *Tirpitz* but before she could fully escape, the first of the explosives from X6 detonated, and she too was forced to surrender. A third submarine was sighted and brought under heavy fire. This was probably X5, which was never seen again.

The attack on *Tirpitz* was a great success, for although the charges did not sink her, the damage they inflicted resulted in the vessel being towed south for repairs. Here *Tirpitz* was at last within range of British bombers, which finally eliminated her a little more than a year later. For the part they played in preventing *Tirpitz* sailing from Norway, Lts Place and Cameron were awarded the Victoria Cross. Midget submarines were used to reconnoitre landing beaches, among other duties, prior to the Normandy invasion in June 1944 and, on D-Day itself, several acted as navigation beacons well inshore to guide the first assault wave. In the Far East they were used to cut submarine cables and sabotage telephone lines (for further information refer to XE Craft Submarines pages 128–30). At best, the secretive operations of midget submarines were hazardous, but many feats of skill and bravery were performed by their crews.

Victoria Crosses
HMS X7 and HMS X6
Lieutenant Basil Charles Place and Lieutenant Donald Cameron

The King has been Graciously pleased to approve the grant of the Victoria Cross to Lieutenant Basil Charles Place, DSC, Royal Navy and Lieutenant Donald Cameron, Royal Naval Reserve. Lieutenants Place and Cameron were the Commanding Officers of two of His Majesty's Midget Submarines X7 and X6 which on the 22nd September 1943 carried out a most daring and successful attack on the German Battleship *Tirpitz*, moored in the protected anchorage of Kaa fjord, North Norway. To reach the anchorage necessitated the penetration of an enemy minefield and a passage of fifty miles up the fjord, known to be vigilantly patrolled by the enemy and to be guarded by nets, gun defences and listening posts, this after a passage of at least a thousand miles from base. Having successfully eluded all these hazards and entered the fleet anchorage, Lieutenants Place and Cameron, with complete disregard for danger, worked their small craft past the closed anti-submarine and torpedo nets surrounding the *Tirpitz*, and from a position inside these nets, carried out a cool and determined attack. Whilst they were still inside the nets a fierce enemy counter-attack by guns and depth charges developed which made their withdrawal impossible. Lieutenants Place and Cameron therefore scuttled their craft to prevent them falling into the hands of the enemy. Before doing so they took every measure to ensure the safety of their crews the majority of whom, together with them-selves, were subsequently taken prisoner. In the course of the operation these small craft pressed home their attack to the full, in doing so accepting all the dangers inherent in such vessels and facing every possible hazard which ingenuity could have devised for the protection in harbour of vitally important capital ships. The courage and utter contempt for danger in the immediate face of the enemy shown by Lieutenants Place and Cameron during their determined and successful attack were supreme.

22 February 1944

X Craft Submarines – Main Characteristics

Overall Length/ Beam/Draught	51ft 3in x 5ft 9in x 5ft 9in (minimum)
Displacement	27 tons surfaced / 30 tons submerged
Power	1 x 42bhp Gardner diesel engine for surface propulsion
	1 x 30bhp Blackman electric motor for submerged propulsion
Diving Depth	300ft
Speed	6.5 knots surfaced / 5.5 knots submerged
Propeller	1
Endurance	1,300 miles at 4 knots surfaced / 80 miles at 2 knots submerged
Armament	2 x 2-ton side cargoes of HE attached to the boat by a threaded bolt and released from the inside of the hull by turning a hand wheel
	Could also carry limpet mines
Complement	4

XE Craft Submarines and XT Craft Submarines

6 of each built on behalf of the Royal Navy

Army munitions were made by Vickers-Armstrongs at Barrow, Crayford, Chertsey, Dartford, Elswick, Manchester, Scotswood and elsewhere, as well as by the English Steel Corporation at Sheffield, by other Vickers' companies, and by Metropolitan-Cammell who were only half Vickers. These munitions ranged from large artillery pieces to leather cloth for tank seats; from hotwater bottles for army hospitals to complete AA predictors; from constructional steel to anti-gas protective clothing; and from ammunition of all kinds to bags to put it in.

Vickers – A History by J.D. Scott

XE1	(Yard No.939)	Built and completed December 1943 – January 1945
XE2	(Yard No.939)	Built and completed December 1943 – January 1945
XE3	(Yard No.939)	Built and completed December 1943 – January 1945
XE4	(Yard No.939)	Built and completed December 1943 – January 1945
XE5	(Yard No.939)	Built and completed December 1943 – January 1945
XE6	(Yard No.939)	Built and completed December 1943 – January 1945

Vickers archives show Yard No.939 as an order for six XE Craft, numbered XE 20 to 25 which is incorrect. In reality Vickers built XE 1 to 6. XE 7 to 12 were built as follows: Broadbent of Huddersfield (XE7 and XE8); Marshall of Gainsborough (XE9 and XE10); Markham and Chesterfield (XE11 and XE12). A further six boats (XE14 to XE19) were ordered but subsequently cancelled. We are unable to explain the anomaly in the Vickers archives – a slip of the archivist's pen perhaps.

XT1	(Yard No.927)	Completed 18 January 1944
XT2	(Yard No.927)	Completed 26 January 1944
XT3	(Yard No.927)	Completed 4 February 1944
XT4	(Yard No.927)	Completed 15 February 1944
XT5	(Yard No.927)	Completed 25 February 1944
XT6	(Yard No.927)	Completed 14 March 1944

The XT Craft midget submarines were quite simply training versions of the XE Craft boats. The Royal Navy originally ordered twelve XTs – six from Barrow and six from Broadbents – but, in the event, the Broadbents order was subsequently cancelled. The Barrow Yard built all the six boats ordered from them.

The XE Craft, with air conditioning and extra stowage space, were designed for employment in the Far East. Spring-loaded legs made it easier for these midget submarines to rest on the seabed, and an airlock allowed a diver to leave the submarine and place limpet mines on the hulls of enemy ships. Vickers built the first six vessels of the class, the most famous and successful of which was HM Midget Submarine XE3.

Commanded by Lt Ian Fraser, RNR, XE3 attacked the Japanese heavy cruiser *Takao* on 31 July 1945. After being released from the towing submarine, XE3 spent more than twenty-four hours getting into a position to attack the *Takao*, which was moored in the Jahore Strait, Singapore. After his first attempt failed, Fraser circled the target and put his boat under the great ship's hull. Despite being hampered by weed and barnacles as well as a leak in his diving equipment, the boat's diver, Leading Seaman James Magennis, swam along the cruiser's hull placing limpet mines. Exhausted, he re-entered the submarine and XE3 pulled clear. During the next stage of the attack, a jammed limpet container prevented the jettisoning of the side cargoes of explosives, which gave the submarine an uncontrollable list. Magennis volunteered to go back outside and spent fifteen minutes freeing the load. All this time the submarine and the diver were vulnerable, lying in the crystal clear water. XE3 eventually made her escape and, whilst returning to base unscathed, the charges detonated – sinking the 11,000-ton vessel. Lt Fraser and Leading Seaman Magennis were both awarded the Victoria Cross for their bravery in performing this operation. Bradford Cathedral has a plaque in memory of Leading Seaman Magennis.

Admiral James Fife, USN, said of the crews of the XEs prior to their mission to sink the Japanese heavy cruisers *Takao* and *Nachi* that: 'You're the little guys with a lotta guts', sentiments that could be applied to all the men of the midgets.

An XE5 Craft midget submarine in Devonshire Dock with storage tank. The Corn Mill can be seen in the background. *(Barrow Museum Service CAT 0139)*

15 August 1945 was VJ Day (Victory over Japan). Within two months of that date, in unseemly haste, XEs 1 to 6 were scrapped in the breakers yard at Cockatoo Island, Sydney Harbour. The apparent reason for breaking was that Sydney was suffering from power strikes and the boats' portable generators were required.

During 1943 and 1944, Vickers built six XT Craft submarines for training purposes. Having an endurance of only 500 miles at 4 knots, the XT Craft boats were a simplified X5 Class (XE Craft) submarine – without the side-cargo release gear, night periscope or automatic helmsman. In addition their day periscope, projector compass and air-induction trunk were fixed in the 'up' position. Six more vessels, ordered in 1943 from Broadbents of Huddersfield, were cancelled before completion. The six Barrow-built boats were scrapped at the end of the war.

XE Craft Submarines – Main Characteristics

Overall Length/ Beam/Draught	53ft x 5ft 9in x 5ft 10in (minimum)
Displacement	30 tons surfaced / 34 tons submerged
Power	1 x 42bhp Gardner diesel engine for surfaced propulsion
	1 x 30bhp Blackman electric motor for submerged propulsion
Diving Depth	300ft
Speed	6.5 knots surfaced / 6 knots submerged
Propeller	1
Endurance	1,350 nautical miles surfaced / 80 nautical miles submerged
Armament	2 x 2-ton side cargoes of HE attached to the boat by a threaded bolt and released from the inside of the hull by turning a hand wheel
	Could also carry limpet mines
Complement	4

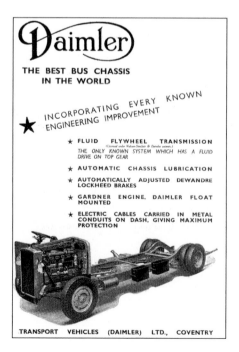

This pre-war advertisement (c.1938) is of interest because the Gardner engine depicted is of the type used in the midget submarines constructed at Barrow-in-Furness (and elsewhere).

XT Craft Submarines – Main Characteristics

Overall Length/ Beam/Draught	51ft 4in x 5ft 9in x 5ft 11in (minimum)
Displacement	26.5 tons surfaced / 29.6 tons submerged
Power	1 x 42bhp Gardner diesel engine for surface propulsion
	1 x 30bhp Blackman electric motor for submerged propulsion
Diving Depth	300ft
Speed	6 knots surfaced / 5 knots submerged
Propeller	1
Endurance	500 miles surfaced / 80 miles submerged
Armament	None
Complement	3

Victoria Cross

HMS XE3

Lieutenant Ian Edward Fraser

The King has been Graciously pleased to approve the grant of the Victoria Cross for great valour to Lieutenant Ian Edward Fraser, DSC, Royal Naval Reserve. Lieutenant Fraser commanded His Majesty's Midget Submarine XE3 in a successful attack on a Japanese heavy cruiser of the Atago Class at her mooring in the Jahore Strait, Singapore, on 31st July 1945. During the long approach up the Singapore Straits, XE3 deliberately left the believed safe channel and entered the mined waters to avoid suspected hydrophone posts. The target was aground, or nearly aground, both fore and aft, and only under the amidships portions was there just sufficient water for XE3 to place herself under the cruiser. For forty minutes XE3 pushed her way along the seabed until finally Lieutenant Fraser managed to force her right under the centre of the cruiser. Here he then placed the limpets and dropped his main side charge. Great difficulty was experienced in extricating the craft after the attack had been completed, but finally XE3 was clear, and commenced her long return journey out to sea. The courage and determination of Lieutenant Fraser are beyond all praise. Any man not possessed of his relentless determination to achieve his objective in full, regardless of all consequences, would have dropped his side charge alongside the target instead of persisting until he had forced his submarine right under the cruiser. The approach and withdrawal entailed a passage of eighty miles through water which had been mined by both the enemy and ourselves, past hydrophone positions, over loops and controlled minefields, and through an anti-submarine boom.

13 November 1945

Victoria Cross
HMS XE3
Leading Seaman James Joseph Magennis

The King has been Graciously pleased to approve the grant of the Victoria Cross for great valour to Temporary Acting Leading Seaman James Joseph Magennis. Leading Seaman Magennis served as a Diver in His Majesty's Submarine XE3 for her attack on 31st July 1945, on a Japanese Cruiser of the Atago Class. Owing to the fact that XE3 was tightly jammed under the target, the diver's hatch could not be fully opened and Magennis had to squeeze himself through the narrow space available. He experienced great difficulty in placing his limpets on the bottom of the cruiser owing to both the foul state of the bottom and to the pronounced slope upon which the limpets would not hold. Before a limpet could be placed therefore, Magennis had thoroughly to scrape the area clear of the barnacles and in order to secure the limpets he had to tie them in pairs by a line passing under the cruiser's keel. This was very tiring work for a diver and he was moreover handicapped by a steady leakage of oxygen which was ascending in bubbles to the surface. A lesser man would have been content to place a few limpets and then return to the craft. Magennis, however, persisted until he had placed his full outfit before returning to the craft in an exhausted condition. Shortly after withdrawing, Lieutenant Fraser endeavoured to jettison his limpet carriers, but one of these would not release itself and fell clear of the craft. Despite his exhaustion, his oxygen leak and the fact that there was every probability of his being sighted, Magennis at once volunteered to leave the craft and free the carrier rather than allow a less experienced diver to undertake the job. After seven minutes of nerve-racking work he succeeded in releasing the carrier. Magennis displayed very great courage and devotion to duty and complete disregard for his own safety.

13 November 1945

XT5 berthed in Devonshire Dock. (Barrow Museum Service CAT 0145)

Second V Class Submarines

14 built on behalf of the Royal Navy

Perfection of the technique of the welded joint in substitution for riveting brought many advantages. The joint is homogenous and superior in strength, and by elimination of overlaps and connecting angle pieces, effects a substantial saving in material. In a riveted ship, as every Owner knows, each rivet is a potential leak when the structure is overstrained, or suffers minor damage, but the welded joint is inherently watertight and remains so under the most severe stress.

Ships by J.S. Redshaw

HMS *Venturer*	(Yard No.860)	Launched 4 May 1943
HMS *Viking*	(Yard No.861)	Launched 5 May 1943
HMS *Veldt*	(Yard No.862)	Launched 19 July 1943
HMS *Vampire*	(Yard No.863)	Launched 20 July 1943
HMS *Vox*	(Yard No.864)	Launched 28 September 1943
HMS *Vigorous*	(Yard No.865)	Launched 15 October 1943
HMS *Virtue*	(Yard No.866)	Launched 29 November 1943
HMS *Visigoth*	(Yard No.867)	Launched 30 November 1943
HMS *Upshot*	(Yard No.886)	Launched 24 February 1944
HMS *Urtica*	(Yard No.887)	Launched 23 March 1944
HMS *Vineyard*	(Yard No.888)	Launched 8 May 1944
HMS *Variance*	(Yard No.889)	Launched 22 May 1944
HMS *Vengeful*	(Yard No.890)	Launched 20 July 1944
HMS *Vortex*	(Yard No.891)	Launched 19 August 1944

Twenty-two V Class submarines were built for the Royal Navy in the early 1940s, with a further twenty ordered but subsequently cancelled. Six of these cancelled boats were to have been constructed at the Barrow Shipyard. As it was, the Barrow Yard built fourteen of the twenty-two boats which were ultimately commissioned into the Royal Navy. The V Class boats were of the same design as the Group Two U Class submarines but were of partially welded construction.

In 1941, modifications were made to the design of the U Class submarines in order to quickly obtain a type of boat which, while retaining the same characteristics, would be stronger but simpler and less expensive. The resultant V Class were slightly longer than the U Class boats and, because of a partially welded pressure hull, had a greater operational depth – 300ft as opposed to 200ft. The electric welding of hull assemblies also gave a quicker building time. The Admiralty were supportive of welding from the onset of war in respect of surface vessels and by 1943 would state: 'subject to satisfactory design arrangements welding results are superior to riveting results, alike under tension, alternating stress, and shock. Our war experiences have given full proof for the above statement.'

The Admiralty possessed sufficient evidence, for both submarines and surface vessels, that welded hulls could better withstand the punishment from battle than those that were riveted. Additionally, there were other benefits which made welding attractive; welding lent itself to pre-fabrication (units of up to 60 tons were produced at Barrow) and the production time for an all-welded (as opposed to riveted) submarine was cut by two thirds; a welded hull was lighter than a riveted hull, the consequent weight saving being of benefit to the engines; and the Admiralty and Shipyard management considered it to be quicker to train a proficient welder than proficient riveters and caulkers. Fourteen of the class were built at Barrow and the first eight submarines were ordered in 1941. Large numbers were planned, and forty-two V Class boats were ordered between 1941 and 1943.

However, with the capitulation of Italy in 1943, the need for coastal submarines in the Mediterranean decreased and twenty of the class were subsequently cancelled when the end to hostilities in Europe seemed imminent. None of the fourteen V Class submarines built at Barrow were lost during the war and the lead ship, HMS *Venturer*, distinguished herself by sinking two German submarines: one in November 1944, the other in February 1945. *Venturer* was transferred to the Royal Netherlands Navy following the war, and many other V Class vessels served with Allied navies (particularly Greece, Norway and Free France) during and after the conflict. The last of the class in service with the Royal Navy was scrapped in 1958.

Second V Class Submarines – Main Characteristics

Overall Length/ Beam/Draught	204ft 6in x 16ft x 15ft 10in
Displacement	545 tons surfaced / 740 tons submerged
Power	2 x 800bhp diesel engines for surface propulsion
	2 x 760bhp electric motors for submerged propulsion
Diving Depth	300ft

HMS *Upshot*, one of fourteen V Class submarines built at Barrow. *(Barrow Museum Service CAT 0085)*

Speed	13 knots surfaced / 9 knots submerged
Propeller	2
Endurance	4,700 miles at 10 knots surfaced / 30 miles at 9 knots submerged
Armament	4 x 21in torpedo tubes in bow (8 torpedoes carried)
	1 x 3in gun
	3 x .303in machine guns
Complement	37

Second A Class Submarines

10 built on behalf of the Royal Navy

The Vickers empire thus contained many kingdoms, widely diverse in products and location, and the men leading them inevitably thought first and foremost of the strength and success of their own activities. They competed for available resources and chaffed against the pull of the reins from Vickers' House. Traditionally this was particularly true of the shipbuilders, and at Barrow it was further intensified by the fierce local pride of all Barrovians. From their isolated position on the Furness peninsula, facing southwards across Morecambe Bay, they regarded all non-Barrovians with suspicion and took deep pride in their own down-to-earth competence and self-sufficiency. Barrow was Vickers and, for them, Vickers was Barrow – a belief fostered by the frequency with which Barrovians who moved to other parts of the Group seemed to rise to the top.

Vickers: Against The Odds, 1956-77 by Harold Evans

HMS *Amphion*	(Yard No.903)	Launched 31 August 1944
HMS *Astute*	(Yard No.904)	Launched 30 January 1945
HMS *Auriga*	(Yard No.905)	Launched 29 March 1945
HMS *Aurochs*	(Yard No.906)	Launched 28 July 1945
HMS *Alcide*	(Yard No.907)	Launched 12 April 1945
HMS *Alderney*	(Yard No.908)	Launched 25 June 1945
HMS *Alliance*	(Yard No.909)	Launched 28 July 1945
HMS *Ambush*	(Yard No.910)	Launched 24 September 1945
HMS *Anchorite*	(Yard No.911)	Launched 22 January 1946
HMS *Andrew*	(Yard No.912)	Launched 6 April 1946

The end of the Second World War curtailed the intended mass production of the Second A Class submarines, indeed none were actually completed in time to see active service during that war. The original intention had been to build forty-six boats in this class but in the event only sixteen were completed, ten of these at the Barrow Shipyard. Of the thirty cancelled boats, Barrow was earmarked to construct ten of these before peace intervened. Some of the cancelled hulls were used in tests or as targets.

Construction of A Class submarines: HMS *Anchorite* is in the centre of the picture in the foreground. *(Barrow Museum Service CAT 0222)*

On the morning of 7 December 1941, the US Fleet suffered more damage in one hour than during the whole of the First World War, when Japanese aircraft bombed Pearl Harbor – the United States' largest naval base – and the airfields which were an essential part of its defences. The attack lasted from 7.55 a.m. to 9.15 a.m., and initiated the Pacific Ocean as one of the war's major battlegrounds. This distant theatre of war heralded a change in British submarine policy. As none of the existing submarines had adequate range, a new class – representing the only new submarine design produced by the Royal Navy during the Second World War – was adopted, which had a much greater range and increased surface speed. The opportunity was also taken to introduce major technical advances, of which the most important was an all-welded hull.

An indication of the strength of a well-designed welded hull was shown during Admiralty trials in which an A Class hull was lowered to 880ft before collapsing. It was such strength that saved *Anchorite* when she collided with an uncharted rock in 1960 in the Havriki Gulf off New Zealand. Although over 100ft down she was able to surface and reach harbour. These new A Class submarines were basically an enlargement of the T Class, with a construction that was simple, fast and so arranged as to utilise many of the materials set aside for the T Class boats. The A Class, perhaps the most successful of all 'traditional' types of pre-nuclear submarine, were fitted with: an effective air conditioning system; air warning radar which could function at periscope depth; a high flared bow for excellent sea performance; formidable armament of ten 21in torpedo tubes; and an appreciably reduced underwater noise level. Forty-six A Class boats were ordered under the 1943 Programme, and the first-of-class *Amphion* was laid down at Vickers on 14 November 1943 and launched on 31 August 1944.

Only *Amphion* and *Astute*, also Barrow-built, were completed before the end of the war, but neither was involved in any hostilities. With the conclusion of the war imminent, thirty of the forty-six ordered boats were cancelled – of the sixteen that remained, Vickers constructed ten.

A Class submarines were over 280ft long and displaced 1,385 tons (surfaced). Their two Admiralty diesels developed 4,300bhp, which gave a surface speed of 18.5 knots. The submerged speed was 8 knots, produced by two English Electric motors generating 1,250bhp. The radius of action of the A Class was 10,500 miles on the surface at 11 knots and up to ninety miles submerged at 3 knots. The heavy armament consisted of six 21in bow tubes (two external) and four 21in stern tubes (two external) – with twenty torpedoes carried. The class were also fitted with one 4in gun forward of the conning tower, one 20mm Oerlikon cannon and three portable .303in machine-guns. As the final act was being played in the theatre of war, it is interesting to recall the words Winston Churchill used to express to the submarine branch of the Royal Navy the nation's gratitude for the difficulties and dangers it faced during the Second World War: 'Of all the branches of men in the Forces there is none that shows more devotion and faces greater perils than the submariner ... Great deeds are done in the air and on the land, nevertheless nothing surpasses your exploits.'

After the war, the A Class, and other submarines, were fitted with a 'Snort' (Schnorkel) mast, which was a device by which air could be taken into a submarine so that it could continue to use its diesel engines when submerged. To demonstrate the effectiveness of the system, the Vickers-built HMS *Andrew* completed a record fifteen-day, 2,500-mile submerged passage from Bermuda to England. She surfaced in the English Channel on the

HMS *Alliance* under construction on the slipway. *(Barrow Museum Service CAT 0223)*

eve of the Coronation in 1953, just in time for the feat to be reported in the same news bulletin as the first ascent of Mount Everest. In the spring of 1951, as if to remind submariners of the hazardous nature of their profession, disaster again struck the Royal Navy Submarine Service. Leaving Portsmouth on a training cruise on 16 April, HMS *Affray* dived at 9.00 p.m. in the extreme western part of the English Channel. She vanished with all her crew plus twenty-three submarine officers under training and some Royal Marine Commandos – a total of seventy-five men. The importance of affecting a quick rescue was hampered by the fact that the commander's brief was very wide-ranging.

Alas, *Affray* remained undiscovered until late June, when an underwater television camera searching north of Guernsey found her in 278ft of water. Pictures revealed her snort mast was snapped off, but no explanation was ever given as to why she had sunk, why nobody escaped or why she was never salvaged. HMS *Affray* has the unfortunate honour of being the last Royal Navy submarine to be lost. Between 1955 and 1960, A Class boats were modernised on the same lines as the T Class, with a complete rebuilding of the forward and after hull sections, lengthening and streamlining. The two external torpedo tubes forward and aft were also removed, leaving a total of six.

From 1967 onwards, these fine submarines were progressively scrapped. In 1972, HMS *Aeneas* was hired by Vickers for successful trials of SLAM (Submarine-Launched Air Missile) – being six Blowpipe missiles clustered around a TV guidance unit. The navy did not persist with the use of SLAM, their range was too short and the boat unhealthily exposed during firing. As the Barrow-built HMS *Andrew* awaited disposal in 1977 the end of an era was signalled – she was the oldest submarine in service, the last to carry a deck gun and the last submarine designed during the Second World War to be still at sea.

The first-of-class HMS *Amphion* having just been launched in 1944. The loose timbers from the launch are visible just to the left of the boat. *(Barrow Museum Service CAT 2365)*

HMS *Astute*. A view of the starboard bow as she runs on the surface in Walney Channel. *(Barrow Museum Service CAT 0991)*

As the world moved into a new era of peace, Barrow's contribution to the national war effort makes a fascinating catalogue. To quote from *A Century of Shipbuilding* by Tom Clark: 'A cursory check has made it four aircraft carriers, three cruisers, ten destroyers, ten cargo ships, eleven landing craft and ninety-nine submarines!' An amazing total of 137 vessels, built in under six years. The majority of the submarines were handed over in the four years of 1941 to 1944, and the peak rate of production was reached in 1942 when an average of over two boats per month was achieved.

On the Victoria Embankment of the Thames, approximately halfway between the Blackfriar and Waterloo bridges, is the magnificent bronze 'to the memory of the officers and men of the British Navy who lost their lives serving in submarines 1914–1918 & 1939–1945'. Commencing with AE1 (which disappeared in St George's Strait between New Britain and New Ireland in September 1914) and concluding with XE11 (lost as a result of a collision in Loch Striven on 6 March 1945) are the names of the boats lost. HMS *Alliance* (Yard No.909) is a poignant and permanent exhibit at the Royal Naval Submarine museum, Gosport.

HMS *Ambush* which was launched at Barrow in September 1945.

Second A Class Submarines – Main Characteristics

Overall Length/ Beam/Draught	281ft 6in x 22ft 3in x 17ft
Displacement	1,385 tons surfaced / 1,620 tons submerged
Power	2 x 4,300bhp diesel engines for surface propulsion
	2 x 1,250bhp electric motors for submerged propulsion
Diving Depth	350ft
Speed	18 knots surfaced / 8.5 knots submerged
Propeller	2
Endurance	10,500 miles at 11 knots surfaced / 90 miles at 3 knots submerged
Armament	10 x 21in torpedo tubes (4 bow, 2 stern, 2 external bow, 2 external stern)
	1 x 4in gun
	1 x 20mm Oerlikon cannon
	3 x .303in machine guns
	20 torpedoes carried
Complement	61

5
Cold War Submarines
(1954 to 1970)

EX Class Experimental Submarines

2 built on behalf of the Royal Navy

> *We need not waste time over the refinements of the latest propulsive methods. The layman would be merely bemused among the permutations and combinations of the standard systems that are now applied for different purposes; for which of us, not being an engineer, could grasp or even appreciate the difference between, say, geared turbines and diesel-electric drive.*
>
> British Ships and Shipbuilders by George Blake

HMS *Explorer*	(Yard No.979)	Launched 5 March 1954
HMS *Excalibur*	(Yard No.980)	Launched 25 February 1955

Vickers Shipyard at Barrow built both the EX Class boats ordered by the Royal Navy, their purpose being to assess the use of hydrogen peroxide submarines. This type of submarine was eventually made obsolete by the advent of nuclear-powered boats.

As early as 1911, Germany was conducting laboratory experiments with closed-cycle propulsion systems that did not breathe, hoping that it would be possible to build a true submarine, one that was designed to stay submerged, as opposed to a submersible boat. By the start of the Second World War research had gathered momentum and, in 1940, following the trials of a prototype hydrogen peroxide-driven submarine – the odd little Walter turbine-propelled V80 – a number of experimental boats were built. In 1946, one such experimental boat, the U-Boat 1407, which had been scuttled at the German collapse, was salvaged, and, after a long delay, commissioned into the Royal Navy as HMS *Meteorite*. U-1407's chief designer, Professor Walter, and his German staff worked at Vickers to oversee the rebuild. Her recovery led to a British development programme which resulted in two 1,120-ton submarines, *Explorer* and *Excalibur*, being constructed at Barrow. Built for speed trials only, they were purely experimental, unarmed submarines. Their high-test hydrogen peroxide (HTP) engines were basically steam turbines, with the steam being supplied from the heat generated by the interaction of high-test hydrogen peroxide, a catalyst and diesel oil. HTP has the ability to expand its volume 500 times!

The dangers of HTP were well known to the Admiralty; an unarmed torpedo with HTP propellant exploded in HMS *Sidon* in 1955. *Sidon* sank within minutes with the loss of thirteen of her crew. The Russian Navy persisted with the use of this volatile substance

Pictured here, running on the surface, is HMS *Explorer*, one of the two EX Class submarines built at Barrow.

which, in August 2000, was rumoured to have been the major contributory factor to the loss of the *Kursk*. HMS *Explorer* had so many teething problems that her first captain never took her to sea. However, when she eventually made an appearance, in 1958, she was impressively fast – submerged speeds of 25 knots were achieved – with retractable superstructure fittings aiding the streamlined hull-form. Provisionally accepted from Vickers in March 1958, HMS *Excalibur* was built at a cost of £1,142,000. It is also worth bearing in mind that at that time HTP was, in Britain, difficult to resource and store and initial costs were £350 to £400 a ton (although the Admiralty expected the eventual cost to reduce to £100 a ton).

Both *Explorer* and *Excalibur* were fitted with the latest submarine escape arrangements, including the one-man escape chamber. They were equipped with the most modern escape breathing apparatus for use by the ships' company in the event of an emergency. *Explorer* and *Excalibur* were, not unnaturally, known as the 'blonde' submarines, because of their peroxide fuel, and they served a useful purpose in as much as they gave the Royal Navy's anti-submarine forces some valuable practice against fast targets.

Their main use, however, was to prove finally that the HTP system was only a stop-gap. HTP proved difficult to the point of being dangerous, and there was more than one contemporary report of explosions in the two submarines, and at least one instance when the entire crew was forced to stand on the casing to avoid the noxious fumes which had suddenly filled the boat. 'I think the best thing we can do is to try to get it adopted by potential enemies,' said one RN submariner. Cdr Christopher Russell, who captained HMS *Explorer* – which was known locally as 'Exploder' because of the huge fireballs from her exhausts when starting up – recalled the dangers of working with HTP thus:

> *The high-test peroxide was a very volatile substance and was carried in special bags outside the pressure hull. Occasionally there would be a 'whoomph' as one of them exploded. Looking into the engine room, which was unmanned when we were under way, one could see flames dancing along the top of the combustion chamber. We did not look upon her as being dangerous. The crew took the bangs and fires as a matter of course. Fire drills became a very practised affair.*

The development of the hydrogen peroxide engine did not go well, and a lot of steam went out of the project, in quite a literal sense. When the Americans succeeded in designing a nuclear reactor suitable for fitting in submarines, a new era began and the HTP project was abandoned. A number of years later Vickers would again become involved in a lengthy series of trials and tests to develop the use of HTP as an alternative power source. This project was discontinued in the late eighties. Neither *Explorer* nor her sister *Excalibur* (known locally as 'Excruciator') had much contribution to make in those circumstances, and they were scrapped in 1969/1970.

U-1407

This was one of the three Type XVII B Boats completed by Blohm & Voss, Hamburg, out of a total of twelve ordered. This class were comparatively small, with approximate dimensions of 136ft length x 11ft beam x 15ft depth, a submerged displacement of 340 tons and armed with two forward torpedo tubes. Two Type XXI boats, U2502 produced by Blohm & Voss, Hamburg, and U3017 produced by Deschimag, Bremen, were also believed to have been subjected to inspections and tests at the Barrow Yard. The XXI Class were considered to be exceptionally good boats and although not the best of surface sea keepers, would, if produced in the numbers projected (1,400), have been a formidable opponent to the allies.

Pre-fabricated sections being aligned on the slipway during the construction of HMS *Explorer*. *(Barrow Museum Service CAT 2043)*

EX Class Experimental Submarines – Main Characteristics

Overall Length/ Beam/Draught	225ft 6in x 15ft 6in x 16ft
Displacement	780 tons surfaced / 1,120 tons submerged
Power	Diesel engines, electric motors and HTP driven steam turbines
Diving Depth	Unknown
Speed	30 knots surfaced / 25 knots submerged
Propeller	2
Endurance	Unknown
Armament	None
Complement	*Explorer*, 49; *Excalibur*, 41

X Class Submarines

4 built on behalf of the Royal Navy

> *Reference has already been made to the experimental 'Nordenfelt' submarine back in the 'eighties', but commencing with the 'Holland' boats at the beginning of the present century they became pioneers in the construction of submarines in this country, and systematically concentrated the efforts of one section of their establishment on this work. Hundreds of submarines for the British Admiralty and others for foreign navies have been produced in the succeeding years culminating in their mass production by pre-fabricating methods during the later part of the war. One of the 'high lights' which could not be disclosed until the end of the war was the designing and building of the midget submarines which will long be remembered for the amazing exploits of their gallant crews.*
>
> *Ships* by J.S. Redshaw

X51 (*Stickleback*)	(Yard No.1037)	Launched July 1954
X52 (*Shrimp*)	(Yard No.1037)	Launched October 1954
X53 (*Sprat*)	(Yard No.1037)	Launched 30 December 1954
X54 (*Minnow*)	(Yard No.1037)	Launched 5 May 1955

Just four X Class submarines were ordered by the Royal Navy, all four being constructed at the Barrow Shipyard.

X51–X54 were the 'improved' boats based on the success of the earlier midgets. The Admiralty considered that X51–X54, or improved successors, would be used to deliver nuclear mines against harbours and dockyard installations belonging to Cold War opponents. Other than carrier-based aircraft, Britain had no way to carry nuclear weapons to the USSR. The boats were of a fairly simple construction being basically four compartments: an engine room, control room, battery room and the 'wet and dry' lock from which a diver could operate to attach limpet mines or cut nets. Some of the boats were used to test harbour defences in Britain, the USA and Sweden, and X51 was sold to the Swedish Navy. They were eventually subject to economic cuts in the fifties and were the last midgets to be built for the Royal Navy. X51 was returned to Britain in 1977 and placed on display at the Imperial War Museum, Duxford. Vickers would, however, be involved in construction aspects for the two-man Pisces submersibles, including their commercial application, and the Leonard Redshaw series.

Piranha, the submarine that never was, reached the design stage with what appeared to be tremendous support and interest from abroad. It formed part of a package including small diesel-electric submarines and surface vessels intended primarily for Middle East navies. The package included development of a naval support facility for build/maintenance of warships and the training of crews.

X Class Submarines – Main Characteristics

Overall Length/ Beam/Draught	53ft 9in x 6ft 3in x 7ft 6in
Displacement	36 tons surfaced / 41 tons displaced
Power	1 x 6-cylinder Perkins diesel engine for surface propulsion
	1 x electric motor for submerged propulsion
Diving Depth	350ft
Speed	7 knots surfaced / 6 knots submerged
Propeller	1
Endurance	Unknown
Armament	Two side cargoes of either mines or limpets
Complement	5

X51 (*Stickleback*) on a low loader ready for transportation from the workshop to Devonshire Dock. (*Barrow Museum Service CAT 0147*)

A builder's model of an X Class midget submarine. *(Barrow Museum Service CAT 2658)*

X52 (*Shrimp*).

Piranha

In September 1985 the Barrow-built *Piranha* journeyed to Portsmouth (as the star attraction at the Royal Navy Equipment Exhibition) – by road! The 18-ton boat (a full-size wooden mock-up intended as a manufacturing aid) would, it was hoped, encourage sales of the real thing, and was carried in three sections on low-loader lorries for the 300-mile 'voyage'. *Piranha* was just one of a number of exhibits displayed by the then VSEL (Vickers Shipbuilding & Engineering Ltd) who were projecting their new company image prior to privatization. *Piranha* was intended to be diesel and battery-driven and was designed for surveillance, minelaying, attacks on moored shipping by combat swimmers and attacks on land targets by special forces. Her intended submerged displacement was 150 tons with a diving depth of 100m and a range of 800 nautical miles from base under the control of a seven-man crew. Far larger than the wartime and post-war midgets, *Piranha* was nevertheless an extension of their philosophy and possibly a missed opportunity by the MoD's procurement executive. *Piranha* generated tremendous interest amongst many navies in many countries but, unfortunately, no sales.

Second Porpoise Class Submarines

3 built on behalf of the Royal Navy

In 1956 the Admiralty had asked Vickers, Rolls-Royce and Foster Wheeler to enter into combination to construct a prototype of nuclear propulsion machinery for a British submarine for experimental work on shore, and Vickers Nuclear Engineering Limited had been formed to co-ordinate this work. Some research had already been done at Harwell, but the United Kingdom Atomic Energy Authority had been directing its resources towards the development of a natural uranium graphite-moderated gas-cooled reactor of a kind which could not be suffi-ciently reduced in size for submarine use.

Vickers – A History by J.D. Scott

HMS *Porpoise*	(Yard No.1029)	Launched 25 April 1956
HMS *Rorqual*	(Yard No.1030)	Launched 5 December 1956
HMS *Narwhal*	(Yard No.1031)	Launched 25 October 1957

By a strange twist of fate, or perhaps by design, Barrow built just three of the Royal Navy's eight Second Porpoise Class submarines – the first-of-class *Porpoise* plus *Rorqual* and *Narwhal*. They had built three boats of the first Porpoise Class years earlier, again the first-of-class *Porpoise* plus *Rorqual* and *Narwhal*!

Submarines with diesel-electric power units still had an important role to play in anti-submarine warfare and against surface ships. Their underwater endurance was not as great as that of nuclear submarines, but they were fast, silent and difficult to detect. The Royal Navy Patrol Submarine Fleet consisted of this Porpoise Class and the Oberon Class (see pages 150-55). Designed in the early 1950s as replacements for the second A Class boats, the Porpoise Class were the first post-war-built operational submarines to be accepted into service. As with the earlier minelayer submarines of the same class name, ordered in the 1930 Admiralty Programme, whether by accident or design, the first-of-class *Porpoise*, *Narwhal* and *Rorqual* were all built at Barrow. Of the other five submarines of the class, *Finwhale*, *Grampus* and *Sealion* were built at Cammell Laird and *Cachalot* and *Walrus* at Scott's.

Porpoise Class submarines were fitted with two Admiralty standard range 16-cylinder diesel generator sets which together supplied 3,300bhp, to provide a surface speed of 12 knots. The submerged speed of 17 knots was attained from two massive main batteries which drove the propulsion motors to develop 5,000bhp. The decision to double the battery size was determined at a very late stage when drawing office work was well advanced. Fortunately the drawing offices were able to meet the challenge that decision posed. Having beautifully clean welded hulls and a high yet silent underwater speed, these submarines were among the best conventional boats in the world. Long patrol endurance was a primary design requirement of the Porpoise Class, and the snort equipment was designed to give maximum snort charging facilities and to operate in rough sea conditions in any part of the world. When required, oxygen replenishment and carbon dioxide and hydrogen eliminators made it possible for the class to remain totally submerged for several days without 'snorting'.

When snorting, these submarines could remain submerged for as long as six weeks. They were fitted with apparatus to distil freshwater from seawater for drinking purposes and this,

The launch of HMS *Porpoise* on 25 April 1956. *(Barrow Museum Service CAT 0305)*

together with stowage capacity for large quantities of stores and provisions, enabled them to remain independently operational for months without any outside support. With the ability to stay at sea for such long periods, habitability standards had to be of the highest quality, and an air-conditioning plant, which provided drying and either heating or cooling of the air as appropriate for arctic or tropical service, was an important installation in the Porpoise Class.

The commissioning of *Porpoise* (on 14 April 1958) was reported in the *North Western Evening Mail* as follows:

The submarine Porpoise, *name-ship of a class which has high underwater speeds and can stay under for a long time in any part of the world, was commissioned at Barrow yesterday. The new submarine is one of three of the class ordered from Messrs. Vickers-Armstrongs Ltd. at Barrow, and the first to be completed. She is also the first operational submarine designed since the war to be accepted into service. The* Porpoise *is commanded by Lt-Cdr B.C.G. Hutchings, RN, and will have a crew of six officers and sixty-four ratings. Two hundred and ninety feet long and with a beam of 26½ feet, the submarine is believed to displace about 2,000 tons when submerged. The design of her hull and superstructure reflect her capabilities in the way of high speeds under water and great diving depth. Stress has been laid on long endurance, both on the surface and when submerged and whether operating on battery-driven motors or using the 'snort'. Diesel-electric drive from Admiralty standard range diesel engines will be used when the ship is operating on the surface or 'snorting', and a large battery will drive the ship's electric motors when submerged. The snort equipment has been so designed as to give maximum snort-charging facilities and to operate in rough sea conditions. Both air and surface warning radar can be operated at periscope depth as well as when surfaced. The new submarine sets a high standard of accommodation for ships of her type. Laminated plastic and wood has been used for panelling; there is strip lighting and nylon curtains; and to combat the tedium of long periods of submerged patrol a cinema projector and tape recorder are available. Each member of the crew will have a bunk with a foam latex mattress. The ship has an air conditioning plant which will provide either drying, heating or cooling of the air for Arctic or tropical service. Oxygen replenishment and carbon dioxide and hydrogen eliminators will make it possible for* Porpoise *to remain totally submerged without even using her 'snort' for several days. There is apparatus for the distillation of fresh water from sea water for drinking purposes, and stowage is provided for large quantities of stores and provisions so as to enable the* Porpoise *to remain on patrol for months without any outside support.*

Speaking to them after the blessing of the new submarine, Capt. H.S. Mackenzie, representing Admiral B.W. Taylor, Flag Officer, Submarines, said that many a day would pass before the country had a nuclear fleet. Capt. Mackenzie said Admiral Taylor was in Malta. He had been first lieutenant on the Porpoise's *predecessor, a submarine minelayer, when she was being built at Barrow in 1934. He had wanted to wish them, personally, all the best of luck. The Porpoise Class was well designed and well equipped for its tremendous job. He said, 'You have got a fine ship.'*

To mark the commissioning of the first post-war operational submarine, Capt. Mackenzie handed over a commemorative plaque. It was received by Mr L. Redshaw, a director of Vickers-Armstrongs (Shipbuilders) and shipbuilding general manager at Barrow and Walker-on-Tyne. This plaque recorded the service between 1941 and 1944 of the 10th Submarine Flotilla in the Mediterranean. The flotilla was composed entirely of U-Class submarines, most of them built by Vickers. The religious service was conducted by the ship's commanding officer, Lt-Com. B.C.G. Hutchings, and the Revd D. Welsh, chaplain to the Adamant, *depot ship of the 3rd Submarine Flotilla based at Faslane. Present were the ship's company drawn up on the dockside at the Submarine Dock, their families and Vickers' representatives. Many of the men who helped to build the new ship looked on.*

Second Porpoise Class Submarines – Main Characteristics

Overall Length/ Beam/Draught	295ft 3in x 26ft 6in x 18ft
Displacement	2,030 tons surfaced / 2,410 tons submerged
Power	Diesel-electric arrangement, with 2 x Admiralty Standard Range 116VMS diesels delivering 3,300hp (2745kW) and 2 x electric motors delivering 5,000hp (4475kW) to two shafts
Diving Depth	650ft when operational (1,115ft maximum)
Speed	12 knots surfaced / 17 knots submerged
Propeller	2
Endurance	10,350 miles at 12 knots surfaced
Armament/ Electronics	6 x 21in bow torpedo tubes for 20 x Mk 24 Tigerfish wire-guided dual-role torpedoes (up to 50 x Mk 5 Stonefish and Mk 6 Sea Urchin mines in place of torpedoes)
	1 x Type 1006 surface-search and navigation radar
	1 x Type 2051 Triton active/passive search and attack hull sonar (or 1 x Type 187 active/passive search and attack hull sonar)
	1 x Type 2007 long-range passive flank sonar
	1 x Type 186 sonar
	1 x Type 2024 passive search clip-on towed-array sonar
	1 x DCH action information and fire-control system
	1 x Manta UAL or UA4 ESM system with warning element
	Various communication and navigation systems
	Various decoys
Complement	69

Oberon Class Submarines

3 built on behalf of the Royal Navy
3 built on behalf of the Brazilian Navy

Even during the period when Vickers was the only great armament company in Britain, it was always more than an armament company. As a shipbuilding company it had been part of the shipbuilding industry; as a steel company, part of the iron and steel industry; as an engineering company, part of the engineering industry; and as an aircraft company, part of the aircraft industry.

Vickers – A History *by J.D. Scott*

For the Royal Navy

HMS *Orpheus*	(Yard No.1059)	Launched 17 November 1959
HMS *Olympus*	(Yard No.1060)	Launched 14 June 1961
HMS *Osiris*	(Yard No.1064)	Launched 29 November 1962

For the Brazilian Navy

Humaita	(Yard No.1087)	Launched 5 October 1971
Tonelero	(Yard No.1088)	Launched 22 November 1972
Riachuelo	(Yard No.1096)	Launched 6 September 1975

In total thirteen Oberon Class submarines, very similar to the preceding second Porpoise Class boats, were constructed for the Royal Navy. The Barrow Yard built just three of these boats for the Royal Navy but, some years later, built three further of the class for the Brazilian Navy. The Oberons are memorable as the first submarines to use plastic in their construction.

Between 1959 and 1964, thirteen Oberon Class submarines were constructed for the Royal Navy, three of which – *Olympus*, *Orpheus* and *Osiris* – were built at Barrow. Although they had the same dimensions, displacement and machinery as the Porpoise Class, the Oberons did incorporate some important developments, such as improved detection equipment and the ability to fire homing torpedoes. It was on this class the Royal Navy developed a 'gulping' technique for snorting which amounted to extending the induction and exhaust masts for only limited lengths of time. This effectively reduced the length of time in which the boat offered itself as a radar target, emitted noise or more latterly provided a heat signature. Perhaps the most radical change that occurred with the introduction of the Oberon Class was the fact that for the first time in British submarines plastic was used in the superstructure construction – before and aft of the bridge, in most units, the superstructure was mainly glass fibre laminate.

In addition, the superstructure of the second boat, the Vickers-built *Orpheus*, was of aluminium. Eight boats of the class underwent a modernization programme. Having acquired an enviable reputation for reliability and quietness, a total of fourteen Oberons have been sold to foreign buyers since 1962, and they were regarded as the best conventional submarine available at that time.

Just a little after noon on 5 October 1971 the Brazilian submarine *Humaita* slid into Walney Channel, the first of an order from the Brazilian Navy for three such boats from the Barrow Yard (the others being *Tonelero* and *Riachuelo*). A contemporary report in the local paper, the *North West Evening Mail*, provides an accurate description of the boat and the class:

When completed, Humaita *will displace 2,030 tons on the surface and 2,400 tons submerged and she will be driven by two 16-cylinder Admiralty Standard Range diesel engines, developing 3,680 brake horse power and two electric motors developing 6,000 horse power. The*

HMS *Osiris*. (Campbell McCutcheon)

diesels have been built by Vickers Shipbuilding Group and the electric motors are products of
the AEI – English Electric concern.

Capable of a speed of more than 15 knots submerged, Humaita will be armed with eight
torpedo tubes, six mounted in the bow and two at the stern. She will also be able to engage in
minelaying operations if required. With a length of 295 feet and a 26½ feet beam Humaita
is similar in most details to the successful British Oberons. She will be manned by seven officers
and fifty-six men, and their accommodation is arranged in the traditional submarine manner
with bunks and cots replacing hammocks. Her equipment includes sonar, modern navigational
aids and a fire control system recently developed by Vickers. The order for the two vessels is
part of an impressive naval construction programme being carried out by the Brazilian
Government. The Oberon-type vessel is considered by the British Navy to be the quietest sonar
platform in the world. Their design, construction and general capabilities influenced the
Brazilian government in buying them and in placing a contract for their construction of two
with a British firm. Glass reinforced plastic has been used extensively in the superstructure of
the vessel.

The glass fibre laminate used in the 'sail' (conning tower) and casing for one of the
submarines has been manufactured and fabricated by Slingsby Sailplanes Limited, at
Kirkbymoorside, a company in the Vickers Shipbuilding Group which is beginning to specialise
in fabricating plastic laminates for marine use, as well as in aircraft. The Humaita is the third
submarine of the Brazilian Navy to bear the name, which commemorates a naval action in the
river war against Paraguay on February 21, 1868. She is the ninth Brazilian warship to be
built at Barrow and the 307th submarine to be launched from the Vickers Yard. She will be
followed on the berth by a sister ship, the Tonelero, due to be launched next year and to
commission in 1973.

Riachuelo was not referenced in the above report as she was still to be ordered by the Brazilians
at this point in time. What is interesting to note in the above *Evening Mail* report is the use
of the American term 'sail' rather than the British 'fin'. Note also the reference to the

'Vickers-developed fire control system' which is perhaps more accurately described as an integrated information organization and weapon control system – a system which, because of its extensive use of Ferranti computers and components, helped to maintain Ferranti's factory in Park Road, Barrow, in full employment a little longer than originally scheduled.

Tonelero, the second of the class, would undergo the twin ordeals of fire and flood, the former before her career commenced and the latter in the twilight of her career. In the early hours of Tuesday 2 October 1973, spilt diesel oil was accidentally ignited during welding operations in the boat's control room. The workforce safely evacuated the boat as the works' and town fire brigades fought to control the fire and smoke which, despite their valiant efforts could not be subdued with the immediacy they required. Consequently, hatches and water-tight doors were shut to prevent the ingress of air and to contain the blaze.

Police forces co-operated with the fire brigades in locating fire-fighting equipment and material from specialist suppliers in Penrith and Lancaster. In one of the more dramatic events, a desperate need for CO_2 was satisfied after the police, along with ICI, were able to identify a CO_2 tanker located at Carlisle. The tanker was escorted with utmost haste to the Yard and its load of 16.5 tons of liquid CO_2 was discharged into *Tonelero*'s control room. The special equipment required to assist the discharge of CO_2 into the boat was rushed from Penrith by 'Cumberland Fire Services' (a specialist commercial company). Additional foam was rushed from Lancaster to supplement dwindling local supplies.

HMS *Osiris* being launched on 29 November 1962. *(Barrow Museum Service CAT 2638)*

The official statement at the time was thus:

> *A fire was discovered aboard the Oberon Class submarine Tonelero early today and has damaged the control room area aboard the vessel despite the efforts of our works' brigade and Barrow Fire Brigade. A quantity of oil was involved. The fire was brought under control by isolating the compartments affected, by closing the watertight doors. As a secondary measure the hull was closed up. This prevented the ingress of air so as not to feed the fire. Foam was then introduced through the top hatch and this was finally followed by the injection of carbon dioxide from a large tanker. … We have not yet had time to assess the damage although it is expected that we will be able to inspect it this afternoon. Preliminary reports suggest that damage might be serious enough to delay completion of the submarine.*

The press release was correct about completion delay as *Tonelero* was taken to Portsmouth Dockyard to have a replacement section and equipment fitted. This work could not be done at Barrow due to the existing workload which required availability of all existing resources.

Tonelero was eventually returned to Barrow to complete sea trials and commissioning in 1977. *Tonelero*, along with *Humaita* (stricken in 1996) and *Riachuelo* (now a memorial/museum boat), gave good service to the Brazilians but, as previously stated, *Tonelero* had a second ordeal to face, this time through uncontrolled flooding. In February 2001, *Tonelero* sank at her moorings in Rio in 25ft of water while under repair. The maintenance crew were not harmed and an investigation into the cause of the sinking will take place when *Tonelero* is salvaged. It is reasonable to assume *Tonelero* will be beyond economic repair when drying out costs are taken into consideration.

HMS *Humaita*, built at Barrow-in-Furness for the Brazilian Navy.

The Oberon Class submarines were without doubt the finest submarines of their type in the world in the late 1960s and it wasn't until 1993 when the last of the thirteen built for the Royal Navy (HMS *Opossum*) was withdrawn from service. So successful was the class that the navies of Australia, Canada and Chile bought Oberon boats, as of course did the Brazilians. Midway through their life the Royal Navy's Oberon Class boats were fitted with a Type 2051 sonar (a highly automated design) and were upgraded to enable them to fire both the Tigerfish torpedo and the Royal Navy Sub-Harpoon missile. These improvements contributed in no small way to their long service life which included missions all over the world.

> *The commissioning ceremony marks the entry of a ship into the Brazilian Navy as a unit of the operating forces. At the moment of raising the commissioning pennant begins the responsibility of the Commanding Officer. He, together with the ship's officers and men will have the duty of preparing and maintaining her in constant readiness for any mission required by our nation in peace or war.*
>
> *Humaita*'s Commissioning Brochure

Oberon Class Submarines – Main Characteristics

Overall Length/ Beam/Draught	295ft 3in x 26ft 6in x 18ft
Displacement	2,030 tons surfaced / 2,400 tons submerged
Power	Diesel-electric arrangement, with 2 x Admiralty Standard Range 116VMS diesels delivering 3,680bhp (2745kW) and 2 x electric motors delivering 6,000bhp (4475kW) to two shafts
Diving Depth	650ft when operational (1,115ft maximum)
Speed	12 knots surfaced / 17 knots submerged
Propeller	2
Endurance	10,350 miles at 12 knots surfaced
Armament/ Electronics	6 x 21in bow torpedo tubes for 20 x Mk 24 Tigerfish wire-guided dual-role torpedoes (up to 50 x Mk 5 Stonefish and Mk 6 Sea Urchin mines in place of torpedoes)
	1 x Type 1006 surface-search and navigation radar
	1 x Type 2051 Triton active/passive search and attack hull sonar (or 1 x Type 187 active/passive search and attack hull sonar)
	1 x Type 2007 long-range passive flank sonar
	1 x Type 186 sonar
	1 x Type 2024 passive search clip-on towed-array sonar
	1 x DCH action information and fire-control system
	1 x Manta UAL or UA4 ESM system with warning element
	Various communication and navigation systems
	Various decoys
Complement	69
Notes	The Brazilian boats were generally similar to the Royal Navy's boats but had the Vickers-designed TI0SB fire control system.

Dreadnought Class Submarine

1 built on behalf of the Royal Navy

> *Within Vickers the arguments ran into cross-currents of rivalry between the Engineers and Shipbuilders at Barrow about who should be in the lead. Traditionally the Engineers had undertaken responsibility for machinery design and installation and the Admiralty had placed with them the main contracts for producing the machinery and for building the land-based facilities at Dounreay, in northern Scotland, to test it. The view taken by the Engineers, crudely expressed, was that building a hull was a relatively simple business for which the Shipbuilders could have a sub-contract. The Shipbuilders on the other hand took the view, again crudely expressed, that building a submarine was an art understood only by themselves and all the engineers had to do was to supply the equipment to go inside it.*
>
> *Vickers: Against The Odds, 1956-77* by Harold Evans

| HMS *Dreadnought* | (Yard No.1062) | Launched 21 October 1960 |

HMS *Dreadnought* was a one-off boat built at Barrow, the first nuclear-powered submarine in the Royal Navy. Costing £18.5 million to build, the aft end was very similar to the US Navy Skipjack Class of submarines. *Dreadnought* was a forerunner of the Valiant and Improved Valiant Classes.

The *Dreadnought* souvenir supplement to the November 1960 issue of *Vickers News* (the Vickers house paper at that time) described matters thus:

> *She was launched in just over eighteen months from the time the first steel plates were delivered to the shipyard. This meant a great deal of intensive work by a very large number of people at Barrow. The new type of alloy steel used for the hull presented a host of difficult welding problems alone, but, of course, all the difficulties were successfully overcome and the experience gained in building Britain's first nuclear submarine will be of invaluable assistance in building the second. Something of the measure of the task can be seen from examples of the quantity of materials used in the construction of this great submarine. Over one million welding electrodes were used, nearly 8,000 test plates were completed and over 7,300 x-rays were taken.*

The supplement contained the address to HM Queen Elizabeth II from Viscount Knollys GCME, MBE, DFC, to whom it fell as 'Chairman of Vickers, the parent company of our Group, to welcome Your Majesty on this historic occasion.' The final lines of her Majesty's response were: 'I wish *Dreadnought* and all who serve in her every good fortune and success. Fear God and dread nought.'

The following is a *Link* (the Shipyard's in-house magazine) article of February 1983 describing the Royal Navy's first nuclear-powered submarine:

Following the progress made by the United States in the revolutionary field of nuclear-powered submarine propulsion, a mid-1950s policy decision announced that, instead of developing an all-British nuclear submarine, much time and money would be saved by accepting the American lead and taking advantage of US nuclear technology. Therefore, the first British nuclear-powered Fleet submarine, HMS Dreadnought, *comprised an American 'kit of parts' in a Vickers-built hull. Specially designed to hunt and destroy enemy underwater craft,* Dreadnought *was laid down on 12th June 1959 and launched by Her Majesty the Queen on Trafalgar Day (21st October) 1960.* Dreadnought's *preliminary trials, which began early in 1962, progressed very satisfactorily – considering that Britain had not built a nuclear-powered submarine before – and she made her first dive, in Ramsden Dock, on 10th January 1963. At the time of her completion – 17th April 1963 – she was one of the most formidable attack submarines in the world.* Dreadnought *is handled by means of telemotor controls, using a type of joystick and elaborate instrument panel similar to those in the cockpit of a modern aircraft. At high underwater speed she also behaves and handles like an aircraft and can be set on course and depth by an 'automatic pilot'. She is also capable of performing 'aquabatics'. Comprehensive air conditioning and purification equipment maintains safe and comfortable atmosphere control and enables* Dreadnought *to operate for more than two months without recourse to air from the surface – a pint of distilled sea-water an hour, passed through electrolysers, provides enough oxygen for a 100-man crew. Food supplies are the only factor which limits submerged endurance.*

In the after end of Dreadnought, *which is almost totally American and is known as the 'American sector', electricity is produced for less than 1p a kilowatt hour; water produced on the same basis costs about 7.5p a gallon. Accommodation is of an unprecedented standard, even in surface vessels, and the crew appreciate shower baths, laundry and washing facilities; amenities that weren't installed in earlier submarines. Separate mess spaces are provided for senior and junior rates, arranged on either side of a large galley, equipped for serving meals on the cafeteria system. Particular attention was paid to the decoration and furnishing of living quarters and recreational spaces – which include cinema equipment, an extensive library and tape recordings; features which help to offset the monotony associated with prolonged underwater voyages. During her career,* Dreadnought *has been on many varied patrols. On 24th June 1967 she was ordered to sink the wrecked and drifting German ship* Essberger Chemist. *Three torpedoes hit along the length of the target; the gunners of HMS* Salisbury *finished the job by piercing the tanks which were keeping the* Essberger Chemist *just afloat. In the mid-60s,* Dreadnought's *visits included trips to Norfolk Va, Bermuda, Rotterdam and Kiel. She was at Gibraltar in 1965, 1966 and 1967, and on 19th September, 1967 she left Rosyth for Singapore on a sustained high-speed run. The round trip finished as 4,640 miles surfaced and 26,545 miles submerged.*

Apart from minor hull cracking problems, Dreadnought *proved to be a reliable vessel, popular with her crews. In 1970 she completed a major refit at Rosyth, in the course of which her nuclear core was refuelled and her ballast tank valves were changed to reduce noise. She re-commissioned on 10th September 1970 – and she has a commemorative postal cover to prove it. On 3rd March, 1971, she became the first British submarine to surface at the North Pole.* Dreadnought *is now at Rosyth Naval Dockyard, laid up indefinitely while her radioactive contamination decays. Her nuclear fuel has been removed and she has been stripped of useful equipment. She will eventually be sunk deep in the Atlantic or broken up for disposal in some other way.*

Becoming used to *Dreadnought*'s S5W reactor and propulsion machinery wasn't just a major leap in technology for the Royal Navy. Fitting and testing that equipment in the biggest submarine hull ever to go on a British berth would require innovative solutions from the Barrow workforce. The keel section was laid down by the Duke of Edinburgh on 12 June 1959, thereafter to be followed by a series of fabricated sections weighing up to 150 tons which would eventually be welded together to form the hull. This hull would be built to unprecedented levels of accuracy to permit *Dreadnought* to operate at previously unconsidered depths (and consequently greater pressures) at high speeds.

The sections were produced in the Assembly Shop and conveyed to the berth, some 500yds away, by the biggest road transporter available in Britain at that time. (The Yard would, some thirty years hence, transport 1,800-ton sections of submarines from the Assembly Shop, approximately half a mile away, to the Devonshire Dock Hall (DDH), and, by 2000, use similar methods to transport 2,350-ton sections of surface vessels to the same destination.) Welding the sections, and the hull, would require new and varied techniques, as would welding many of the pipe systems. New test methods would be required to test the integrity of hull, pipe systems and electrical systems. New departments would be required with a workforce trained to conduct the tests and to evaluate their results. The workforce would also be required to understand American technology and terminology.

New drawing offices were built. HM Dockyard, Portsmouth would build a new floating dock to house *Dreadnought* for some of her fitting-out requirements (Admiralty Floating Dock 59 – AFD59). A special progress department would be created to track, on a daily basis,

The launch of HMS *Dreadnought*, the Royal Navy's first nuclear submarine.

HMS *Dreadnought* after her launch.

every item of equipment so that potential bottlenecks would be eliminated. Giant portable covers would be built to protect the activities of personnel working on the hull from the vagaries of Barrow weather and the prying eyes of people who did not have a need to know about the boat. *Dreadnought* was very much a giant advance in submarine construction at the Barrow Yard but even as the half-British half-American fleet submarine nearing completion, her new, all-British sisters, *Valiant* and *Warspite*, were, respectively, being built and ordered.

In a speech to the Commons in 1964 the Civil Lord of the Admiralty would, amongst other items, advise the House on *Dreadnought* that: 'The Royal Navy's first nuclear submarine had steamed about 20,000 miles since her completion and had gone faster and dived deeper than any other previous British submarine.' Within that proud statement lay the harbinger of a problem which would arise when *Dreadnought* had seen little more than a year's service with the navy. In the late summer of 1965 *Dreadnought* was in Rosyth Dockyard for 'repairs and modifications' made to the hull after the discovery of hairline cracking in her internal bulkheads. By February 1966 *Dreadnought* was considered satisfactory to return to sea for trials.

On her return she was subjected to rigorous non-destructive examination, reported in the *North Western Evening Mail* thus:

> *Obviously this was a very thorough examination. We used new radiographic and ultrasonic methods of testing and these take far longer than usual to evaluate.' The Ministry of Defence spokesman pointed out that the Dreadnought was the first of its kind. He said, 'We were literally breaking new ground in achieving a thoroughly new order of operational performance. This necessitated new steel not used in submarine construction before, which required investigating all major stress areas in the hull. Dreadnought was the deepest-diving, fastest-turning submarine of its kind.*

That spokesman's report only partially endorsed an earlier statement issued by Maritime Headquarters, Pitreavie, Dunfermline, which was more explicit: 'The tendency for the welds to have cracked was accelerated by an unprecedented programme of deep dives, fast turns and full-speed underwater runs.'

The navy was well aware they were accelerating ageing of the hull in their 'unprecedented programme' and presumably they wanted and needed to know how far the hull performance could be 'safely' pushed. Whatever it was that the Ministry of Defence (MoD) gained in their trials and tests it was, at the very least, confidence that *Dreadnought* could do the job demanded of her. Prior to her first refit in 1970 she had steamed over 150,000 miles in completing that first commission reported in the above *Link* article. At a cost of £18.5 million 'SSN01' had done all that the navy required. Although *Dreadnought* was designated as a 'fleet submarine' by the navy, as the only one of her class and bearing in mind her 'unprecedented programme of deep dives, fast turns and full-speed underwater runs', she would appear to have been a proving ground, an experimental boat, designed to give the navy a taste of what was to come.

★ ★ ★

To give an idea of the shipbuilding expertise available in Barrow at the time *Dreadnought* was laid down, in June 1959, the following are some examples of the vessels under build or completion: HMS *Hermes*, a 23,000-ton aircraft carrier; two 2,730-ton Chilean destroyers, Almirantes *Williams* and *Riveros*; two Oberon Class boats – *Orpheus* and *Olympus* (see pages 150-55); and one of the great liners, the Orient Co.'s 42,000-ton *Oriana*.

Imagine if you will the work done by Engineering and Armaments in support of the vessels (in addition to their own contracts), all too numerous to mention for this publication, and you have an indication of the diversity of the Barrow Yard at that time.

Dreadnought Class Submarine – Main Characteristics

Overall Length/ Beam/Draught	265ft 9in x 32ft 3in x 26ft
Displacement	3,500 tons surfaced / 4,000 tons submerged
Power	A steam turbine powered by a Westinghouse S5W Pressurised Water Reactor
Diving Depth	1,000ft
Speed	Surfaced speed unknown / 28 knots submerged
Propeller	1
Endurance	100,000 miles
Armament/ Electronics	6 x 21in torpedo tubes in bow
	1 x radar – search: 1-band
	Sonar Type 2001
	Sonar Type 2007
Complement	88

Valiant Class Submarines

2 built on behalf of the Royal Navy

As a fleet submarine her most important role is to provide aggressive anti-submarine escort for surface task forces, and to hunt down and destroy enemy submarines and surface forces. Torpedoes are her main armament, and she is fitted with the latest sonar (underwater detection) equipment, navigation and communication aids. Like other modern submarines, she is capable of communication with her base while submerged. The submarine is handled by means of powered controls, using a type of joystick and elaborate instrument panel similar to those in the cockpit of a modern aircraft. At high underwater speed she also behaves and handles like an aircraft and can be set on course and depth by an 'automatic pilot'.

HMS *Valiant*'s Commissioning Brochure

HMS *Valiant*	(Yard No.1066)	Launched 3 December 1963
HMS *Warspite*	(Yard No.1072)	Launched 25 September 1965

The Barrow Shipyard built both *Valiant* and *Warspite*, the only two submarines in the Valiant Class. The construction/completion costs for these two fleet submarines were £24.9 million for *Valiant* and £21.5 million for *Warspite*.

The following summary of the Valiant Class submarines appeared in the *Link* edition of December 1982:

Fleet submarines are the nuclear-powered capital ships of the modern navy. They are the main striking power of the Fleet and are themselves the single most effective anti-submarine weapon available. Fitted with complex computer-assisted sensors and the latest torpedoes, they can silently shadow a target for long periods at high speeds while hundreds of feet below the surface, ready to attack with deadly effectiveness when required. During Dreadnought's *build, Rolls-Royce and Associates, in collaboration with the United Kingdom Atomic Energy Authority, were developing a completely new nuclear propulsion system. On 31 August 1960, Britain's second nuclear-powered submarine was ordered from Vickers and, fitted with Rolls-Royce's nuclear steam raising plant,* Valiant *was the first all-British nuclear submarine. Although the name originally chosen for her was* Inflexible, *Britain's second nuclear submarine was commissioned as HMS* Valiant *on 18 July 1966. Derived directly from HMS* Dreadnought, Valiant's *near-perfect streamlining gives maximum underwater efficiency, whilst her fin-like conning tower is intended to reduce 'drag' to a minimum. As early as April 1967,* Valiant *set a record submerged passage for a British submarine when she completed the 12,000-mile homeward voyage from Singapore in 28 days. Month-long submerged voyages have since become routine. Vickers' third 'nuke',* Warspite, *was launched on 25 September 1965, and commissioned on 18 April 1967. Unfortunately, completion of the Valiant Class was held back to speed work on the Resolution Class Polaris submarines. However, as soon as* Resolution *was launched, no time was lost in completing the Valiant Class and starting work on a repeat Valiant Class – the Vickers-built* Churchill *and* Courageous, *together with Cammell Laird's* Conqueror, *the only British Fleet submarine to be built outside Barrow. On the 15 March 1983, HMS* Warspite *returned to her base at Faslane, after a 111-day patrol off the Falklands – the longest ever made in peacetime by a British submarine. With a 110-man crew, her Commanding Officer, Cdr J.G.F. Cooke, said the only things left in the submarine's deep freeze 'are three herrings and two lemons'.*

Prior to the announcement of the order for '1066' the *Times* carried an article concerning the Yard: 250 specialist craftsmen currently working on *Dreadnought* would be laid off following completion of the vessel due to a lack of follow-on orders. However, far from the predicted 'lay-offs' there would, following more orders, be an enormous build-up of personnel so that by the time *Polaris* came on the scene the workforce would be growing by thousands. The problem to come would be to attract people to the very specialised nature of manufacturing within the Yard. Aspects of manufacturing on the first 'nukes' are contained in Appendix VII of this book. The Admiralty were determined that the Valiant Class boats would be substantially quieter than *Dreadnought*; consequently design of the British propulsion plants required separate condensers for the main turbines and the turbo-generators, with the main turbines and gearbox being mounted on a raft resiliently isolated from the hull. Indeed, all mechanical equipments were, if possible, seated on resilient mounts and the connections to the equipments would be made with flexible hoses and expansion pieces.

HMS *Valiant* running on the surface.

Additionally, electrical equipment would be mounted on leaf spring-type mounts. This would not only assist to reduce radiated noise but would also reduce shock transmission in the event of a collision or depth charging. Although noise reduction had been developed to an incredible extent on the Oberons, the nuclear boats presented a whole new series of challenges. The important thing to remember is that with the exception of the hull shape (as per *Dreadnought*) the remainder of the boat, in respect of electrical and mechanical equipment, was new, including a new reactor and new propulsion system.

Notwithstanding the land-based test facility at Dounreay, the leap to the all-British design was perhaps as far removed from *Dreadnought* as *Dreadnought* was from the Oberons – there were bound to be problems along the way. Tests conducted on materials used in the Dounreay reactor were producing results which indicated that one particular material – Inconel, was, in certain instances, less than satisfactory. Speaking in the Commons in 1964, the then Civil Lord of the Admiralty stated: 'At Dounreay, during the final tests before criticality, unexpected material failures occurred in the prototype... The failures meant that some piping had to be renewed and certain other components altered. This will delay the completion of the plant by a number of months, and that is disappointing. But a prototype is after all to enable difficulties and dangers to be forestalled before the submarines go to sea.'

The Civil Lord went on to advise of the progress made on the Polaris programme, site work on the Polaris base at Faslane in Scotland, preparations to Rosyth Dockyard to refit nuclear submarines and of the assistance received from the US Navy and United States authorities. The problem with the Inconel pipework and components was resolved, albeit at the very highest level. It apparently required the combined intervention of Sir Solly Zuckerman (the government's Chief Scientific Advisor), Admiral of the Fleet the Earl Mountbatten of Burma and Admiral Hyman G. Rickover, US Navy (known as the father of the nuclear submarine) to bring the matter to a safe and satisfactory conclusion. Another problem would arise (as stated in the *Link* article above) with the Admiralty wanting increased resources directed to Polaris construction. The navy were very much between a 'rock and a hard place', they needed Polaris as an effective and credible deterrent to replace the RAF's ageing V-bombers and their free-fall bombs. Equally they needed the patrol and handling experience the all-British fleet submarine could provide while having to be fully aware that *Valiant* was not only a 'first of class' but also a prototype.

For Vickers there were concerns that the Barrow dock system, over which they had little or no control, was going to be closed or left without care and maintenance, as continuing threats by the dock owners, British Transport Docks Board, over a lack of commercial use, loomed. These threats evaporated after a number of years' concern but Vickers were again featuring in local newspapers – appealing against their business rates. In the great scheme of things Vickers' worries may have appeared ludicrous in the context of the Cold War, but Vickers had a business to run, profits to make and shareholders to satisfy. Thus one typical extract from Barrow's *North West Evening Mail* in 1964 headed: 'Appeal on Valuation of Docks' continued in the following vein:

The valuation officer 'is not a hound sniffing up where he can,' the Barrow Rating Valuation Court was told today. Appearing for the valuation officer in an appeal by Vickers-Armstrongs (Engineers) a representative went on to say: 'Vickers are performing one of this country's most important tasks – building nuclear submarines.' Earlier the representative announced the valuation officer had reduced his estimate of Vickers' rateable value from £100,000 to £89,820. He said the main point of the appeal would be the value of the smaller of Vickers' two floating docks – AFD19. 'We see this as a plain case of a piece of plant being as rateable as you can find' he said. Proceeding.

Notwithstanding the valuation appeals, the pursuit of nuclear submarine construction continued at a fast pace; then the shock announcement of *Dreadnought's* weld defects was announced. This was an unexpected challenge to be met and the Admiralty and Vickers met it successfully – through a programme of non-destructive examination, weld repair and heat treatment where appropriate (there being a similar requirement for the Polaris boats). Vickers and the Admiralty were not alone in this problem – it would later emerge that the US Navy and its construction yards were suffering similar setbacks but not from quite the same cause. When the steel specification for the hull was raised it appears none of those involved were privy to the harsh, uncompromising, programme which, for *Dreadnought*, would become routine. Consequently, small traces of non-metallic inclusions within the QT35 steel were, initially, considered as being of no significance. However, once subjected to *Dreadnought's* punishing schedule it was apparent that the steel was inadequate for its role. A further contributory factor was the inflexibility of the weld procedures. The Polaris section (pages 169-77) continues the episode. Then, with *Valiant* just four months away from completion, there was an 'incident'.

The final edition of Barrow's *North West Evening Mail* gave the following account on Wednesday 16 March 1966 under a by-line headed: '*Valiant* flooded by "error"' and repeated the statement provided by a spokesman for Vickers Ltd, Shipbuilding Group management. According to the spokesman, 20 tons of water flooded the new £20 million nuclear submarine *Valiant* when a workman unscrewed the wrong valve.

HMS *Valiant* under construction on the slipway in February 1963. *(Barrow Museum Service CAT PR29)*

But Valiant *was not really in danger of sinking.* [Said the spokesman] *We think this was a case of human error. The substance of the thing is the chap opened the right valve on the wrong ship. About 4,000 gallons of water which flooded* Valiant *would not have made much difference to the draught. As a gallon is equal to ten pounds giving in this case 40,000 pounds of water – that is about 20 tons and it would not make much difference to* Valiant. *The chap has made a full report and we have put it down to human error.*

The *Evening Mail's* reporter interviewed the 'chap' at home who said: 'This was just a mix-up of orders – somebody has to carry the can and it just happened to be me. I had been working on *Valiant.* When I came off I was given a valve number. I was not told the name of the ship. I should have gone on *Warspite* which is in the dry dock alongside.' '…not really in danger of sinking…' said the spokesman – well that isn't how it appeared to those present. The 20 tons of water were not distributed evenly throughout *Valiant's* length, they flooded into the aft end – the motor room – and the boat adopted a slight stern-down attitude with a small, but noticeable list to port. The first warning came by way of a small but measurable tremor and a few degrees list to port. The majority of the boat's workforce believed that a series of water-shots (simulated torpedo firings) were being undertaken so there was no cause for concern.

When the alarm was raised and works' firemen scurried through the boat calling for the workforce to go ashore. Within twenty minutes of the first tremor *Valiant* again shook herself, settling down slightly more at the aft end and a little more to port. Basically *Valiant* was listing and tilting. The time was around 1.00 a.m. and it was noticeable, with only a small nightshift to account for, that several workmen were missing. There was a last dash by the firemen with shouts of 'Get off. The boat's sinking!' *Valiant's* stern-down attitude and list to port was, by now, quite pronounced but she was cleared of personnel. 'Not really in danger,' said the spokesman – the large gathering of worried-looking management standing by the ill-lit aft

HMS *Valiant* under construction on the slipway in March 1963. *(Barrow Museum Service CATPR28)*

gangway clearly thought otherwise. Called from their beds in the middle of the night in the most urgent of circumstances they huddled in the cold March night air, some with hastily donned top-coats only half-concealing a wide variety of striped and paisley-patterned pyjamas. The more unfortunate gently stamped carpet slipper-shod feet against the chill concrete dockside. The crews of Works' fire engines were running hoses into the motor room ready to commence pumping-out operations, and therein lay another significant problem. The motor-room bulkhead door could not be sealed and the incoming water would, upon spilling over the sill of the motor-room door, slowly spread through the main and auxiliary machinery spaces and then through the boat until she sank.

An additional problem was the aft escape tower exiting out of the motor-room. This too could not be sealed and the increasing stern-down attitude brought the open hatch of the escape tower closer and closer to the level of the dock water which would eventually rush in and totally overwhelm *Valiant*. The reason for hatches and water-tight doors in the motor-room being unable to be sealed was the same throughout every compartment in the boat. As was the custom and practice they were left open to permit access of all manner of dockside services. Fume extraction hoses, power lines and cables, welding leads, temporary pipework etc., ran through every door and hatch on the boat. The fire crews had commenced pumping operations virtually at the same time as several of the work-force, including the 'chap', fitted the valve back into position in the most trying of circumstances – and thus *Valiant* was saved.

To ensure there would be no repetition of such an incident a number of solutions were provided, some examples of which included: locking hull valves shut, their status and keys being controlled by one authority – the Dock Test Organization; the provision of purpose-built 'service' hatches, which would allow access to the boat but enable the hatches to be shut and 'services' to be isolated as appropriate; and fitting 'top hats' to escape towers – in particular the aft tower – to artificially raise the level several feet above that of the dock. The spokesman was quite right about negligible electrical damage. *Valiant* joined the fleet in July 1966.

Should it be considered that such an incident couldn't be repeated, both the Royal Navy and other navies would prove some lessons are learned the hard way, albeit in a slightly dissimilar manner and at different locations.

On 16 May 1969 a USN Sturgeon Class nuclear-powered fleet submarine sank at her moorings in the Mare Island Navy Yard. The boat, *Guittaro*, was recovered and dried out at a cost of $25 million. The incident took place while the boat was under construction and was described by a Congressional committee as 'wholly avoidable'.

On 1 July 1971, HMS *Artemis* sank at her moorings in HMS Dolphin, the submarine base at Gosport, Hampshire. The incident was due, amongst other matters concerned with the filling of external and emergency fuel tanks with water, to 'the failure of the aft escape hatch to be shut and clipped' because a shore power cable ran through it. Three crew members were trapped underwater before escaping. *Artemis* was raised by a salvage vessel a week after the sinking and scrapped at Portsmouth the following year.

In January 2001 the Barrow-built Oberon Class boat *Tonelero* sank at her moorings in Rio. The boat was undergoing repair and maintenance at the time of the incident. The Brazilian Navy have said that they will be unable to comment on the cause until the boat is salvaged. (See pages 153-54 for more details on the build history of the *Tonelero*).

★ ★ ★

Warspite steamed back into the Barrow dock system (almost eighteen months after her commissioning) on 23 October 1968. Her return was the subject of much humour within the Yard. She was back for repairs to her bridge fin and superstructure following an underwater collision with ice. The humour, somewhat caustic, was concerned with a MoD statement explaining 'Warspite's collision damage was sustained during navigation exercises.'

With thousands of miles of North Atlantic sea-room available to her, and notwithstanding her highly sophisticated electronic detection systems, *Warspite* had somewhat remarkably been unable to avoid underwater ice! This was the perception of the Yard and the media – £20 million was the cost of the navy's latest boat and it couldn't avoid ice! A MoD spokesman told the media: 'Some of *Warspite*'s 100 crew members had been slightly hurt in the collision but there were no serious injuries. The boat's superstructure and conning tower had been damaged when the boat collided with some kind of projection under the ice.' The spokesman went on to explain, 'The ice varies considerably in depth.' The spokesman was unable to explain if *Warspite*'s latest navigational aids were in use at the time of collision and on being asked as to the likelihood of a Board of Enquiry said, 'It will depend on the circumstance.' The spokesman was able to confirm that there was no radioactive leakage, but could not say whether *Warspite*'s damage was 'serious or whether it would seriously affect her scheduled training and navigational programme or whether her speed had been affected or whether any person had to be transferred to a surface vessel or whether the boat had been trapped for any length of time under the ice.'

Barrow's *North West Evening Mail*, under the by-line '*Warspite* back for repairs' reported the matter thus:

> *Wearing a black mask to hide a kink in her conning tower,* Warspite, *the Barrow-built nuclear submarine, today steamed into the port where she was launched three years ago. The multi-million pound fleet submarine arrived at Barrow Docks shortly after noon today for repairs, after crashing into a roof of ice in the North Atlantic ten days ago. A black tarpaulin was draped across the front of her conning tower hiding the damage as she was towed by a tug into the Barrow docks system. She had sailed from her base at Faslane on the Clyde yesterday, having been escorted there last week by the frigate* Duncan. *Vickers and Admiralty officials watched her arrival today.*

Warspite returned to service some four weeks later on 20 November 1968.

★ ★ ★

On a lighter note in May 1966, the *Times* newspaper, which had already terrified Barrow by advising of the post-*Dreadnought* lay-offs, now raised another matter of national concern:

> *Popularity of beer in the navy is beginning to present a storage problem for submarines. The men are allowed a basic two cans a day which they buy at the canteen. In the Barrow-built nuclear submarine* Valiant *the captain thinks they will be unable to cope because of the space available. With 80 men drawing two cans daily this is going to mean more than 1,000 cans to be stored on a week's patrol.*

Barrow and The Black Mafia

The reader might consider that far more words than necessary have been used to report a relatively minor event bearing in mind that 'some of *Warspite*'s crew had been hurt.' There may, however, be more to this collision than initially appears to have been the case. Consider the following: ice, and occasionally bad weather, have caused problems for the Royal Navy's submarines from the 1950s onwards. The media have frequently carried reports outlining damage from collisions with ice or damage due to severe weather conditions while boats were surfaced. The frequency of these reports appeared, however, to rise in parallel with the intensity with which the Cold War was promoted. Consequently Warspite's 'tarpaulin-draped conning tower' begs the question – was it ice? – or was it a Russian boat?

A former head of the Russian section of the UK's defence intelligence staff offered comments of a non-secret nature on the activities of the navy's submarines in the March 2000 *Legion* magazine. One comment declared that the Royal Navy itself considered its submarine arm so secretive – as if a Sicilian blood-oath never to reveal the nature of certain activities had been sworn by its members – as to christen it 'The Black Mafia'.

In 1984 the BBC were, following negotiations conducted with the MoD over twelve months, permitted to produce the series *Submarine*, during which it was confirmed that one activity was trailing Russian submarines. The manner of the admission was such that it didn't hold any surprises, but it was a first.

The closest intended factual statements have come from an American book *Blind Man's Bluff*, published in late 2000, which, given the American Freedom of Information Act, is biased towards USN activities. The book contains references to Royal Navy activities already publicised by the MoD – with one exception! This exception concerns an incident which took place around 9 October 1968 and for which the American authors, in protecting their Russian source, offer no objective evidence. The Russian source claims there is a report of a British submarine unwittingly attempting to surface underneath a Russian boat with subsequent damage to both boats; the British boat, by now identified as 'conventional', making the safety of a Norwegian NATO harbour several days later.

As already stated there is no evidence to support the above other than the dates and the damage. Rumours circulating several years later claimed *Warspite* was located in Russian territorial waters and deliberately rammed by a Kotlin Class destroyer. One other tenuous piece of 'evidence' comes from the crews of USN boats on courtesy visits to the Faslane naval base. Barrow personnel working at the base were sometimes able to visit the American boats, the crews of which were in open admiration of *Warspite* and would tell the visitors, 'She's the easy rider, she does the Sneaky Petes no other boat can do.' When *Warspite* returned to the navy, on 20 November 1968, she presumably returned to do what she did best – perhaps the Black Mafia will, one day, be permitted to tell us what that was.

Valiant Class Submarines – Main Characteristics

Overall Length/ Beam/Draught	285ft x 33ft 3in x 27ft
Displacement	3,500 tons surfaced / 4,500 tons submerged
Power	1 x Rolls-Royce PWR-1 pressurised water-cooled reactor supplying steam to geared turbines delivering 15,00bhp (11.185kW) to one shaft
	1 x motor for emergency drive
	1 x auxiliary retractable propeller
Diving Depth	985ft when operational (1,640ft maximum)
Speed	In excess of 25 knots surfaced / 30 knots submerged
Propeller	1
Endurance	Unknown
Armament/ Electronics	6 x 21in torpedo tubes in bow (for Mk24 Tigerfish dual-role wire-guided torpedoes). Alternatively up to 64 x Mk 5 Stonefish or Mk 6 Sea Urchin mines instead of torpedoes.
	1 x Type 1006 surface-search and navigation radar
	1 x Type 2020 active/passive search and attack chin sonar
	1 x Type 2007 long-range passive sonar
	1 x Type 2046 passive search towed-array sonar
	1 x Type 2019 active/passive intercept and ranging sonar
	1 x Type 197 passive ranging sonar
	1 x DCB torpedo fire-control system
	1 x Type UAL ESM system with warning element
	1 x SINS
	Extensive communication and navigation systems
	Various decoys
Complement	103

Polaris Class Submarines

2 built on behalf of the Royal Navy

> *…on a cold February morning, on the steep crack which leaves Abraham's Cave; of Barrow lads (whose fingertips grace Polaris nuclear submarines beneath the Polar ice, and who have spent night after midsummer night on the crag) having a tussle with verglas on the gun-barrel chimney along the top traverse, although they would normally be climbing Hard VS. It's not a climb to be underestimated.*
>
> *Classic Rock* by Ken Wilson

Although the above epigraph may not seem apt, it was some of those Barrow lads who initiated, in the late 1960s, what has become one of the Shipyard's great institutions following a challenge laid down by members of the Barrow Mountaineering and Ski Club working on submarines. Their challenge decreased the distance of fifty miles which President Kennedy believed every

American male should be able to walk. Thus was born the 'Keswick to Barrow Walk', a forty-four mile journey which has raised hundreds of thousands of pounds for charities.

HMS *Resolution*	(Yard No.1074)	Launched 15 September 1966
HMS *Repulse*	(Yard No.1075)	Launched 4 November 1967

> The Barrow Shipyard was responsible for building two of the Royal Navy's four Polaris Class submarines, including the first-of-class *Resolution*. The other two boats in this class, sometimes known as Resolution Class or Ballistic Missile Carrying Submarines, were both built at Cammell Laird on Birkenhead. They were *Renown* and *Revenge*.

It is unlikely that the great majority of Barrow Shipyard personnel soon to be involved in the construction of *Resolution* and *Repulse* considered the implications of the new boats in respect of their size, sophistication and complexity. 'Polaris? Just like Valiant with a 140 feet section of missile space stuck in the middle.' Certainly the quantum leap, from preparing SSNs (Ship Submersible Nuclear) to deliver sanction via a torpedo with an 800lb conventional warhead from a distance of 1½ miles, to preparing SSBNs (Ship Submersible Ballistic Nuclear) to deliver ultimate sanction in the form of a Polaris missile with a thermonuclear warhead from a distance of 2,500 miles, did not go completely unnoticed by the Yard's tradesmen. Their construction helmets would, in future, carry the totally unofficial 'magic marker' drawing of a leaping shark carrying a missile under one fin instead of the usual torpedo. Nor can the incongruity of the situation have been lost on the navy. In Barrow, boat crews were training on a mock-up designed to prepare them for the use of the 'most powerful weapon ever produced' whilst earlier in the decade O Class boats involved in the Indonesian conflict had been fitted with a 20mm Oerlikon cannon. A contemporary view of the SSBNs, their construction and role, is given in the extracts taken from the HMS *Repulse/Resolution* souvenir pamphlet prepared by Vickers Shipbuilding Technical Publications Department in November 1968. These are included in Appendix VII.

In March 1983 the *Link* included the following article relating to the Polaris programme:

A Challenge Met
Polaris Submarines

The mid-1950s development of the submarine-launched Polaris ballistic missile by Lockheed and the US Navy led, eventually, to the signing of the Polaris Sales Agreement between Prime Minister Harold McMillan and President John F. Kennedy. It was decided that the United Kingdom would have four Polaris submarines to carry the latest A-3 missiles; that the submarines would be British designed and built; that the whole weapon systems and equipment, except warheads, would be purchased from the United States; and that the warheads would be British. The Government directive was explicit; the four SSBNs were to be deployed at the earliest possible date and the programme executed within the allotted budget. 'A challenge had been issued and a challenge was going to be met.'

The programme was authorised in February 1963; the submarines were to be built in pairs, with maximum speed, by Vickers (Lead Yard) and Cammell Laird. The order for a fifth SSBN was announced in 1964, but was cancelled by a new Government the following year. The planning and design effort which went into the Polaris submarine programme was colossal: 500,000 man-hours of planning, preparation of more than 10,000 carefully detailed drawings all to be translated into the physical business of construction. Additionally, a full-scale wooden 'mock-up' was built. Not only did this allow the exact positioning of any piece of equipment to be planned and the routes for cables, pipes and trunking to be decided, but, when the crew arrived to stand by their ship, they were able to train on the 'mock-up' and become familiar with their new charge before they even set foot aboard her. In constructing Resolution, *the hull was assembled on the berth from sections pre-fabricated in the Assembly Shop.*

The fore and aft parts of the ship were built up simultaneously, and into the space between were placed the prefabricated missile sections, complete with missile tubes. Thirty months was the time occupied from keel laying to launch – which was carried out by Her Majesty Queen Elizabeth The Queen Mother on 15th September 1966. The autumn of 1967 was an important one in the history of Vickers. Resolution, *having successfully completed her Contractors' Sea Trials, was accepted into the Fleet on 2nd October. To provide an operational submarine of completely new design, with a complete weapon system from the United States and with adequate support facilities, within 4½ years of ordering the vessel, was a truly remarkable performance. 'Vickers' workforce had met their challenge'. Hard on the heels of* Resolution's *delivery to the Fleet came the launch of* Repulse, *on 4th November. This launch was not accomplished without one of those heart pounding incidents which sometimes accompany these occasions.*

Repulse *decided to elude the waiting tugs and remain on display in the Walney Channel*

The launch of the first-of-class Polaris Class submarine HMS *Resolution* into Walney Channel on 16 September 1966.

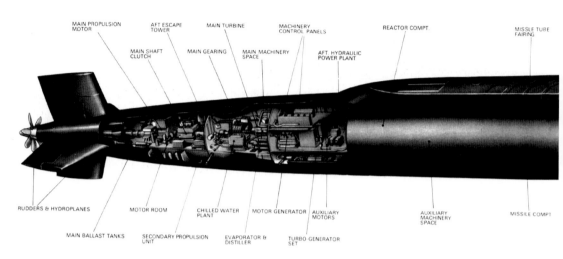

HMS RESOLUTION

Launched	15 September 1966
Displacement	Over 7000 tons
Length	425 feet
Beam	33 feet
Underwater speed	Over 20 knots
Armament	16 Type A3 missiles with a range of 2500 nautical miles
	6 21-inch torpedo tubes.
Main Propulsion	Pressurized water nuclear reactor providing steam
	to geared turbines
Complement	13 officers, 130 ratings

A cut-away representation of HMS *Resolution*.

until the next high tide. Repulse *was fitted-out in Devonshire Dock, and joined the Fleet,* *ahead of time, on 28th September, 1968. Her sister ships,* Renown *and* Revenge, *built at* *Cammell Laird, were commissioned in November 1968 and December 1969, respectively. One* *of the most important events in the work-up of a Polaris submarine is the Demonstration and* *Shakedown Operation (DASO), which is conducted off Cape Kennedy in Florida. This* *operation culminates in the firing of a Polaris missile down the US Air Force Eastern Test Range* *to a target up to 2,500 nautical miles away. The Ministry of Defence planned, in 1963, to fire* *Britain's first Polaris missile at 11.15 Eastern Standard Time on 15th February, 1968 – HMS* Resolution *failed to achieve this by 15 milliseconds, but the firing was otherwise fully successful!*

Being the United Kingdom's contribution to NATO's strategic nuclear deterrent, at least one *Polaris submarine is constantly on patrol, sailing submerged 'one knows not where', but always* *carrying her deadly 'cargo' of two-stage ballistic missiles. 'Sherwood Forest' is the nickname given* *to the compartment housing these missiles, which are 31 feet long, 4½ feet in diameter and weigh* *28,000 pounds. Fired from the submerged submarine, the multiple nuclear warheads can soar* *into the stratosphere and devastate a target 2,500 nautical miles away. One Polaris submarine* *carries more destructive potential than the total amount of explosives expended by all sides in the* *Second World War. When a Polaris submarine heads out into the open sea, the crew settles down* *to a life of routine, where days pass relatively quickly, but time seems to stand still. Their main* *activities are devoted entirely to ensuring that the secrecy of their position is preserved, and that* *the deadly missiles are always ready to fulfil their ultimate purpose. To make the fullest use of* *Polaris submarines, each has two crews – known as Port and Starboard – which take turn and* *turn-about in the two month patrol cycle. Food assumes an importance beyond its intrinsic value,*

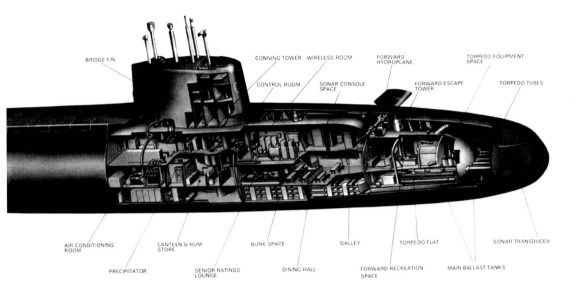

BRIDGE FIN

CONNING TOWER WIRELESS ROOM

FORWARD
HYDROPLANE

TORPEDO EQUIPMENT
SPACE

CONTROL ROOM

SONAR CONSOLE
SPACE

FORWARD ESCAPE
TOWER

TORPEDO TUBES

AIR CONDITIONING
ROOM

CANTEEN & RUM
STORE

BUNK SPACE

GALLEY

TORPEDO FLAT

SONAR TRANSDUCER

PRECIPITATOR

SENIOR RATINGS
LOUNGE

DINING HALL

FORWARD RECREATION
SPACE

MAIN BALLAST TANKS

and plays a large part in influencing the morale of those onboard. From the small galley of a *Polaris* submarine, three cooked meals a day are prepared for the 143 officers and men – in an eight-week patrol, the equivalent of feeding a family of four for five years. The primary source of power for the *Polaris* submarines is a pressurised water nuclear reactor which provides steam for the propulsion turbines and turbo-generators. Systems for every-day running range from high and low voltage electrical power, steam, hydraulic, pneumatic, lubricating oil and water for essential ship's services, to fresh water, air conditioning and refrigeration for domestic purposes. A network of communications and control systems is used for the transmission of information, for direction of remote services, and for round-the-clock monitoring of conditions throughout the ship.

Polaris submarines are designed to carry, and maintain in a state of readiness to fire, 16 Type A-3 Polaris missiles in addition to their conventional torpedo armament. The Admiralty believe that if the missiles are ever employed they will have failed in their purpose of preventing war. But to quote Vice-Admiral Sir Hugh Mackenzie (ex Chief Polaris Executive): 'It is no use pretending to be able to do the job. The stakes are too high to rely on bluff.' Such is the fearsome capability of HMS Resolution, Renown, Repulse and Revenge that, even in peacetime, the 'opposition' is extremely unlikely to subscribe to that proverbial saying 'Out of sight, out of mind'.

This *Link* article covered the successful completion of an immensely sophisticated project but without reference to any of the trials and tribulations that inevitably arise with such contracts.

★ ★ ★

The late Rear Admiral Hugh Mackenzie (Chief Polaris Executive) believed the then modern management technique employed so successfully on the USN Polaris programme, would, suitably adapted for British use, be the way ahead for both the Admiralty and Vickers. Consequently, the previously unheard of Critical Path Analysis, Programme Evaluation Review Technique and Programme Management Plans, were, amongst other matters, revealed to a, possibly, initially dubious Vickers. Mackenzie had written on a number of occasions of 'having to drag Vickers, and Cammell Laird, screaming and kicking into the twentieth century', and he believed that while Vickers may have been 'expert in steel working and the construction and fitting out of conventional ships' hulls' they had no concept of what they were taking on in building, fitting out, testing and tuning an SSBN. Consequently, the assembly, installation and rigorous testing of thousands and thousands of 'items of equipment', many extremely complex, to be supplied by hundreds of sub-contractors in Britain and America, all in accordance with a strict timetable, needed detailed planning.

Vickers apparent reluctance to allot appropriate resources to planning would, in Mackenzie's opinion, jeopardise the timely completion of the contract. A series of increasingly acrimonious exchanges between Mackenzie's staff and the Barrow Yard, throughout the latter half of 1964, was to lead in early 1965 to an extremely serious exchange of view between the main protagonists, Mackenzie for the Admiralty and Leonard Redshaw (later Sir Leonard), the then Managing Director of Vickers-Armstrongs (Shipbuilders). Given the reputations of both men as tough, single-minded and authoritarian, damaging delays to the project must have appeared inevitable. However, their professionalism came to the fore and the matter was settled amicably. Mackenzie would write of the incident in later years saying that what had threatened to become a critical row was settled with a happy outcome that established friendly relations between himself and Len Redshaw that would permit future problems on the project to be successfully resolved.

Amongst those future problems would be the weld hair-line cracking (described in Valiant Class Submarines, pages 161-69) and concerns with the supply of hull steel. The submarine construction programme included, in addition to the SSBNs, two fleet submarines of the 'Improved Valiant' class and supplies of the pressure hull steel QT35, used for plate and castings, were becoming difficult to locate. The scarcity was due to the manufacturers being unable to find a supplier for molybdenum, essential in the make-up of the material. Fortunately a supply was found before the construction timetable was compromised – the source, amazingly, was Russia! Further problems then arose when laminations were found during examination of some of the early supplies of QT35. Following further examination and testing the laminations would be found to fall into the precisely defined category of 'acceptable defects'. Ultimately the supply of QT35 became more and more difficult to obtain and was eventually replaced by the American manufactured hull material HY80.

★ ★ ★

Rear Admiral Mackenzie's publicised opinions regarding 'dragging Vickers into a modern age' and Vickers being required 'to mend their ways and devote more effort to planning' are not supported by the Vickers' personnel involved. Their privately held views remain that Vickers were keen to implement the new methods and, once proved, applied them most professionally. Additionally they considered that the root cause of the acrimony between the parties was a result of Mackenzie and his staff trying to dictate how the boats should be built – a matter clearly unacceptable to Vickers and one which would come to a head early on in the build during the missile compartment construction. The Admiralty/MoD wanted the missile compartment built the Electric Boat (EB) way, i.e. to cut oversize holes in an already complete hull, insert the missile tubes and closing plates and then complete the welding. This method was reliably reported as being described as 'butchery' by Sir Leonard Redshaw who had witnessed the EB approach. Vickers' proposal was to build adjacent missile tubes into each shop fabrication for subsequent transfer to the berth and welding into the hull. This method was, with Vickers' facilities, better than the EB approach, assisting as it did the maintenance of circularity and reducing the amount of welding required at the berth. Known as the 'Redshaw Method' it became the adopted system and it appeared it did not sit well with Mackenzie, who allowed this early clash to tarnish his view of the company to the extent that he would still write critically of Vickers some thirty-odd years later. Members of Mackenzie's team, however, would also write of the expertise and professionalism of the Yard. Indeed one leading member of the Mackenzie team would write of Vickers devising a 'significantly more elegant' method of installing the missile tubes into the hull.

★　★　★

A little more explanation on the grounding of *Repulse* following her launch, initially mentioned on pages 171-172, will reveal some of the worries surrounding that event. Leonard Redshaw would tell the Press, following *Repulse*'s refloating, that had the tugs not pulled her from the sandbank within thirty-six hours, then *Repulse* would have stayed where she was for at least another month when the next suitable tides would have been available. The initial attempts to free *Repulse* were foiled by a fast-ebbing tide and the three tugs attempting the task left *Repulse* and went to wait for the next high tide, immediately after midnight on Saturday 5 November, along with reinforcements in the shape of four tugs from Liverpool. All of this must have been some consolation for the Campaign for Nuclear Disarmament (CND), some forty of whose supporters were arrested during a sit-down demonstration after having their pleas to the launch crowd not to cheer firmly ignored.

HMS *Repulse* departing from Devonshire Dock, with the High Level Bridge raised to allow the boat to exit..

Shortly before midnight, under the glare of arc lights, the seven tugs with extended tow ropes commenced preparing for the refloating operation. In addition to the critical gaze of the media, Admiralty, Navy and Yard personnel, a further estimated 1,500 spectators described as 'listening to transistor radios and eating fish and chips' also witnessed events. As a little over 10,000bhp gently took the strain, *Repulse* gave up the unequal fight and a little after midnight, after thirteen hours aground, allowed herself to be towed to the docks system with the enthusiastic cheers of watchers ringing across the Walney Channel. *Repulse* didn't go totally quietly – she collided with a dock gate – but submarines are, as Mr Redshaw told the Press, 'immensely strong units'. Her grounding and minor collision did no more than scratch the paintwork, as subsequent inspections showed.

The government of the day decided that there would not be a fifth Polaris boat; had there been, she would have carried the name *Ramillies*. When the first Polaris patrol commenced in 1968, East-West tension was so high that it is highly unlikely that any politician or member of the armed forces believed that by 1994 Britain and Russia would have signed pacts agreeing not to target one another's nuclear forces. Even so, when by May 1996 *Repulse* completed her sixtieth and the final Polaris deterrent patrol, 229 in total, it was only because *Trident* had become the replacement 'Big Stick'.

Polaris Class Submarines – Main Characteristics

Overall Length/ Beam/Draught	425ft x 33ft x 30ft
Displacement	7,600 tons surfaced / 8,500 tons submerged
Power	1 x Rolls-Royce PWR-1 pressurised water-cooled reactor supplying steam to geared turbines delivering 15,000bhp (11.185kW) to one shaft
	1 x motor for emergency drive
	1 x auxiliary retractable propeller
Diving Depth	1,150ft when operational (1,525ft maximum)
Speed	20 knots surfaced / 25 knots submerged
Propeller	1
Endurance	Unknown
Armament/ Electronics	6 x 21in torpedo tubes in bow (for Mk24 Tigerfish dual-role wire-guided torpedoes)
	16 x vertical launch tubes for 16 UGM-27C Polaris A3TK under-water-launched ballistic missiles
	1 x Type 1006 surface-search and navigation radar
	1 x Type 2001 long-range active/passive hull sonar
	1 x Type 2007 long-range active/passive hull sonar
	1 x Type 2046 retractable towed-array passive sonar
	1 x Type 2019 passive intercept and ranging sonar
	1 x SLBM fire-control system
	1 x underwater weapons fire-control system
	1 x ESM system with UA-11/12 intercept elements

	1 x SINS
	Various communication and navigation systems
	Various decoys
Complement	143
Notes	Missile tubes were big enough to allow modification to carry the Poseidon system though this modification was never carried out. However, a British warhead upgrade, Chevalene, was installed.

Improved Valiant Class Submarines

2 built on behalf of the Royal Navy

The majority of the crew are watch keepers, working four hours on duty and eight hours off. However, the eight hours 'off' is not entirely free as everyone has a further task to perform of either maintenance of the many equipments or housekeeping and cleaning. In addition, working hours are taken up with continuous training. In the evening there is time for relaxation: film shows, quiz competitions, indoor games and literature being popular. The ship's internal radio system provides classical and popular music. This usual pattern of life is of course interspersed with periods of intense activity day or night when carrying out the operational purpose of the patrol.

HMS *Valiant*'s Commissioning Brochure

| HMS *Churchill* | (Yard No.1076) | Launched 20 December 1968 |
| HMS *Courageous* | (Yard No.1077) | Launched 7 March 1970 |

Several sources fail to differentiate between the Valiant Class and these Improved Valiant Class submarines. However they were undisputedly different. There were three boats in the Improved Class: two being built at Barrow and one at Cammell Laird of Birkenhead. The Barrow Shipyard built the first-of-class HMS *Churchill*, a fact which results in some sources referring to these boats as the Churchill Class. The first boat of the three was named after Sir Winston Churchill while the great man was still alive. Unfortunately he died not long after the order was placed so never saw the boat in the water.

The Improved Valiant Class comprised *Churchill*, *Courageous* and Cammell Laird's *Conqueror* and retained the dimensions and hull form of the Valiant Class. There were, however, significant improvements in equipment, and machinery layout, an upgraded sonar, improvements in motor cooling that would reduce and in some cases cancel out the need for cooling water, and far better arrangements for the reduction of noise. Speed, range and operating depths remained as per the Valiant Class but the improved sonar permitted, amongst other things, detection, identification and tracking much earlier and the reductions in the use of cooling water and various noise forms made for a far better noise and heat signature.

HMS *Courageous* running on the surface.

The new class would greatly complement the intelligence gathering and surveillance activities of the Valiants. Boats of both classes would be involved during the Falklands conflict and *Conqueror* would become the first, and at the time of writing the only, 'nuke' to fire torpedoes in anger when she sank the Argentinian cruiser *General Belgrano*.

While *Churchill* was under construction on the berth, the building of a Shock Test Vessel (STV) was reaching completion. The STV was a box-shaped barge, very similar to the facilities barges in Sub Dock supporting build and test activities, which, within her confines, replicated aspects of a 'nuke's' main machinery space and equipment. Special instruments to measure and record the reaction of the replicated equipment under conditions of explosive shock were later fitted at Rosyth Naval Dockyard. The first descriptions of the STV and its intended role were described by the media in the early 1970s, apparently to the great concern of the MoD who had wished to conduct the STV's activities without attendant publicity. However, almost unnoticed in the briefest of paragraphs, Barrow's own *North West Evening Mail* was sharp enough in a 1969 edition to note the completion of the STV, at a cost of £1 million, and its transfer to Rosyth. Researchers should note that the STV was not identified with a Yard No. and is not therefore referenced in the build list.

By the early 1990s the Valiant Class and Improved Valiant Class submarines were laid up and awaiting disposal. There can be no doubt the navy had obtained the most exacting performance from these two classes of fleet submarines. The cost of an Improved Class boat was approximately £30 million.

★ ★ ★

As of necessity, vessel crews and Yard personnel are involved with one another during construction and completion activities, and in many instances the involvement leads to friendship. Consequently the Falklands conflict was the cause of much mixed emotion in those involved with the build at Barrow and the supervision of build in Argentina's La Plata Naval Dockyard of Type 42 destroyers. There is a grim irony in the fact that within five minutes of the launch of the first-of-class Type 42, HMS *Sheffield* (Yard No.1084), the first section of Argentina's equivalent was laid – *Hercules* (Yard No.1089).

In 1966, approximately one year prior to *Churchill* being laid down, the scrupulous cleanliness required in the building of nuclear submarines was stressed in a paper submitted to the Royal Institute of Naval Architects at a meeting in London. The paper was read by Mr H.J. Tabb, Deputy Director of Naval Construction and Deputy Technical Erector, Polaris Executive, and Mr S.A.T. Warren, Constructor, Polaris Submarine Design Section. Nuclear submarines had been in the forefront of the need for clean conditions and the authors of the paper emphasised the conditions of almost surgical cleanliness applied to nuclear engineering.

HMS *Churchill*, first of the Royal Navy's pump-jet boats.

Improved Valiant Class Submarines – Main Characteristics

Overall Length/ Beam/Draught	285ft x 33ft 3in x 27ft
Displacement	3,500 tons surfaced / 4,500 tons submerged
Power	1 x Rolls-Royce PWR-1 pressurised water-cooled reactor supplying steam to geared turbines delivering 15,000hp (11.185kW) to one shaft
	1 x motor for emergency drive
	1 x auxiliary retractable propeller
Diving Depth	985ft when operational (1,640ft maximum)
Speed	In excess of 25 knots surfaced / 30 knots submerged
Propeller	1 (*Churchill* was fitted with a prototype propulsor)
Endurance	Unknown
Armament/ Electronics	6 x 21in torpedo tubes in bow (for Mk24 Tigerfish dual-role wire-guided torpedoes). Alternatively up to 64 x Mk 5 Stonefish or Mk 6 Sea Urchin mines instead of torpedoes.
	1 x Type 1006 surface-search and navigation radar
	1 x Type 2020 active/passive search and attack chin sonar
	1 x Type 2007 long-range passive sonar
	1 x Type 2046 passive search towed-array sonar
	1 x Type 2019 active/passive intercept and ranging sonar
	1 x Type 197 passive ranging sonar
	1 x DCB torpedo fire-control system
	1 x Type UAL ESM system with warning element
	1 x SINS
	Extensive communication and navigation systems
	Various decoys
Complement	103

6

Modern Submarines
(1971 to 2003)

Swiftsure Class Submarines

6 built on behalf of the Royal Navy

The latest air conditioning and purification equipment is installed along with a water distilling plant of improved design. Shower baths and a fully equipped laundry have been provided as in previous Fleet submarines, and separate messes for senior and junior ratings are laid out on either side of a big modern galley. From this galley meals will be served on a cafeteria system.

HMS *Swiftsure*'s Commissioning Brochure

HMS *Swiftsure*	(Yard No.1078)	Launched 7 September 1971
HMS *Sovereign*	(Yard No.1086)	Launched 17 February 1973
HMS *Superb*	(Yard No.1090)	Launched 30 November 1974
HMS *Sceptre*	(Yard No.1092)	Launched 20 November 1976
HMS *Spartan*	(Yard No.1097)	Launched 7 April 1978
HMS *Splendid*	(Yard No.1099)	Launched 5 October 1979

All six Royal Navy Swiftsure Class submarines were built at Barrow-in-Furness, from the first-of-class HMS *Swiftsure* through to the final boat HMS *Splendid*.

Following the luncheon after the launch of the Polaris Class boat *Repulse*, on 4 November 1967, Mr L. Redshaw was able to describe the next challenge awaiting the Yard workforce. The challenge was represented by the order for a new class of 'deep divers' announced in a telegram from Mr Roy Mason, Minister of State, MoD, with special responsibility for equipment. Mr Redshaw described the impact on Yard design and drawing resources thus: 'In terms of drawing and design office effort the order for SSN07, the Royal Navy's latest submarine, is equal to two and a half of the longest possible passenger liners and seven of the world's largest tankers, each of a different design.' '07' commenced life with the Admiralty in the very early 1960s as SSN0X (a number wasn't designated because it couldn't be determined how the new class would evolve chronologically). Shipyard intelligence at Barrow had been aware of the new 'super boat' well in advance of any formal announcement, but precisely what 'snocks' (as she was known locally) would entail in her construction was known only to a select few. Almost eight years would pass between SSN07 commencing as a design and specification at the Admiralty to being laid down as a pre-fabricated section on 15 April 1969. It would be another thirty months before she could be launched as HMS *Swiftsure* on 7 September 1971 and another twenty months to her commissioning on 17 April 1973.

Swiftsure represented a major change when compared to the existing Improved Valiant Class. Swiftsures would be required to dive deeper and be much faster and quieter. To achieve this, the hull form would be changed and the internal layout of machinery and equipment would be totally different to anything previously seen. To permit *Swiftsure* to dive deeper there would be fewer seawater inlets, starting with a reduction in the number of torpedo tubes from six to five, plus new designs for seawater-cooled equipment which would also reduce the number of inlets and improve the heat signature.

Her hull would be 13ft shorter but would retain a greater length of parallel body – with the resultant loss of the familiar hump-back outline, the forward hydroplanes were sited much lower in the hull (they would not be visible when the boat was surfaced), the bridge fin was much shorter and the rudder profile was changed. The main machinery space was much larger. Main turbines, gear-box and turbo-generators were set on a single main machinery raft which could be resiliently isolated from the hull. A flexible coupling fitted between the gear-box and the main shaft ensured there would be a sufficiency of compensation for any misalignment induced by manoeuvres (at high speeds the raft would be hydraulically locked in position). Class follow-on boats to *Swiftsure* are fitted with a shrouded pump-jet propulsor. Quite why this was not fitted to *Swiftsure* is not known by the authors of this book, but it is assumed that the evaluation of HMS *Churchill*'s prototype unit was not complete by this time.

It may even have been the subject of second thoughts by the MoD following an incident alleged to have taken place during *Churchill*'s Contractor Sea Trials; *Churchill* had been fitted with the prototype pump-jet unit. The trials included a surface-run manoeuvre during which the boat was required to go from 'full-ahead' to 'full-astern'. Fractionally, prior to going full-astern, the boat's bow was deliberately dipped to assist in the reduction of forward momentum. The dipping was, however, outwith the operating procedures for that manoeuvre with the consequence that a 'kick' was transmitted to the intermediate shaft positioned between the gear box and the clutch. The resulting eccentricity the kick produced into the shaft was of extreme concern, as was the distinct possibility of damage to the gear box, clutch and pump-jet. The intermediate shaft was uncoupled and revolved on rollers (within the boat) to locate the maximum eccentricity. (This was measured in thousandths of

HMS *Superb* running on the surface with *Piel Castle* in the background.

an inch and there was no enormous deformation of the shaft.) The offending portion of the shaft was heated by blow-lamp, in an extremely small and very localised area, to the instructions of a team of metallurgists and technicians from Rosyth. The shaft duly returned to its required concentricity and was re-coupled with the gear box and clutch which, along with the pump-jet unit, had been subjected to rigorous tests and inspections and found to be satisfactory. Trials activity was resumed and *Churchill* returned to Barrow having successfully carried out all the necessary tests and manoeuvres despite the alleged incident. The pump-jet is much more efficient than a propeller, perhaps 50% more so; consequently at its theoretical best the pump-jet produces the same speed as a propeller but for half the revolutions. The overall noise signature was further reduced by ensuring all pipework connections to equipment on the main machinery raft were invested with suitable expansion/coupling connections. The US Navy and Royal Navy have worked together for many years and noise reduction has remained one of the major requirements for both navies. Consequently the US Navy were sufficiently impressed with the main shaft flexible coupling to secure licensing arrangements permitting their manufacture in America. The final link to complete the noise reduction chain was the use of anechoic tiling.

The Swiftsure Class were conceived and constructed during the Cold War, having been created as quiet running, fast attack submarines intended to locate and destroy enemy submarines and surface shipping. Their role involved intelligence and surveillance missions and, according to reports, the surveillance came within touching distance on some occasions.

HMS *Sceptre* collided with a Russian 'nuke' in 1981 while, in 1986, HMS *Splendid* lost her towed array following a near collision with a Soviet submarine. HMS *Splendid* became the first Royal Navy submarine to fire Tomahawk Block 3 missiles, launching them against Serb targets during the Kosovo conflict. Defence Minister, John Spellar, in answer to a parliamentary question, advised the decommissioning dates for the Swiftsure Class boats. *Swiftsure* is already laid up and will be followed by *Sovereign*, *Superb*, *Sceptre*, *Spartan* and *Splendid* between 2005 and 2008. These boats are scheduled to be replaced by the Astute Class from 2005 onwards. However, a projected three-year delay in the Astute Class construction may lead to amendments of the replacement dates.

HMS *Swiftsure*'s first refit was to provide her with an undesirable record (hopefully there won't be other contenders) for continuous lying-up time – five years' duration – due to a paucity of class spares and dockyard disputes.

Swiftsure Class Submarines – Main Characteristics

Overall Length/ Beam/Draught	83m x 10m x 8m
Displacement	4,000 tons surfaced / 4,900 tons submerged
Power	1 x PWR reactor
	2 x 15,000bhp GEC steam turbines (11.2MW)
	2 x W.H. Allen Turbo-Generators (3.6MW)
	1 x 1,900bhp Paxman Diesel Generator (1.42MW)
	1 x motor for emergency drive
	1 x auxiliary retractable propeller
Diving Depth	In excess of 1,000ft

Speed	In excess of 25 knots surfaced / 30 knots submerged
Propeller	1 x propeller (Swiftsure only) – remainder of class fitted with shrouded pump-jet propulsor
Endurance	Unknown
Armament/ Electronics	5 x 21in bow torpedo tubes
	McDonnell Douglas UGM-84B Sub-Harpoon anti-surface missiles
	Marconi Spearfish torpedoes
	Marconi Tigerfish Mk24 Mod2 torpedoes
	Hughes Tomahawk Block III cruise missiles (Splendid only)
	Various decoys
	Various Sonars (including hull-mounted passive low-frequency, passive search towed array, passive intercept and ranging, and high-frequency short-range classification)
Complement	97

Type 540 Class Submarines

3 built on behalf of the Israeli Navy

In 1976 Sir Leonard Redshaw departed Vickers Shipbuilders but agreed to act as non-executive chairman of the Offshore Engineering Group in whose formation and development he had played a key role. The following is just one of the many tributes.

> *No executive can have served Vickers with greater distinction and dedication. Under his leadership Vickers Shipbuilding have enhanced their already high international reputation and he has established himself as a leading personality in the British shipbuilding industry.*
>
> Lord Robens speaking about Sir Leonard Redshaw in 1976

Gal (Wave)	(Yard No.1093)	Launched 2 December 1975
Tanin (Crocodile)	(Yard No.1094)	Launched 25 October 1976
Rahav (Sea Monster)	(Yard No.1095)	Launched 8 May 1977

Although referenced by various naval authorities as IKL/Vickers Type 206 Class patrol submarines, or the Gal Class submarines, these three submarines, built on behalf of the Israeli Navy, were designated by Vickers as the 540 Class.

The design of the 540 Class Israeli submarines was developed by Vickers in collaboration with Ingenieurkontur Lübeck (IKL) and Howaldtswerke (HDW), both of, what was then, West Germany. The design was based on the existing, and successful, Type 206 Class patrol submarines which were introduced into the German Navy from the early 1970s onwards; a number of that class having been built by HDL at their Kiel Yard. The Vickers/IKL/HDW design collaboration included several types of diesel-electric boat commencing with a Type 100, then a 500 Class and a 1100 Class. The 540s could not be built in West Germany for political reasons and were eventually contracted to Vickers for construction, which thrust them into an unenviable position of being subject to boycott by Arab states.

Vickers had considerable investment in the British Aircraft Corporation (BAC) at the time and BAC's crucial role in military aircraft production, and particularly the Jaguar, Tornado and Rapier anti-aircraft missile, was, along with other aero-space equipments, worth some £750 million in export orders. Particularly large contracts were held with Iran and Saudi Arabia. Vickers could not afford to jeopardise such matters and a difficult political balancing act was required for several years. (Some twenty-four years later BAC would, having become BAE Systems in the meantime, become owners of the Barrow Yard.) The 540s were, with the exception of the midget boats, the smallest class of submarine to be built by Vickers since the Second World War V Class.

As first of class, *Gal*'s launch was viewed with some interest by Yard workers who turned up to give the customary cheers as she slid down the 'ways and into Walney Channel. However, the cheers turned to cries of alarm as *Gal* listed violently to starboard as she entered the water, almost pitching the launch team on the casing into the channel. Many of the onlookers believed cradle retaining studs had sheared on the bow cradle permitting excess movement. The Vickers spokesman described the incident as 'a mishap caused by ballast displacement which caused the vessel's incorrect trim but the boat was brought onto an even keel within a short time.' The onlookers preferred the media's version which was 'Submarine Launching Nearly A Disaster.'

Gal completed her build and trials successfully but, having almost completed transit to her home port, a navigation error caused her to run aground off Haifa and suffer damage. A tragic accident caused the death of three crew members during Israeli navy-conducted exercises at Loch Gilphead (possibly a diver lockout incident) and reports in the media re-ignited the

Israeli submarine *Gal*.

Gal running on the surface.

spectre of boycott. Consequently, *Rahav* was constructed on a pontoon in Buccleuch Dock, with as least fuss as possible, and her naming ceremony was classed as her launch. There would be one final minor media-reported incident when Israeli sailors casually strolled to their boat with shouldered automatic rifles. A number of the workforce deduced a terrorist attack was in the offing, but there wasn't and the Israeli Navy were politely instructed to discontinue that particular habit whilst in the Yard.

Opinions vary as to which boat was fitted with SLAM. Most sources agree *Rahav* was a recipient and a few believe all three boats possessed the launchers. Interestingly enough, several Middle Eastern navies would eventually show sufficient interest for Vickers to combine with Costains in the early and middle 1980s to market boats from the Vickers/IKL/HDW collaborations. The complete package included a full naval construction/maintenance facility (including a shiplift) complete with necessary training. Unfortunately the interest never developed into a customer stage.

540 Class Submarines – Main Characteristics

Overall Length/ Beam/Draught	146.7ft x 15.4ft x 12ft
Displacement	420 tons surfaced / 600 tons submerged
Power	Diesel-electric arrangement, with two MTU 12V493 TY60 diesels powering AEG generators supplying current to one electric motor delivering 1.345kW (1800bhp) to one shaft
Diving Depth	1,000ft operational (1,640ft maximum)
Speed	11 knots surfaced / 17 knots submerged
Propeller	1
Endurance	Unknown
Armament/ Electronics	8 x 21in torpedo tubes in bow (10 torpedoes carried including anti-submarine torpedoes or alternatively 20 mines) No gun armament (though may have SLAM launcher for Blowpipe surface-to-air missiles) 1 x Plessey surface-search and navigation radar 1 x Plessey active/passive search and attack hull sonar 1 x TIOS torpedo fire-control system 1 x ESM system with warning element Extensive communications and navigation systems Various decoys
Complement	22

Trafalgar Class Submarines

7 built on behalf of the Royal Navy

The heart of the nuclear power plant of a Fleet submarine is a Pressurised Water Reactor. It is a collection of fissile uranium fuel elements arranged in a heavily shielded pressure vessel. The enormous release of energy produced by fissioning uranium nuclei – 1 ton of the fissionable material is equivalent to 2½ million tons of best coal – manifests itself as heat in the fuel elements. The fission rate in the reactor is controlled by special rods which are inserted between the fuel elements to absorb fission-producing neutrons.

HMS *Turbulent's* Commissioning Brochure

HMS *Trafalgar*	(Yard No.1100)	Launched 1 July 1981
HMS *Turbulent*	(Yard No.1101)	Launched 1 December 1982
HMS *Tireless*	(Yard No.1103)	Launched 17 March 1984
HMS *Torbay*	(Yard No.1104)	Launched 8 March 1985
HMS *Trenchant*	(Yard No.1105)	Launched 3 November 1986
HMS *Talent*	(Yard No.1107)	Launched 15 April 1988
HMS *Triumph*	(Yard No.1108)	Launched 16 February 1991

There were a total of seven Trafalgar Class boats, all of which were built (over a ten-year period) at the Shipyard at Barrow-in-Furness.

Lessons learned from the Swiftsure Class boats were applied to the Trafalgar Class (originally termed Improved Swiftsure), the most obvious changes being increased length and displacement as the general characteristics table shows. The Trafalgar Class boats were given an improved reactor and the main and auxiliary machinery spaces were much modified. The eternal pursuit of noise reduction would indicate its continuing success following navy statements in the mid-eighties, when they were able to declare the noise levels on *Trafalgar* (as recorded on the noise test ranges) as being less than those of the Oberon Class boats. That astonishing achievement came as part of an ongoing process of tests and research conducted by the MoD in conjunction with Vickers and several hundred or more equipment suppliers. Although there are specific requirements concerning installed equipments/systems in respect of noise reduction, the subject was largely ignored during the Second World War with the exception of the most rudimentary application to midget submarines. As the Cold War intensified, the 'Silent Service' became aware they were not as silent as they should, or would wish to be with the result that much greater resources were applied to the matter.

Thus, in 1973, Vickers formed its Noise and Vibration Engineering Department (NAVED), which would become the recipient of a number of MoD contracts placed to permit the conduct of 'a variety of trials, tests and mathematical investigations aimed at reducing the noise radiated by submarines'. Clearly those contracts have proved to have been repaid with maximum value. However, improvements are not restricted to noise. They continue through all aspects of boat construction and indeed throughout their service life. Consequently, even within a class, each successive boat will differ to a greater or lesser degree by an improvement over its predecessor. Descriptions of the reactor compartment and the main machinery space, or its auxiliary spaces, are not permitted but a brief and non-technical outline of the boat forward of the reactor compartment forward bulkhead is allowed. The use of masts (such as attack and search periscopes) which do not penetrate the hull must wait until the Astute Class is developed, so, even with two continuous decks to attempt to reduce the through movement of non-essential personnel, the control room (the boat's brain) continues to have little room to spare. Either side of the control room, which lies amidships on One Deck, are the navigation centre to starboard and the weapons information/action information console to port. Immediately forward of those spaces are the Chief PO's and PO's accommodation and the sound room. Immediately aft of the control room is the CO's accommodation and the communications office. One Deck also accommodates the radar and sonar offices and equipment which various authoritative works reference as being highly sophisticated and very capable.

Down on Two Deck is the remainder of the accommodation and mess rooms, galley, laundry, etc. Various auxiliary machinery spaces are sited throughout both One and Two Deck – life support equipment such as CO_2 scrubbers, oxygen production equipment, air conditioning equipment, CO/H_2 burners, primary H_2 burners and hydraulic and cooling pumps, etc. The torpedo room, or more properly the weapons storage compartment, is down on the third level (Three Deck). Both the forward and aft end of the boat contain escape towers, as per SSNs and SSBNs, so that in the highly unlikely event of an incident personnel can escape individually or via a Deep Submergence Rescue Vehicle (DSRV) which is capable of locking on to the escape tower. Trafalgar Class construction and launch continued until *Talent*, which, on 15 April 1988, became the last submarine at the Yard to undergo dynamic launch – thus ending 102 years of tradition started in 1886 with the first Nordenfelt boat (excepting of course the 'midget' boats and the Israeli *Tanin* and *Rahav*). Several traditions were broken at *Talent*'s launch which took place five minutes and five seconds later than scheduled. One tradition was broken when speeches commenced immediately after the main course to permit HRH Princess Anne, the sponsor, to keep to a schedule severely compromised by bad weather. A second tradition was broken when the Princess requested cheques for selected charities rather than be given the more usual sponsor gift. A third tradition was broken when the launching bottle of Pusser's Rum and its ribbon were lost in Walney Channel during the launch, thus preventing the shipbuilder from presenting the bottle remains and ribbon to *Talent*'s complement.

★ ★ ★

In 1988 the Yard announced that *Talent* would be the last dynamic launch, as that method of putting a vessel into the water is one of the most stressful events in its life. The announcement has been partly fulfilled as submarines have, since that date, been lowered into Devonshire Dock via the synchronised shiplift, though surface vessels continue to be launched in the traditional dynamic manner. A traditional (dynamic) launch from the slipway provides a dramatic and exciting spectacle for the onlooker. For those involved in the organization, it provides a lot of work and some concerns. A dynamic launch lasts just sixty seconds from the moment the triggers release the vessel on her journey down the slipway and into Walney Channel. However, during that time, the vessel is under considerable stress, particularly so when the stern is afloat and tremendous weight bears down on the forward poppet (the bow cradle) which is still sliding down the slipways. Some figures which illustrate those stresses are taken from Swiftsure Class boat *Spartan*'s launch:

Total launch weight	3,780 tons
Weight of drag chains	360 tons
Weight on fore poppet when stern lifts	400 tons

Slipway preparation commences some three months prior to launch but the first calculations are prepared even before the build contract is signed. A shiplift launch has practically none of the risks attendant to a dynamic launch and considerably less manual and office work. The 24,000-plus tons lifting capacity of the £50 million shiplift was the world's heaviest when the Yard commenced using the equipment in late 1986. The SSK *Upholder* and SSN *Trenchant* were early beneficiaries of the lift's powerful abilities with each being hoisted from Devonshire Dock.

★ ★ ★

Wednesday 6 April 1988 was the first of several days of major embarrassment for the Yard when, via a leaked report, the media obtained the story of one of *Triumph*'s units having been welded upside down and, like a dog with a bone, the National Press would not let go. 'Atom Sub's Builders Admit a Mix-Down' tittered the *Daily Telegraph*; 'Down Periscope' jeered the *Daily Mirror*; 'Sub-Standard' screamed the *Sun*. These are just three examples of the headlines which appeared in the nation's major newspapers and all were accompanied by cartoons with a theme to match.

The story was correct, but several weeks later the *Link* was able to make the following statement: 'The facts are that one of the hoops that make up the submarine was welded in an inverted position. This mistake occurred in the New Assembly Shop. A standard, detailed internal inspection, carried out after welding, identified the problem which the subsequent examination showed was not critical.' Earlier in a Parliamentary reply to a question from a Labour MP, the Secretary of State for Defence Procurement said, 'SSN hull units contain a slightly thicker section at the keel to provide an internal corrosion element. The incorrectly welded unit has been measured and found to contain a sufficient element for corrosion and it is therefore intended to leave the unit where it is presently positioned. The performance and life of the submarine will not be affected.' *Triumph* was the last of the Trafalgar Class of submarines and was commissioned into the Royal Navy in 1992.

With that momentary hiccup overcome, the opportunity was taken to implement, somewhat ironically, a newly determined build strategy for the reactor compartment. The standard approach to the construction of a boat's reactor compartment, both in British and American yards, was for the compartment to be constructed as a section of the submarine hull. Following completion of the structure the top third of the reactor compartment was cut out to permit the reactor equipment (including pressure vessel and steam generators) to be shipped in. The problem with that method is that it can cause delays on immediately adjacent major outfitting work until the cut out section is reinserted and satisfactorily rewelded. The new method was to eliminate those delays by shipping the reactor equipment through an open end of the hull prior to welding up the reactor compartment. That method was the

The launch of HMS *Turbulent*.

result of the work of a team which included draughtsmen, welding engineers, QC Inspectors and construction and outfit department representatives. The team worked together for almost eight months to develop the method which, to use the most basic of descriptions, consisted of a system of monorails and skidways capable of handling the reactor equipment, the heaviest item weighing 140 tons. A full analysis showing that the method was both feasible and time-saving was presented to the Yard's directors, senior management, MoD officials and Rolls-Royce & Associates members before permission to use the method was given.

Millennium year brought consternation to the Admiralty and public alike following the highly publicised and discussed matter (at least by the press) of the reactor coolant system leaks which, following rigorously conducted examinations, were found to be present in seven of the navy's twelve SSNs. Of the five unaffected boats, four were undergoing scheduled main-tenance/refit work and were thus operationally unavailable. Consequently for a very brief period *Triumph* carried the burden of being Britain's only operational nuclear submarine.

Regrettably that brief period of strain was exacerbated by *Triumph's* sharp contact with the seabed while undergoing diving manoeuvres off the Scottish coast, which necessitated repair to what the MoD described as 'superficial damage' – leaving the country without a single serviceable SSN. Future governments might consider the fact that the minimum number of SSNs required to maintain a credible force in the light of scheduled/unscheduled mainte-nance/refit programmes is eighteen.

Trafalgar Class Submarines – Main Characteristics

Overall Length/ Beam/Draught	85.4m x 9.8m x 9.5m
Displacement	4,740 tons surfaced / 5,208 tons submerged
Power	1 x Rolls-Royce PWR1 nuclear reactor
	2 x GEC turbines (15,000bhp – 11.2MW)
	2 x W.H. Allen turbo generators (3.2MW)
	2 x Paxman diesel alternators (2,800bhp – 2.1MW)
	1 x motor for emergency drive
	1 x auxiliary retractable propeller
Diving Depth	Unknown
Speed	Surface speed unknown / 32 knots submerged
Propeller	1 x pump-jet propulsor
Endurance	Unknown
Armament/ Electronics	5 x 21in torpedo tubes in bow (for 18 x Spearfish and
	Mk 24 Tigerfish and Spearfish wire-guided dual-role torpedoes;
	alternatively up to 44 Mk 5 Stonefish and Mk 6 Sea Urchin mines)
	1 x Type 1007 surface-search and navigation radar
	1 x Type 2046 or Type 2076 passive search and intercept hull sonar
	1 x Type 2019 passive intercept and ranging sonar
	1 x Type 2046 towed array passive sonar
	Extensive communication and navigation systems
	Various decoys
Complement	148

Type 2400 Class Submarine

1 built on behalf of the Royal Navy

Into the 21st Century
New warship building facilities currently under construction at Barrow herald the end of tradi-
tional dynamic slipway launches for all but the smaller export boats, replaced by a gentle
lowering into the water on an electric shiplift. A large construction hall will accommodate up to
six boats, or a mix of submarines and surface vessels, in various stages of build at the same
time.

By 1990, these new VSEL shipbuilding yard facilities, augmented by the recent acquisition
of the ultra-modern Cammell Laird shipyard, will be ready to meet the challenge of the 21st
Century, staffed by a workforce with the experience that only a century of continuous warship
building development can bring, and taking pride in our determination to maintain the quality
of ships and submarines for which we are known throughout the world.

1886 – 1986 A Century of Barrow-Built Submarines,
a Shipyard Technical Publication

HMS *Upholder*   (Yard No.1106)   Launched 2 December, 1986

Sometimes known as the Upholder Class, the Type 2400 Class submarines were designed to replace the Oberon Class boats. It was originally thought that up to eighteen were planned but in the event just four were built, the first-of-class HMS *Upholder* at Barrow and the others (*Unicorn*, *Unseen* and *Ursula*) at Cammell Laird at Birkenhead. Interestingly at this time the Cammell Laird Shipyard was owned by the Barrow-in-Furness Shipyard, though *Unicorn*, *Unseen* and *Ursula* can never be considered Barrow-built submarines. The 1993 defence cuts saw the entire class paid off and all four boats were mothballed at Barrow prior to their being leased (with an option to buy) to the Canadian Navy.

HMS *Upholder* (SSK 01) was commissioned into the Royal Navy on 9 June 1990, the first of a new class intended to replace the Oberon Class boats. She was considered by her many admirers in Britain and abroad to be the finest of all diesel-electric boats. With her tear-drop hull and the sensors and weapons capability of a Trafalgar Class boat she was ideally suited for the role of a NATO picket. The propulsion system comprises two high-speed diesels, each coupled to a 1.4MW generator, and a double armature main motor driving a single propeller. The generators are able to be used to provide power to the main motor directly to charge the main battery. Submerged duration is considerably greater than that of the Oberons by virtue of the comprehensive air purification regeneration system, and osmosis technology ensures plenty of fresh water. The maximization of remote control and automatic surveillance systems enables a much smaller complement to operate the boat (as a compar-ison a similarly equipped Fleet submarine would require some 120 personnel as against Upholder's 46).

The well thought out design takes into account the use of good self-diagnosis in machinery fault-finding systems and the widespread use of printed circuit boards to ensure electronic equipment is reliable and easier to repair. External communication systems take into account the requirement to receive and transmit across a wide spectrum of military and other radio bands and frequencies. A fully integrated computerised sonar suite enables long-range detection and shadow/attack ability. Sensor-provided information is processed and linked to a computer, for display to a Command Team, in a system that also processes data from periscope, radar and ESM masts and navigation inputs. The weapons system allows *Upholder* to defend herself by means of six bow-mounted weapons discharge tubes (torpedo tubes) capable of discharging a varying payload of torpedoes, missiles and mines. Two main bulkheads divide the pressure hull into three primary compartments, with the forward and aft compartments containing escape towers and the middle compartment containing a diver lock-out within the bridge fin. All the above is packaged in a pressure hull manufactured from Naval Quality 1 (NQ1) steel as post-1970s nuclear submarines, and the boat is fast, can run deep and is very quiet. '*Upholder*,' said the Royal Navy, 'is a very fine addition to the Fleet.'

There had, however, been a time when it appeared as if *Upholder* might not join the Fleet, as if she were doomed to an endless cycle of ill-luck and repeated trials all reported by an ill-informed, and at times merciless, national media. *Upholder* completed her basin dives and trim and incline trials with both the MoD and the Yard's Naval Architects Department pleased with the results. Also satisfactorily completed were an extensive range of trials and tests which could only be undertaken during basin dives: sonar, signal ejectors, escape towers, garbage ejectors and, most importantly, the blow systems (which assist the boat to surface by blowing water out of the ballast tanks). Those examples are just a small selection of the wide-ranging and rigorous trials and tests, the satisfactory completion of which is mandatory prior to any boat proceeding to the next stage – Contractor Sea Trials (CSTs). There was one aspect of the second basin dive which had not been totally satisfactory – the weapons discharge system – but that was due to design shortcomings outside of VSEL's control. Nevertheless a dummy weapon was fired from each weapon discharge tube followed by a salvo discharge, all to the satisfaction of the inspecting officer. However, to ensure absolute safety, the outer boundaries of the tubes were locked prior to CSTs because, as VSEL would state: 'Under deliberate operation in controlled conditions they can be operated but for safety reasons they are not fully operational. The problem is being tackled and a solution is in sight.'

Upholder returned from CSTs under tow, causing much speculation by the press, some of which made Garrett's adventures with the Nordenfelts seem mundane in comparison. VSEL appeared to be sufficiently concerned by the speculation as to allow *Upholder*'s Boat Manager to respond in a *Link* article in September 1989. The article was, although entirely objective, rather more aggressive than usual for a generally conservative in-house journal. The wilder media reports about 'plunging 1,000 feet', 'lying on the seabed for three hours', 'surfacing stern first', and so on, were swiftly dismissed as exciting but purely fictional stories. The *Link* article contradicted inaccurate media articles concerning propulsion problems:

> *At about 250 feet, rising and still moving ahead, virtually all electrical power was lost and it went very dark and quiet. The boat continued to rise, with the after hydroplanes in air control (as opposed to hydraulic) until the boat stopped. At that point we blew to the surface, main-taining a level trim throughout, all under the calm control of the ship's staff.*

HMS *Upholder*.

The article echoed the earlier Royal Navy comment publicised prior to the CSTs: 'The trials are a major challenge because there are many items of equipment and systems on *Upholder* that have never been to sea on any other vessel' and '*Upholder* is not only a first-of-class submarine, she is a prototype.'

The final paragraph of the article summed up the Boat Manager's anger and frustration: 'It is a pity the world only sees VSEL on the (bridge) fin and attributes all the snags to us – especially when the two major problems at present have little to do with the company. It is still a boat we can all be proud of.' Many within VSEL believed, rightly or wrongly, that the MoD were themselves irresponsible in not undertaking more rigorous pre-installation trials and testing of the 'two major problems', namely the weapons discharge system and propulsion motor. CSTs would need to be repeated but *Upholder*'s problems were eventually satisfactorily resolved and she would be followed into service by her three sister boats which were constructed at Birkenhead in the VSEL wholly-owned subsidiary Cammell Laird. Those three boats were HMS *Unseen*, HMS *Ursula* and HMS *Unicorn*.

There would be one last public airing of *Upholder*'s shortcomings when an all-party parliamentary commission concluded that VSEL had provided inadequate resources (there had been a three-month labour dispute in the Yard which was also resourcing for the Trafalgar and Trident Class boats) and the MoD had changed its plans far too often on too many matters.

Once in service the SSKs undertook surveillance and picket activities against Warsaw Pact boats. Then, in late 1993, the government decided that part of the post-Cold War peace dividend would be a requirement for the Royal Navy to either give up its SSKs or reduce the number of SSNs. For operational flexibility the choice was to retain the SSNs, so by the mid-1990s the SSKs were moored alongside the Yard's Buccleuch Dock wall on a care-and-maintenance basis while the MoD sought a buyer. Canada had announced its intention to acquire a nuclear submarine fleet in 1987, thus bringing elation to the Yard who believed they had a far better product than the other contender – France. However in 1989 Canada dashed all hopes of renewing her submarine fleet (three Oberons) and the competition between Britain's Trafalgar Class and France's Amethyste Class was over.

The care-and-maintenance routine continued as officials and naval staffs of various countries came and looked and went away, and the SSKs stayed put. Canada had never completely disappeared from the picture though and consideration was given to a joint Anglo-Canadian venture into production of a Canadian variant of the Upholder Class and VSEL had advertised its intent to produce an export variant of the class. Many observers deemed the boats too sophisticated for the majority of navies interested, and too costly by dint of that sophistication. Some concluded the equipment was too sensitive to be used by any other than the most reliable of allies. This brings us back to the earlier statement: 'many items of equipment and systems on *Upholder* that have never been to sea on any other vessel.' There had been constant rumours of the SSKs being used to prove electronics systems to be employed on the Trident Class boats. Whatever the truth of these matters the Canadian government was back in the frame by the late 1990s with the result that now, in a complex arrangement, the SSKs are, subject to satisfactory modification and the satisfactory completion of a rigorous programme of tests and CSTs, being leased (with an option to buy) by the Canadian Navy. Consequently the boats have been reactivated and modified by the Yard and, at the time of writing, the first newly commissioned boat, HMCS *Victoria*, has completed transit to her home port in Halifax, Nova Scotia. *Victoria*, which is also the class designation (she was previously *Unseen*), will be followed at intervals by *Windsor* (*Unicorn*), *Chicoutimi* (*Upholder*) and *Cornerbrook* (*Ursula*). Amongst some of the modifications to the boats are the removal of the mixed weapons package, replaced by eighteen Mark 48 torpedoes whose fire control system is as the Canadian Oberons, as is the towed array. Crew accommodation has been modified to permit the inclusion of females as part of the complement and areas/spaces adjacent to the propulsion units have been changed to align with Canadian requirements.

With large areas of the Pacific, Arctic and Atlantic oceans to patrol, the class require the ability to stay on patrol for at least forty-five days. The boats are expected to be useful well into the twenty-first century and if Canada proposed to buy them at the end of the lease they might give consideration to the installation of an Air Independent Propulsion (AIP) system. The Royal Navy is known to be extremely dissatisfied with having to part with what is, although, as a minimum, ten years old, an outstanding class of diesel-electric boat. The consolation remains that in the hands of the Canadian Navy the boats are with a most trusted friend and a tough, tried and tested, and most professional, submarine service.

★ ★ ★

On 5 June 1990, just four days prior to *Upholder*'s commissioning, a full military funeral was held for Albert Cheale, an ex-submariner of Barrow. Mr Cheale's Union Jack-draped coffin was borne into church by six submariners from *Upholder* and a Royal Navy bugler sounded the Last Post. Mr Cheale was paid these final honours in recognition of long and outstanding service in the navy, not least of which was service in submarines throughout the Second World War without leave. His signalling skills were such that as soon as his boat had docked he would go back to sea on another. Mr Cheale served twenty-six years in the navy, eighteen years of which were on submarines. Included amongst his decorations was the Distinguished Service Medal, awarded for his role with the captured German submarine U570 (later HMS *Graph*) which was brought to Barrow and later turned against the Germans (see also page 111 and Appendix III).

Type 2400 Class Submarines – Main Characteristics

Overall Length/ Beam/Draught	70.3m x 7.60m x 5.50m
Displacement	2,160 tons surfaced / 2,455 tons submerged
Power	Diesel-electric arrangement with 2 x Paxman/GEC Valenta 1600 RPA-200 SZ diesel generators supplying current to one GEC electric motor delivering 5,400bhp (4,030kW) to one shaft
Diving Depth	300m operational (500m maximum)
Speed	12 knots surfaced / 20 knots submerged
Propeller	1
Endurance	9,200 miles at 8 knots surfaced / 310 miles at 3 knots submerged
Armament/ Electronics	6 x 2in torpedo tubes in bow (for 18 x Spearfish and Mk 24 Tigerfish and Spearfish wire-guided dual-role torpedoes; alternatively up to 44 Mk 5 Stonefish and Mk 6 Sea Urchin mines 1 x Type 1007 surface-search and navigation radar 1 x Type 2040 or Type 2075 passive search and intercept hull sonar 1 x Type 2007 passive search flank sonar 1 x Type 2019 passive intercept and ranging sonar 1 x Type 2026 towed array passive sonar 1 x DCC action information and underwater weapons fire-control system 1 x Type UAC ESM system with warning element Extensive communication and navigation system Various decoys
Complement	46

Trident Class Submarines

4 built on behalf of the Royal Navy

VSEL is expected to build four Trident submarines each with a submerged displacement of about 15,900 tons. They will each have 16 missile tubes designed to carry the Trident D5 ballistic missile now being developed by the Lockheed Missiles and Space Company of America.

VSEL's *Link* Magazine – Issue 9, May 1986, announcing the programme to construct the largest submarines ever built in Britain

HMS *Vanguard*	(Yard No.1109)	Launched 4 March 1992
HMS *Victorious*	(Yard No.1110)	Launched 29 September 1993
HMS *Vigilant*	(Yard No.1111)	Launched 14 October 1995
HMS *Vengeance*	(Yard No.1112)	Launched 19 September 1998

All four Trident Class submarines (sometimes known as Vanguard Class) were built at Barrow-in-Furness.

Having successfully completed well in excess of 20,000 inspections, the first Trident Class boat was completed in July 1989. This boat, however, was not intended to go to sea – it was a one-fifth scale model. Such models, first developed at Barrow in the 1970s for the Swiftsure Class boats, were built as a design and development tool to assist technical and production departments to ensure all equipments fit into the actual boat and can be operated and maintained. The Trident model was, as previous models, extremely accurate, finely detailed and divided into a series of 'bases' each of which represented sections of the submarine. Throughout the construction and test programme the model was updated to reflect such matters as MoD required modifications and feedback emanating from boat construction.

The order for the first Trident Class boat, *Vanguard*, was announced in the House of Commons by the Defence Procurement Minister on 30 April 1986 and, including 'first of class' work, was worth £650 million. Notwithstanding the formality of that announcement, contracts were already in place relating to design and drawing work. Additionally, certain construction aspects were already underway (commencing in 1984) and included missile tube manufacture for follow-on boats to *Vanguard* (her missile tubes were under construction in the USA by Babcock & Wilcox). The process of inviting hundreds of specialist manufacturers to tender for the supply of components and equipment was well underway and in many instances the close collaboration necessary between ministry officials, Yard technical and production staff and the suppliers was already well established – indeed in the case of the major suppliers the collaboration was an ongoing routine, unbroken since *Dreadnought's* inception.

The Electric Boat (builders of the American boats) connection was again renewed with personnel from that company providing specialist training in the use of their automatic welding and burning equipment to Yard personnel. Certain aspects of design work commenced in the early 1970s and in 1978 the Yard won a major contract to build an experimental aft section of hull with the reactor and engine room installed within it. The reactor was the Rolls-Royce designed PWR2, powerful enough to propel the almost 16,000 tons displacement of HMS *Vanguard* and her sister boats through the world's seas. The sheer size of the class, more than twice the displacement of a Polaris Class boat, would set the Yard an immense challenge and that challenge would be further extended through a requirement for enormous step changes in technology to be introduced. The challenge was successfully met and, by the time the last of the class was commissioned, the overall programme had been maintained and in real terms was well under budget.

However, it would come as no surprise in such an immensely complex project that there should be some upsets to be overcome and some examples follow below. During the *Trident* prototype main machinery trials serious vibration occurred in the port main turbine necessitating a full turbine stripdown, comprehensive investigation and then repair. The combined effort of GEC (turbine manufacturer) and the Yard's Submarine Machinery Installation and Testing Establishment (SMITE) and Marine Design Department completed the work in six weeks. The trials, successfully re-proving the turbine, resumed four days ahead of the planned programme. It is interesting to note that, due to an overlap between SSN and SSBN programmes, circumstances dictated SMITE would run trials on the main machinery of the

A Trident Class boat exiting the Yard via the dock system.

last Trafalgar Class boat (SSN19-*Triumph*) at the same time as the *Trident* prototype. The combined power output was apparently considerably in excess of anything previously experienced in Yard engine trials – about the equivalent of a small power station.

Vanguard (SSBN05) tribulations came to light following acceptance when it was revealed by the navy to a Commons Defence Select Committee that: torpedoes could not be fired because of the late arrival of computer software, during sea trials the sonar towed array fell off, and the main sonar array was several years late in delivery. Most importantly, however, the navy stated that none of those concerns could be attributed to the Yard as they were all the responsibility of outside contractors.

Possibly less serious (the Yard was quite amused by the pre-emptive launch) was the loss of two hull sections being transported by cargo vessel from the Clyde to the Barrow Yard. The vessel, the *Skellig Rock*, was caught in heavy weather and lost the first section in almost 200ft of water off the Mull of Galloway. The second section was lost in 50ft of water off the coast of Barrow's Walney Island.

Commenting on media headlines stating: 'Experts aim to raise *Trident* parts lost at sea', a Yard spokesman said of the matter that: 'Salvage or write-off costs will not be borne by VSEL – transport is a matter for the manufacturer and their insurers.' Those lost sections (which would eventually be made good) were destined for the Devonshire Dock Hall (the DDH, or Hall). All sections of hull and superstructure, and a vast variety of seats, supports and ancillary steelwork would, by one means or another, eventually find their way to the Hall – there to be positioned and welded into the configuration that would finally produce a finished hull.

★ ★ ★

One of the first sections of *Trident*, a 12m diameter hull ring weighing a little over 80 tons was used in a time trial. The trial was to establish approximately how long the transport of units and sections from the Assembly Shed to the Hall would take, utilising a main thoroughfare of the town. The trial was arranged so that Yard staff, police and council representatives could study re-routing requirements for traffic, bus services and, more importantly, emergency services during the transport of loads.

★ ★ ★

In a construction programme which the government of the time described as 'the biggest, most complex and expensive in Western Europe', one of the more unusual aspects would occur in the spring of 1985, some twelve months prior to the contract award of *Trident*. The reactor primary system and engine room, for the Rolls-Royce designed PWR2 reactor, was built by the Yard and installed into a hull section on the building berth.

The 1,300-ton unit was then 'launched' and shipped on a semi-submersible barge some 380 miles to Sandside Bay in the north of Scotland. The reactor unit's ultimate destination was the Vulcan Naval Reactor Test Establishment at Dounreay. Towing and transport, which included a last over-land mile on air bags on a specially prepared 'road' was undertaken by Smit Internationale, Dutch ocean towing and lifting specialists.

Vengeance, the last of the class, had an extra nine months added to her build programme due to a series of major changes and upgrades requested by the MoD. This is a prime example of the continuous improvement made throughout the life of a class. The final approximate cost of each submarine in the Trident Class was £550 million.

★ ★ ★

The complexity of just some of a Trident boat's main equipment can be judged by reference to the Main Characteristics listed below. Here though are some more facts to go with those characteristics:

• Trident's great size permits the housing of the navy's largest reactor and sixteen missile tubes. It also affords the crews a slightly more luxurious accommodation than the SSNs.

• The hull contains approximately 21,000 lengths of electrical cable totalling some 300 miles in length and around 1.5 miles of ventilation trunking.

• Lowering a Trident boat on the shiplift for 'dunking' (i.e. launch) took approximately 1½ hours at 8in (0.20m) per minute.

• Rolling the boat out of the DDH on the bogies (wheeled cars) took approximately 2½ hours at 1yd (0.91m) per minute.

• Approximately 87,000 noise-reducing tiles cover the hull of each boat.

• Despite the 'finish' of the Cold War the navy has continued to find roles for the Trident boats which have involved a variety of trials, surveys and exercises. It might be considered that the demise of the Cold War was directly due to the existence of the Trident Class boats, that they achieved their desired solution by their very existence.

Trident Class Submarines – Main Characteristics

Overall Length/ Beam/Draught	149.9m x 12.8m x 12m
Displacement	15,900 submerged
Power	1 x Rolls-Royce PWR2 reactor
	2 x GEC turbines (27,500bhp)
	2 x W.H. Allen Turbo-generators (6MW)
	2 x Paxman diesel alternators (2,700bhp)
Diving Depth	In excess of 1,000ft
Speed	Surface speed unknown / 25 knots submerged
Propeller	1 x pump-jet propulsor
	2 x auxiliary retractable propulsion motors
Endurance	Unknown
Armament/ Electronics	4 x 21in torpedo tubes in bow (for Spearfish torpedoes
	16 x Lockhead Trident 2 (D5) three-stage solid fuel rockets
	1 x Type 2054 (Marconi/Plessey) composite multi-frequency sonar suite (incorporating 1 x Type 1007 surface-search and navigation radar, 1 x Type 2043 passive search and intercept hull sonar, 1 x Type 2082 passive intercept and ranging sonar, and 1 x Type 2046 towed array passive sonar)
	1 x Dowty Sema SMCS
	1 x Dowty tactical control system SAFS 3 FCS
	Extensive communication and navigation systems
	Various decoys
Complement	135

Open Hall Hours

The above headline was used by Barrow's *Evening Mail* on 17 April 1990 to report an unusual event involving the Trident Class submarines. The article is reproduced in part here:

> *Love it or hate it, for almost five years VSEL's massive Devonshire Dock Hall has dominated the town. Yesterday it yielded up some of its secrets to the Barrovians who queued up for a privileged tour. For the first time they had a chance to see inside the hall where the first two Trident submarines are taking shape. Some 6,000 shipyard employees and families were invited to look around in the first goodwill exercise of its kind ever attempted by VSEL. The visit to the normally busy hall was only possible because work had slowed down for the bank holiday. Even so, security men were plentiful and visitors kept to a strict route. Sensitive parts of the submarine were hidden from public view. Inside the hall, the air hums from the air conditioning and the overhead cranes move slowly up and down. Light filters down from the roof windows and lamps. Lying on one side of the hall, stretched from one end to the other and surrounded by scaffolding and pipes is* Vanguard, *the first of the Trident submarines. Most people stop to gaze at it for some time. Still in sections, but well on the way towards completion, it is an impressive sight.*

A Trident Class submarine undergoing night-time basin trials in Devonshire Dock, immediately outside of Devonshire Dock Hall.

Its finish date is classified information, VSEL press officer Mike Smith explains. The huge grey shape of Vanguard *dwarfs the last of the Trafalgar Class subs,* Triumph, *being built alongside her. Also taking shape is* Victorious, *sitting behind* Triumph *on the other side of the hall. With a 15,000-ton displacement the Tridents are three times the weight of the Trafalgar Class subs. When she is ready to be launched, little trolley jacks will move the submarine to the centre of the hall, where she can be rolled onto the shiplift. Parts of all four Tridents are under construction, even though the final one has not yet been put out to tender.*

The idea of a public open day was not a new one. A Barrow leisure chief had tried a similar idea some twelve years earlier in 1988, suggesting in a letter written to a local government journal 'Why not have a tour of Vickers' great shipbuilding and engineering plants?'. The suggestion was later floated by a government tourism minister in a speech. At the time a VSEL press officer described the idea as a non-starter.

The Case of the Stolen Tiles

Much has been made of the efforts to reduce radiated noise, but equal effort has gone into reducing the active sonar signal – the 'ping' rebounding from a hull.

One method to reduce that signal has been the development of an anechoic coating for the outside of the hull, usually applied in tile form. That and the internal application of decoupling material is a routine practice undertaken by most submarine-operating navies. Routine as the practice may be, the nature of the materials used and their design remains a closely guarded secret amongst the practitioners. What follows is the story of an attempt by two Barrow men to sell an anechoic tile of the type used on the Royal Navy's SSNs, SSBNs and SSKs.

The story commences with the remand in custody of the men, who were charged under Section One of the Official Secrets Act at a special hearing before Barrow magistrates on Thursday 11 October 1990. The charge was that, on 1 October 1990, for a purpose prejudicial to the safety of interests of the state, they communicated to another person a photograph which was intended to be directly or indirectly useful to an enemy, contrary to Section One of the Official Secrets Act.

The seriousness of the charge required the matter to be held in Preston Crown Court and it was little wonder that in view of the national prominence being given to the subject, the prosecution were giving consideration to applying for the trial to be held in camera, with the press and public barred.

To the charges invoked – 'conspiring to contravene the 1911 Official Secrets Act by seeking to publish or communicate an article or information which was directly or indirectly useful to an enemy' – both men pleaded not guilty.

One of the pair also denied 'theft of an acoustic tile from VSEL', while the other denied a charge of handling the tile knowing or believing it to be stolen.

There would be several more adjournments and a lengthy police investigation before the matter would be brought to a conclusion in July 1991.

By that time both men had pleaded guilty to a charge under the 1989 Official Secrets Act of making a damaging disclosure to a foreign power, with one of the pair pleading guilty to theft of an acoustic tile from VSEL, and the other pleading guilty to handling the tile and knowing or believing it to be stolen. This considerable reduction in the seriousness of the charges was brought about by, as the prosecution explained, the Crown agreeing to charge the men under the 1989 Act rather than the more serious 1911 Act under authority from the Attorney General, as 'the defendants gave no thought to the real gravity of what they were doing.' Additionally, there would be no application by the prosecution for the trial to be held in camera as it was not expected that anything revealed could prejudice national security.

The facts are as follows:

The two men, who shall be known by their prison nicknames – 'Perestroika' and 'Glasnost', decided to offer the tile for money to Russia. The tile had been acquired with relative ease by 'Perestroika', an ex-VSEL security guard who was, when in that role, in a position of special trust.

The pair obtained a phone number (via directory enquiries) for the Soviet Embassy and offered for sale, at £3 million, what 'Perestroika' described as 'a rubber tile that goes on the outside of a submarine'. The Soviet contact asked the purpose of the tile and 'Perestroika' said 'I don't know, they just stick them on submarines.'

They made phone contact with a Russian official of the Soviet Trade Delegation and the official gave his name as Alexander Madrichyk, but, after a trap was laid by Special Branch and the security services, they finally made their deal with a British agent.

The (then) Cumbria CID chief described how 'Perestroika' made phone contact with the embassy on six occasions but nevertheless categorised the pair not as 'spies or traitors' but as 'two greedy men motivated by greed.'

The chief disclosed that the police were alerted to the situation by a tip-off but declined to identify the source. Speculation as to how Britain's secret service picked up the Embassy calls centred on the signals intelligence facility, GCHQ, Cheltenham.

Defence experts believe that key words, such as submarine, are picked up from calls monitored at specific locations.

Police investigations commenced with the checking of records of thousands of Yard employees who could have been involved with tiles and then moved on to the aspects of former employees whereupon 'Perestroika's' name topped the list.

The security services then placed a series of advertisements in the *Barrow Evening Mail* asking a 'John Stuart' (the alias 'Perestroika' had used with the Soviets) not to call London numbers but to get in touch with Alexander M via a given phone number or mailbox number.

The advertisements were considered by many of the *Mail's* readers to be of a coded sexual nature and were eventually considered to be unsuitable for publication by the paper who considered it their duty to protect the Furness public from this kind of advertisement. The ban clearly did nothing to upset the Secret Service's trap.

On 10 July 1991 the trial judge Mr Justice Brooke was 'carefully handed the plain, one-foot square tile at the centre of the court room drama', while the two men who tried to sell it to the Soviets sat silently in the dock. At 11.30 a.m. the two men were each sentenced to fifteen months imprisonment.

According to some defence experts, if 'Perestroika' and 'Glasnost' had succeeded in their ploy 'the Russians could have gained vital information about British submarines. Laboratory analysis would have revealed the formula which allowed the foot-square tiles to absorb sonar sound waves making the vessels sitting ducks for enemy detectors.'

In view of those last remarks many considered the sentences to be remarkably lenient.

These three small ads were placed by the British Secret Service, and *Evening Mail* tele-ad manager Linda McCoy thought they 'looked funny'. *(Microfilm Archives)*

Astute Class Submarines

3 to be built on behalf of the Royal Navy

> *Dear John*
> *I am sorry to have to advise you that, following analysis of the two bids received in response to the invitation to tender for the design, build and initial support of up to three Batch 2 Trafalgar Class (B2TC) submarines, our intention is to take the bid from GEC-Marconi forward to the next stage of the B2TC and Swiftsure and Trafalgar Update programme. I know that this will be disappointing news for VSEL, that their design is not the preferred option; it will be for GEC as their parent company to determine the eventual apportionment of work on the B2TC.*
> *Yours ever,*
> *James Arbuthnot.*
>
> Letter from Defence Procurement Minister James Arbuthnot
> to John Hutton (Barrow's MP) dated 20 December 1995

Astute	(Yard No.1122)	Not yet built
Ambush	(Yard No.1123)	Not yet built
Artful	(Yard No.1124)	Not yet built

To date three Astute Class submarines have been ordered by the Royal Navy, but it is widely thought that an order for a further three will follow, with the potential for a further three after that, giving a total of nine. These are also to be built at the Barrow Yard.

Astute, originally scheduled to enter service in 2005, and the rest of her class, could be the last boats of their kind if MoD predictions on the alternative means of delivering what a submarine does come to fruition. The navy is forecasting a new generation of unmanned submersible weaponry will provide a considerable portion of their capability needs. Apparently the word 'submarine' is no longer used when determining plans for the type of underwater vessels expected to enter service around 2025.

In a project titled 'Maritime Underwater Future Capability' it is envisaged a range of what will be known as 'Unmanned Underwater Vehicles' (UUVs) will replace and exceed much of the role the Astutes are designed to fulfil. UUVs are seen as being brought into action by warships, aircraft or even a manned boat which could be responsible for monitoring and directing the UUVs in such tasks as the detection and destruction of remotely armed weapons, intelligence gathering and surveillance missions and torpedo, mine or missile attack. The Yard owners BAE do not rule out that manufacturing capacity could, in twenty to twenty-five years' time, be dedicated to producing UUVs – a task in which their aerospace skills would certainly come to the fore.

BAE have confirmed they will be working in partnership with the navy and MoD to see how best to apply new technology, but security and research requirements preclude more meaningful comment. That is possibly the future – the present is *Astute*.

By October 2000, and within nine months of the departure of the last Trident boat, HMS *Vengeance*, leaving the Barrow dock system, the first of the new class of hunter-killer was under construction with the hull section for the reactor compartment almost complete along with the forward dome end. What is an Astute boat? Well, according to its website it is 'the next generation SSN, the largest and most powerful attack submarine ever ordered for the Royal Navy, designed for littoral, deep sea or ocean deployment worldwide.' In early 2001 Defence Procurement Minister Baroness Symons presided at the first-of-class keel laying and advised that following *Astute* would be four more boats with a decision to be made on a sixth boat in 2002, by which time *Ambush* would be well into her construction phase and *Artful* commencing hers.

The MoD believes the Astute programme will provide employment for 5,000 people, including Yard personnel and the main sub-contractors, and that the bill for each boat will be £745 million. Although based on the Trafalgar Class, the Astute boats are nevertheless almost one third bigger. Their designers have discarded the previous philosophy of designing a boat as small as possible to improve performance following studies which showed a larger boat would be easier and cheaper to build and maintain than previous classes. Also it would be easier to install the new, bigger reactor. What the navy gets for £745 million should please them when a comparison is made against the Trafalgar Class.

The Astutes are scheduled to be built 20% faster and through-life costs are calculated at 10% less. Immense improvements in machinery and electronics technology will allow a proposed complement of 100 to operate the boat and the complement will have much-improved accommodation. A single core – Core H – Mark 2 pressurised water reactor (PWR2) will drive the boat throughout her service life – estimated to be twenty-five to thirty years. This cuts out costly and time-consuming refuelling and much reduces environmental impacts. *Astute* will have the latest in command and sensing systems, and will be both stealthier and much harder to detect than its predecessors. One of a number of innovative systems to be used, is the use in some areas of the boat of 'floating decks'. The US Navy has been a long-time user of such a system but it is a first for the Royal Navy. There is a 50% increase in fire

An artist's impression of the Royal Navy's latest submarine (the Astute Class) which will be constructed at the Barrow Shipyard.

power, there being six torpedo tubes (as against five in the Trafalgar boats) and a mix of thirty-eight weapons available which includes different types of torpedo and Tomahawk land attack cruise missiles. Non hull penetrating optronic periscopes are also fitted to the Astute boats.

The immense technical challenges posed in the design and construction of an Astute boat makes them some of the most complex products on earth, where the level of technical expertise required ranges – to quote in the most general fashion – from the absolute state-of-the-art software engineering and control systems to flawless welding in the pressure hull. In mentioning the pressure hull, BAE were reporting that its welding was exceeding the high standard set on *Trident*. Not only is the welding faster but the defect rate is reduced to 11mm in every 600m. Both BAE and the MoD run websites for those wishing to keep updated on the Astute Class construction.

Notwithstanding the above comment, the construction programme was dramatically curtailed in late 2002 as failure to make a satisfactory transition from existing CAD/drawing/model-based systems to a total CAD system manifested itself. Both BAE and the MoD agreed that they had drastically underestimated the problems that had arisen. In 2003, agreement was made with Electric Boat, which had undergone a similar and equally traumatic experience on their Sea Wolf programme, for the provision of assistance in overcoming the problems.

The programme may be delayed by three years.

Astute Class Submarines – Main Characteristics

Overall Length/ Beam/Draught	97 metres x 10.4 metres x 11 metres
Displacement	6,500 tons (surfaced/7,200 tons (submerged)
Power	1 x Rolls-Royce PWR2 (Core H) nuclear reactor
	2 x GEC turbines
	2 x diesel alternators
	2 x motors for emergency drive
Diving Depth	Unknown
Speed	Surface speed unknown / 29 knots submerged
Propeller	1 x pump-jet propulsor
	1 x auxiliary retractable propeller
Endurance	Unknown
Armament/ Electronics	6 x 21in torpedo tubes for missiles and Spearfish torpedo – total of 36 carried
	BAE Sema SMCS Combat Data System
	Sub Harpoon Surface-to-Surface Missiles
	Tomahawk Block III Submarine Launched Cruise Missiles
	Countermeasures – ESM, Decoys
	I-Band Navigation Radar
	Thompson Sintra Type 2076 Sonar
Complement	100 (including 12 officers)
Notes	Astute is classed as an evolving design. These characteristics may change.

Appendix 1
Barrow-Built Submarines at a Glance

Nordenfelt Submarines

Yard No.143   *Nordenfelt I*   Launched 14 April 1886

The first submarine boat built at Barrow. Commissioned into the Turkish Navy on 3 April 1888 as *Abdul Hamid* but considered too dangerous to be used operationally. Ended life as a rusting hulk. Scrapped in 1921.

Yard No.149   *Nordenfelt II*   Launched 26 March 1887

Wrecked off the coast of Jutland during transit to Russia where it was to take part in trials and demonstrations for the Russian Navy. Bought by the insurers and disposed of as scrap.

Holland Class Submarines

Yard No.280   HMS *Holland 1*   Launched 2 October 1901

Completed 1902. The first submarine in the Royal Navy. Sold for scrap to T.W. Ward in 1913 but foundered while under tow to the breakers yard. Raised in 1982 and now displayed at the Royal Navy Submarine Museum, Gosport.

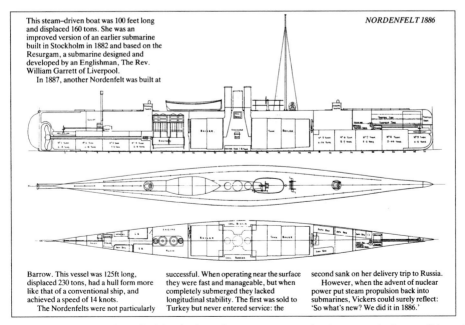

This steam-driven boat was 100 feet long and displaced 160 tons. She was an improved version of an earlier submarine built in Stockholm in 1882 and based on the Resurgam, a submarine designed and developed by an Englishman, The Rev. William Garrett of Liverpool.

In 1887, another Nordenfelt was built at Barrow. This vessel was 125ft long, displaced 230 tons, had a hull form more like that of a conventional ship, and achieved a speed of 14 knots.

The Nordenfelts were not particularly successful. When operating near the surface they were fast and manageable, but when completely submerged they lacked longitudinal stability. The first was sold to Turkey but never entered service: the second sank on her delivery trip to Russia.

However, when the advent of nuclear power put steam propulsion back into submarines, Vickers could surely reflect: 'So what's new? We did it in 1886.'

NORDENFELT 1886

An engineering drawing of *Nordenfelt I*, the first submarine constructed at the Barrow-in-Furness Shipyard.

HMS *Holland 2* with several of her crew posing in going-ashore gear. *(Barrow Museum Service CAT 3441)*

Yard No.281   HMS *Holland 2*   Launched 21 January 1902
Sold for scrap to Pollack & Brown in 1913.

Yard No.283   HMS *Holland 3*   Launched 9 May 1902
Sold for scrap to Ryadyk in 1913.

Yard No.284   HMS *Holland 4*   Launched 23 May 1902
Deliberately sunk by gunfire experiments in October 1912.

Yard No.282   HMS *Holland 5*   Launched 10 June 1902
Foundered under tow to breakers in 1912.

First A Class Submarines

Yard No.285   HMS A1   Launched 9 July 1902
First all-British designed and built submarine to serve with the Royal Navy. Originally laid down as *Holland 6*. Sunk in collision off Portsmouth 1904. Later raised and used for target practice and sunk in 1910. Relocated in 1988 with consideration for raising.

Yard No.294   HMS A2   Launched 16 April 1903
Dismantled in 1920 after grounding in Bomb Ketch Lake (Portsmouth). Sold in 1925 to Pounds of Portsmouth.

Yard No.295   HMS A3   Launched 9 May 1903
Sunk in collision with HMS *Hazard* off Isle of Wight in 1912. Salvaged and used as target and sunk in 1912.

Yard No.296   HMS A4   Launched 9 June 1903
Sunk by steamer wash off Portsmouth 1905. Raised, sank again, and raised and sunk in gunfire experiments in 1912. Salvaged again in 1920 and sold to J.Lee of Bembridge.

Yard No.303   HMS A5   Launched 3 March 1904
Dismantled in 1920 at Portsmouth Dockyard.

Yard No.304   HMS A6   Launched 3 March 1904
Sold for scrap in 1920 to J.Lee of Bembridge.

Yard No.305   HMS A7   Launched 23 January 1905
Foundered inexplicably off Plymouth on 16 January 1914. After unsuccessful efforts were made to raise her, the burial service was held at sea 12 March 1914.

Yard No.306   HMS A8   Launched 23 January 1905
Sank in 1905 with loss of crew. Recommissioned and continued in service until it was sold for scrap in 1920. Scrapped by Philips of Dartmouth.

Yard No.307   HMS A9   Launched 8 February 1905
Discarded in 1919 or 1920.

Yard No.308   HMS A10   Launched 8 February 1905
Sold for scrap in 1919 to Ardrossan Dockyard Co., Scotland.

Yard No.309   HMS A11   Launched 8 March 1905
Scrapped in 1920 at Portsmouth.

Yard No.310   HMS A12   Launched 8 March 1905
Sold for scrap in 1920 to J.Lee of Bembridge.

Yard No.311   HMS A13   Launched 18 April 1905
Fitted with Hornsby-Ackroyd heavy oil engine. Discarded in 1920.

B Class Submarines

Yard No.312   HMS B1   Launched 25 October 1904
Laid down as HMS A14. Sold for scrap in 1922 to Smith's of Poole.

Yard No.320   HMS B2   Launched 19 August 1905
Sunk in collision with the SS *Amerika* off Dover in 1912.

Yard No.321   HMS B3   Launched 1 September 1905
Sold for scrap 1919 to J. Jackson.

Yard No.322   HMS B4   Launched 31 October 1905
Reported variously as sold for scrap in 1919, and lost prior to 1914. It is generally believed to have been sold to Ardrossan Dockyard Co., Scotland in 1919.

Yard No.323   HMS B5   Launched 14 November 1905
Sold for scrap in 1922 to Smith's of Poole.

Yard No.324   HMS B6   Launched 30 November 1905
Sold for scrap in Italy in 1919.

Yard No.325   HMS B7   Launched 30 November 1905
Sold for scrap at Malta in 1919.

Yard No.326   HMS B8   Launched 23 January 1906
Sold for scrap in 1919.

Yard No.327   HMS B9   Launched 26 January 1906
Sold for scrap in Italy in 1919.

Yard No.328   HMS B10   Launched 28 March 1906
Bombed and sunk in dock at Venice by an Austrian aircraft, 9 August 1916. Later raised then scrapped. B10 was at one time under the command of Lt C.W. Craven, later a Vickers chairman.

Yard No.329   HMS B11   Launched 24 February 1906
On 13 December 1914, when under the command of Lt-Com. Holbrook, she dived under some five rows of mines and torpedoed the Turkish battleship *Messoudieh* in the Dardanelles, for which Holbrook was awarded the VC. In 1919 she was sold for scrap in Italy.

C Class Submarines

Yard No.334   HMS C1   Launched 10 July 1906
Was filled with dynamite and scheduled to be blown up 23 April 1918 at Zeebrugge Mole, but was spared because, due to navigational errors, she did not make the rendezvous. Sold for scrap in 1921 to Young's of Sunderland.

Yard No.335   HMS C2   Launched 10 July 1906
Sold for scrap in 1921 to Madden & McKee.

Yard No.336   HMS C3   Launched 3 October 1906
Filled with explosive and blown up to destroy the viaduct at Zeebrugge Mole on 23 April 1918 (St George's Day) in a daring and hazardous raid which would see her CO, Lt R.D. Sandford, awarded the VC.

Yard No.337   HMS C4   Launched 18 October 1906
Sold for scrap in 1922 to Hollamshire Metal Co.

Yard No.338   HMS C5   Launched 20 August 1906
Scrapped at Malta in 1919.

Yard No.339   HMS C6   Launched 20 August 1906
Sold for scrap in 1919 to J.A. Walker.

Yard No.340   HMS C7   Launched 15 February 1907
On 5 April 1917 she torpedoed and sank UC-68 off Schouwen, Holland, and in November
of the same year U-63. She was sold for scrap in 1919 to J. Jackson.

Yard No.341   HMS C8   Launched 15 February 1907
Sold for scrap in 1921 to Young's of Sunderland.

Yard No.342   HMS C9   Launched 3 April 1907
Sold for scrap in 1922 to Stanlee.

Yard No.343   HMS C10   Launched 15 April 1907
Sold for scrap in 1922 to Stanlee.

Yard No.346   HMS C11   Launched 17 May 1907
Sunk in collision with SS *Eddystone* off Cromer in 1909.

Yard No.351   HMS C12   Launched 9 September 1907
Sank in 1916 following collision after main motors failed. Raised within a few days and re-
commissioned. Scrapped in 1920 by J.H. Lee.

Yard No.352   HMS C13   Launched 14 January 1907
Sold for scrap in 1920 to J.H. Lee.

Yard No.353   HMS C14   Launched 7 December 1907
Sank after collision with a hopper in Plymouth Sound in 1913. Sold for scrap in 1921 to C.A.
Beard of Upnor.

Yard No.354   HMS C15   Launched 21 January 1908
Torpedoed and sank UC-65 in Dover Straits 3 November 1917. Sold for scrap in 1922 to
Hallamshire Metal Co.

Yard No.355   HMS C16   Launched 19 March 1908
In 1922 she was accidentally rammed and sunk by a British destroyer, HMS *Melampus*. After
being salvaged she was declared a constructive total loss and sold to C.A. Beard of Upnor.

Yard No.375   HMS C21   Launched 26 September 1908
Sold for scrap in 1921 to C.A. Beard of Upnor.

Yard No.376   HMS C22   Launched 10 October 1908
Sold for scrap in 1920 to J.H. Lee.

Yard No.377   HMS C23   Launched 26 November 1908
Sold for scrap in 1921 to C.A. Beard of Upnor.

Yard No.378   HMS C24   Launched 26 November 1908
On 23 June 1918 she torpedoed and sank U–40 some fifty miles SE by S of Girdle Ness. Sold for scrap in 1921 to B. Fryer of Sunderland.

Yard No.379   HMS C25   Launched 10 March 1909
Sold for scrap 1921 to C.A. Beard of Upnor.

Yard No.380   HMS C26   Launched 20 March 1909
Blown up at Helsingfors to avoid capture by the advancing Germans on 4 April 1918. Salvaged in August 1953 and scrapped in Finland.

Yard No.381   HMS C27   Launched 22 April 1909
On 20 July 1915, in conjunction with the trawler *Princess Louise*, she sank U–23 off Fair Isle. She was blown up to avoid capture at Helsingfors 5 April 1918.

Yard No.382   HMS C28   Launched 22 April 1909
Sold for scrap in 1921 to B. Fryer of Sunderland.

Yard No.383   HMS C29   Launched 19 June 1909
Sunk after being towed into a minefield by the trawler *Ariadne* on 29 August 1915.

Yard No.384   HMS C30   Launched 19 July 1909
Sold for scrap in 1921 to B. Fryer of Sunderland.

Yard No.387   HMS C31   Launched 2 September 1909
Lost 4 January 1915 off the Belgian coast. Cause unknown.

Yard No.388   HMS C32   Launched 29 September 1909
Stranded in the Gulf of Riga and blown up to avoid capture in October 1917.

Yard No.391   HMS C35   Launched 25 May 1909
Blown up at Helsingfors to avoid capture 5 April 1918.

Yard No.392   HMS C36   Launched 30 November 1909
Scrapped in China 1919.

Yard No.393   HMS C37   Launched 12 January 1910
Scrapped in China 1919.

Yard No.394   HMS C38   Launched 10 February 1910
Scrapped in China 1919.

D Class Submarines

Yard No.350   HMS D1   Launched 16 May 1908
Sunk as a target 23 October 1918.

Yard No.390   HMS D2   Launched 25 October 1910
Her captain was swept overboard and drowned on 23 November 1914. She was lost in late 1914 in the North Sea, cause unknown, but possibly due to mining or gunfire from a German patrol vessel.

Yard No.403   HMS D3   Launched 17 October 1910
On 15 March 1918 she was bombed and sunk in error by a French airship in the English Channel.

Yard No.404   HMS D4   Launched 27 May 1910
The first British submarine to mount a gun. In 1918 she torpedoed and sank UB-72 in the English Channel. She was sold for scrap in 1921 to H. Pounds.

Yard No.405   HMS D5   Launched 28 August 1911
On 3 November 1914 she was sunk by a mine thrown out by a German warship whilst engaged in chasing raiders off Great Yarmouth.

Yard No.406   HMS D6   Launched 25 October 1912
On 28 June 1918 she was sunk by a U-boat (UB-73) off Northern Ireland.

Japanese Submarines

Yard No.366   No.8   Launched 19 May 1908
Built for the Imperial Japanese Navy. Later, in 1924, was designated HA 1. Broken up in 1928.

Yard No.367   No.9   Launched 19 May 1909
Built for the Imperial Japanese Navy. Later, in 1924, was designated HA 2. Broken up in 1928.

E Class Submarines

Yard No.415   HMS E3   Launched 29 October 1912
Fate unknown but sunk on 18 October 1914 by either U-27 off Borkum or SMS *Strassburg* in the Heligoland Bight. The wreck was found in the North Sea off the island of Schiermonnikoog in 1997.

Yard No.416   HMS E4   Launched 5 February 1912

Collided while submerged with E41 which was surfaced on 15 August 1916 off Harwich. All hands lost in this incident. Salvaged and re-commissioned in May 1917. Sold for scrap in 1922 to Upnor Shipbreaking Co.

Yard No.417   HMS E5   Launched 17 February 1912

In December 1915 she sank an armed cruiser off Borkum. She was herself sunk 7 March 1916 in the North Sea by the German cruiser *Strassburg*.

Yard No.418   HMS E6   Launched 12 November 1912

Mined and sunk in the North Sea 26 December 1915.

Yard No.430   HMS E9   Launched 29 November 1913

On 13 September 1914 she torpedoed and sank the German 2,040-ton cruiser *Hela* six miles south of Heligoland. On 6 October 1914 she sank the German destroyer S116 off the mouth of the River Ems. On 28 January 1915 she torpedoed a destroyer three miles east of Moens Klint, Denmark. She torpedoed the destroyer G 194 on 4 June 1915 between Windau and Gothland, and on 7 July 1915 the destroyer S191 in the Baltic. A transport was also sunk in the Baltic on 2 August 1915, and on 18 October 1915 sank the German transport *Pernabuco* off Oxelosund. She torpedoed the destroyer V191 in the Baltic on 17 December 1915. She was finally blown up at Helsingfors to avoid capture on 3 April 1918.

Yard No.431   HMS E10   Launched 29 December 1913

Lost in the North Sea 18 January 1915.

Yard No.432   HMS E11   Launched 25 April 1914

On 22 May 1915 she torpedoed and sank the 880-ton Turkish gunboat *Pelenk-I-Deria* southwest of Seraglio Point, Istanbul. On 2 June 1915 she sank two transports and forced another ashore in the Sea of Marmora, then penetrated the defences of Istanbul to torpedo another transport alongside the Naval Arsenal. She torpedoed the 10,000-ton battleship *Kheiredin Barbarossa* some five miles off Istanbul in the Gulf of Ismid on 8 August 1915. Her next conquest was the 290-ton destroyer *Yar Hissar* on 3 December 1915 in the Sea of Marmora. She was sold for scrap at Malta in 1921.

Yard No.438   HMS E14   Launched 7 July 1914

On 29 April 1915 she torpedoed and sank the Turkish gunboat *Peik-I-Shevket* in the Bosporus Narrows. On 1 May 1915 she sank the 200-ton gunboat *Nurelbahr* in the Sea of Marmora, and on 3 May 1915 torpedoed the 500-ton transport *Gul-Djemal* which was fully laden with troops at the time. Under the command of Lt-Com. A.C. Boyle in 1915 she also sank a transport and two gunboats (an act for which Boyle was awarded the VC). On 27 January 1918 (by now under the command of Lt-Com. G.S. White) she was sunk by gunfire off Kum Kaleh, there being only seven survivors. White himself was killed during this incident but was posthumously awarded the VC.

Yard No.439   HMS E15   Launched 23 April 1914
In 1915 she torpedoed and sank the German destroyer V188 in the North Sea. On 18 April 1915 she was stranded near Kephez Point, Dardanelles, and torpedoed by the picket boats HMS *Triumph* and HMS *Majestic* to avoid capture.

Yard No.440   HMS E16   Launched 23 September 1914
In 1915 she torpedoed and sank U-6 off Stavanger, and on 26 July 1915 torpedoed the destroyer V188 off the German coast. She also accounted for a minelayer in the Heligoland Bight on 22 December 1915. She was herself sunk in the Heligoland Bight by mine on 22 August 1916.

Yard No.452   HMS E17   Launched 16 January 1915
Wrecked off Texel 6 January 1916. The conning tower is preserved at the Royal Naval Submarine Museum, Gosport.

Yard No.453   HMS E18   Launched 4 March 1915
Sunk in surface action with the German Q ship (SMS K) in the Baltic 24 May 1916.

Yard No.470   HMS E19   Launched 13 May 1915
The first addition to the navy's war effort, she was built, launched, completed and delivered inside eight months. On 13 October 1915 she torpedoed and sank a German destroyer off Moen Island, Denmark, and then, on 7 November 1915, sank the 2,715-ton German cruiser *Undine* twenty-two miles off Trelleberg, Sweden. She was blown up at Helsingfors to avoid capture 3 April 1918 and was found by civilian divers in August 2001.

Yard No.471   HMS E20   Launched 12 June 1915
Torpedoed in the Sea of Marmara 6 November 1915 by UB-14. E20 was ambushed by UB-40 following the capture of the French submarine *Turquoise* which failed to destroy secret documents containing details of rendezvous and patrol activities of Allied vessels.

Yard No.472   HMS E21   Launched 24 June 1915
Sold for scrap in 1921 to Peterson & Albeck.

Yard No.473   HMS E22   Launched 27 August 1915
Torpedoed in the North Sea by UB-18 on 25 April 1916.

Yard No.474   HMS E23   Launched 28 September 1915
In August 1916 she torpedoed and sank the 18,900-ton German battleship *Westfalen*, in the North Sea. Sold for scrap in 1922 to Young's of Sunderland.

Yard No.475   HMS E24   Launched 9 December 1915
Mined and sunk in the Heligoland Bight 24 March 1916. The first of the class to be built as a minelayer.

Yard No.419   HMAS AE1   Launched 22 May 1913
Built for the Royal Australian Navy. On 14 September 1914 she struck an uncharted reef and sank off the Bismarck Archipelago. The first Allied submarine to be lost during the First World War.

Yard No.420   HMAS AE2   Launched 18 June 1913
Sunk by the gunfire of Turkish warships in the Sea of Marmara on 30 April 1915.

First V Class Submarines

Yard No.437   HMS V1   Launched 23 July 1914
Sold for scrap in 1921 to J. Kelly.

Yard No.449   HMS V2   Launched 17 February 1915
Sold for scrap in 1921 to J. Kelly.

Yard No.450   HMS V3   Launched 1 April 1915
Completed 1916. Sold for scrap in 1920 to J.W. Towers.

Yard No.451   HMS V4   Launched 25 November 1915
Completed 1916. Sold for scrap in 1920 to J.W. Towers.

Experimental Submarine

Yard No.436   HMS *Nautilus*   Launched 16 December 1914
In 1918 she became a battery charging vessel, and was never operational. She was sold for scrap in 1922 to Cashmore.

G Class Submarines

Yard No.463   HMS G8   Launched 1 May 1916
Lost in the North Sea 14 January 1918. Cause unknown.

Yard No.464   HMS G9   Launched 15 June 1916
Sunk in error by HMS *Petard* off Norway 16 September 1917.

Yard No.465   HMS G10   Launched 11 January 1916
Sold for scrap in 1923 to J. Smith.

Yard No.466   HMS G11   Launched 22 February 1916
Wrecked off Harwich 22 November 1918.

Yard No.467   HMS G12   Launched 24 March 1916
Sold for scrap in 1923 to J.G. Potts.

Yard No.468   HMS G13   Launched 18 July 1916
On 10 March 1917 she torpedoed and sank UC-43 some nine miles northwest of Muckle Flugga Lighthouse, Shetland Islands. She was sold for scrap in 1923 to J. Smith.

K Class and K26 Submarines

Yard No.480   HMS K3   Launched 29 May 1916
Completed 1917. Sold for scrap in 1921 to Barking Shipbreaking Co.

Yard No.481   HMS K4   Launched 15 July 1916
Completed December 1916. On 31 January 1918 she was rammed and sunk by HMS *Inflexible* while engaged in tactical exercises, the same day as her sister K17 (Yard No.492) met the same fate.

Yard No.482   HMS K8   Launched 18 October 1916
Completed 1917. Sold for scrap in 1923 to MacClellan.

Yard No.483   HMS K9   Launched 8 November 1916
Completed 1917. Sold for scrap in 1926 to Alloa Shipbreaking Co., Charlestown.

Yard No.484   HMS K10   Launched 27 December 1916
Completed 1917. Sold for scrap in 1921.

Yard No.492   HMS K17   Launched 10 April 1917
On 31 January 1918 she was rammed and sunk on tactical exercises by HMS *Fearless*. See also K4 (Yard No.481).

Yard No.564   HMS K26   Launched 26 August 1919
Ordered April 1918. Laid down July 1918. Launched at Barrow but completed at Chatham May 1923. In 1924 she undertook a cruise to Colombo and back. She was sold for scrap at Malta in 1931.

L Class Submarines

Yard No.489   HMS L1   Launched 10 May 1917
Laid down as E57. Sold for scrap in 1930 to Cashmore.

Yard No.490   HMS L2   Launched 6 July 1917
Laid down as E58. Sold for scrap 1930 to Ward's of Grays.

HMS L1, L6, L2, L3 and L5 laying alongside HMS *Ambrose* submarine depot ship (camouflaged). (Campbell McCutcheon)

Yard No.495   HMS L3   Launched 1 September 1917
Sold for scrap in 1930 to Metal Industries of Charlestown.

Yard No.496   HMS L4   Launched 17 November 1917
Completed 1918. Sold for scrap in 1934 to Ward's of Grays.

Yard No.510   HMS L11   Launched 26 February 1918
Sold for scrap in 1932 to Young's of Sunderland.

Yard No.511   HMS L12   Launched 16 March 1918
In 1918 she torpedoed and sank UB-90 in the Skagerrak. She was sold for scrap in 1932 to Cashmore.

Yard No.512   HMS L17   Launched 13 May 1918
Sold for scrap in 1934 to Ward's of Pembroke Dock.

Yard No.513   HMS L14   Launched 19 June 1918
Sold for scrap in 1934 to Cashmore.

Yard No.533   HMS L18   Launched 21 November 1918
Sold for scrap in 1936 to Ward's of Pembroke Dock.

Yard No.534   HMS L19   Launched 4 February 1919
Sold for scrap in 1937 to Ward's of Pembroke Dock.

Yard No.535   HMS L20   Launched 23 September 1918
Sold for scrap in 1935 to Cashmore.

Yard No.536   HMS L21   Launched 11 October 1919
Completed 1920. Sold for scrap in 1939 to Arnott Young of Delmuir.

Yard No.537   HMS L22   Launched 25 October 1919
Completed 1921. Sold for scrap in 1935 to Cashmore.

Yard No.538   HMS L23   Launched 1 July 1919
Launched at Barrow but completed by Chatham Dockyard in 1923. In 1944 was sent to Canada for training purposes, and in May 1946 was lost whilst in tow to the breakers.

Yard No.539   HMS L24   Launched 13 February 1919
Completed 1920. Sunk in collision off Portland in January 1924 by the battleship HMS *Resolution*.

Yard No.540   HMS L25   Launched 19 February 1919
Launched at Barrow but completed 1927 by Sheerness Dockyard. Sold for scrap in 1935 to Cashmore.

Yard No.541   HMS L26   Launched 29 May 1919
Launched at Barrow but completed by Devonport Dockyard 1926. In 1944 was sent to Canada for training purposes. She was expended as an anti-submarine target 25 September 1945.

Yard No.542   HMS L27   Launched 14 June 1919
Launched at Barrow but completed by Sheerness Dockyard 1925. In 1944 she was sent to Canada for training purposes and was scrapped there in 1947.

Yard No.547   HMS L32   Launched 23 August 1919
Launched at Barrow but construction cancelled before completion. Sold as a hulk to Leith Salvage Co. of Edinburgh.

M Class Submarines

Yard No.491   HMS M1   Launched 9 July 1917
Laid down as K18. Sunk in collision off Start Point 12 November 1925.

Yard No.494   HMS M2   Launched 15 April 1919
Completed 1920. Laid down as K19. In 1927 she was altered to carry one seaplane. She foundered in 1932 off Portland.

HMS M1.

H Class Submarines

Yard No.499   HMS H21   Launched 20 October 1917
Ordered and laid down December 1916. Completed 1918. Sold for scrap in 1926 to Cashmore.

Yard No.500   HMS H22   Launched 7 September 1918
Ordered December 1916. Sold for scrap in 1935 to Alloa Shipbreaking Co. of Charlestown.

Yard No.501   HMS H23   Launched 29 January 1918
Ordered December 1916. Sold for scrap in 1934 to J. Young's of Sunderland.

Yard No.502   HMS H24   Launched 14 November 1917
Ordered December 1916. Sold for scrap in 1934 to J. Young's of Sunderland.

Yard No.503   HMS H25   Launched 27 April 1918
Ordered December 1916. Sold for scrap in 1935 to Alloa Shipbreaking Co. of Charlestown.

Yard No.504   HMS H26   Launched 15 November 1917
Ordered December 1916. Completed 1918. Sold for scrap in 1928 to Ward's of Pembroke Dock.

Yard No.527   HMS H27   Launched 25 September 1918
Sold for scrap in 1935 to Cashmore.

Yard No.528   HMS H28   Launched 12 March 1918
This boat conducted patrols in both the First and Second World Wars. Scrapped at Troon in August 1944.

Yard No.529   HMS H29   Launched 8 June 1918
In August 1926 she sank in Devonport Dockyard and, after being raised, was scrapped in 1927 by Ward's of Pembroke Dock.

Yard No.530   HMS H30   Launched 9 May 1918
Completed 21 February 1919. Sold for scrap in 1935 to Cashmore.

Yard No.531   HMS H31   Launched 16 November 1918
Completed 21 February 1919. Sank UJ-126 in the North Sea in July 1940. Mined in the Bay of Biscay 24 December 1941.

Yard No.532   HMS H32   Launched 19 November 1918
Scrapped at Troon in November 1944.

First R Class Submarines

Yard No.549   HMS R7   Launched 14 May 1918
Designed as the first hunter-killer submarine. Sold for scrap in 1923 to E. Suren.

Yard No.550   HMS R8   Launched 28 June 1918
Sold for scrap in 1923 to E. Suren.

O Class Submarines

Yard No.621   HMAS *Oxley*   Launched 29 June 1926
Completed 22 February 1927. Built for the Royal Australian Navy – returned to the Royal
Navy in 1931. She served in the Home Flotilla and was torpedoed and sunk in error
10 September 1939 off Norway by *Triton* (Yard No.716). Sadly she was the first Royal Navy
boat sunk in the Second World War (this was an awful coincidence as another Australian
submarine AE1 had suffered the same fate in the First World War).

Yard No.622   HMAS *Otway*   Launched 7 September 1926
Built for the Royal Australian Navy, and in 1931 was returned to the Royal Navy. After
serving in the Mediterranean she was scrapped at Inverkeithing by Thos W. Ward Ltd,
arriving there 24 August 1945.

Yard No.633   HMS *Osiris*   Launched 19 May 1928
Completed February 1929. On 14 August 1940 she torpedoed and sank the 3,296-ton Italian
steamship *Leopardi*, six miles east of Tolmetta in position 32.39N x 21.03E. In September
1940 she torpedoed the Italian destroyer *Palestro* in the Adriatic and in 1943 a caique. She
went to the Eastern theatre as a training ship, and was scrapped at Durban in September 1946.

Yard No.634   HMS *Oswald*   Launched 19 June, 1928
Completed 1 May 1929. Whilst serving in the Mediterranean, on 1 August 1940 she was
rammed and sunk ten miles south-east of Spartevento Bay by the Italian destroyer *Ugolino
Vivaldi*.

Yard No.635   HMS *Otus*   Launched 31 August 1928
Served in the East Indies, in 1940 going on to the Mediterranean, in 1942 to Home waters
and in 1943 to the South Atlantic for anti-submarine training purposes. She was scuttled off
Durban in September 1946.

Yard No.645   *Capitan O'Brien*   Launched 2 October 1928
Laid down 15 November 1927. Completed 19 June 1929. Built for the Chilean Navy.
Scrapped in 1958/1959.

Yard No.646   *Capitan Thompson*   Launched 15 January 1929
Laid down 15 November 1927. Completed 24 August 1929. Built for the Chilean Navy.
Scrapped in 1958/1959.

Yard No.647   *Almirante Simpson*   Launched 15 January 1929
Laid down 15 November 1927. Completed 14 September 1929. Built for the Chilean Navy.
Scrapped in 1958/1959.

P Class Submarines

Yard No.638   HMS *Perseus*   Launched 22 May 1929
Completed 15 April 1930. Served in China, and in 1940 went to the Mediterranean. According to the Allies she was mined 6 December 1941 off Zante, Western Greece, but the Germans say she was torpedoed by the Italian submarine *Enrico Toti* in the Mediterranean 19 December 1941.

Yard No.639   HMS *Poseidon*   Launched 21 June 1929
Sunk in collision 9 June 1931.

Yard No.640   HMS *Proteus*   Launched 23 July 1929
After serving in Chinese waters she served in the Mediterranean 1940 to 1943, after which she was used for training purposes in Home waters. She was scrapped at Troon, arriving there 26 February 1946. During her time in the Mediterranean she sank or damaged a total of eleven Italian transports.

Yard No.641   HMS *Pandora*   Launched 22 August 1929
Completed 30 June 1930. Laid down as *Python*. After serving in Chinese waters and going to the Mediterranean in 1940, she was bombed and sunk at Malta on either 31 March or 1 April 1942. In 1943 the wreck was raised and she was dismantled in 1957.

Second R Class Submarines

Yard No.653   HMS *Regent*   Launched 11 June 1930
Completed 11 November 1930. After serving in Chinese waters she was sent to the Mediterranean in 1940. She was mined and sunk in the Straits of Otranto 18 April 1943.

Yard No.654   HMS *Regulus*   Launched 11 June 1930
Completed 7 December 1930. She was sent to the Mediterranean in 1940 after serving on the China station, and was lost 6 December 1940 in the Straits of Otranto by an unknown cause.

Yard No.655   HMS *Rover*   Launched 11 June 1930
Completed January 1931. Served first in China, then the Mediterranean 1940 to 1943, when she went to the Far East again for training duties. She was scrapped in Durban 30 July 1946.

First Porpoise Class Submarines

Yard No.679   HMS *Porpoise*   Launched 30 August 1932
Laid down 22 September 1931. Completed 11 March 1933. In 1939 she was transferred to Home waters from the Mediterranean. She was back in the Mediterranean briefly in 1941 and in 1944 went to the Eastern Fleet. On 16 April 1940 sank German U-boat U-1 in the North Sea. She was lost in January 1945 while laying mines off Penang, bombed by Japanese

HMS *Porpoise. (Barrow Museum Service CAT 0013)*

aircraft in the Malacca Strait. She was the last submarine lost by the Royal Navy in the Second World War.

Yard No.701   HMS *Narwhal*   Launched 29 August 1935
Laid down 29 May 1934. Completed 28 February 1936. Served in the Mediterranean, West Indies, Home waters, then the Mediterranean again. She was sunk in the vicinity of Trondheim (while on a minelaying mission off Norway) by an unknown cause in July 1940. Having failed to return she was assumed lost on 1 August 1940.

Yard No.708   HMS *Rorqual*   Launched 21 July 1936
Laid down 1 May 1935. Completed 10 February 1937. Cost £350,639. Served in Chinese waters, coming to the Mediterranean in 1940, to the Eastern Fleet in 1944, being scrapped at Newport, Monmouthshire, by John Cashmore Ltd, arriving there 17 March 1946. During active service her mines accounted for two Italian supply ships, three Italian torpedo boats and the Italian submarine *Pier Capponi*.

Thames Class Submarines

Yard No.672   HMS *Thames*   Launched 26 January 1932
Laid down January 1931. Completed 14 September 1932. Based in Portsmouth from 1932 to 1934, she was sent to the Baltic in 1933 to test the boat's ability to work under ice. Transferred to Mediterranean from 1934 to 1939 and completed a journey around Africa in the winter of 1938/1939. On 26 July 1940 she sank *Luchs* (a German torpedo boat) west of the Skagerrak. She herself was lost with all hands in early August 1940, presumed mined off Stavanger, Norway.

Yard No.683   HMS *Severn*   Launched 16 January 1934
Laid down 27 March 1933. Completed February 1935. She was based at Freetown till she was sent to Home waters in 1941, then to the Mediterranean. In 1944 she went to the Far East. She was scrapped at Bombay in 1946. During active service she sank three ships off

Norway (between 1940 and 1941) and an Italian submarine *Michele Bianchi* in the Adriatic (October 1941).

Yard No.684   HMS *Clyde*   Launched 15 March 1934
Laid down 15 May 1933. Completed April 1935. Cost £459,886. Firstly based at Freetown, then Home waters, then in 1941 to the Mediterranean, and in 1944 to the Far East. She arrived 30 July 1946 at Durban for scrap. Her successes in active service included the sinking of two ships in the Mediterranean between 1941 and 1942.

Portuguese Submarines

Yard No.685   *Delfim*   Launched 5 May 1934
Built for the Portuguese Navy. Scrapped in the 1950s.

Yard No.686   *Espadarte*   Launched 30 May 1934
Built for the Portuguese Navy. Scrapped in the 1950s.

Yard No.687   *Golfino*   Launched 30 May 1934
Built for the Portuguese Navy. Scrapped in the 1950s.

HMS *Severn*.

Portuguese submarine *Espardarte*. (*Barrow Museum Service CAT 0034*)

Estonian Submarines

Yard No.705   *Kalev*   Launched 7 July 1936
Built for the Estonian Navy. Mined in the Gulf of Finland 1941.

Yard No.706   *Lembit*   Launched 7 July 1936
Built for the Estonian Navy. Became a museum/memorial ship in 1978.

T Class Submarines

Yard No.716   HMS *Triton*   Launched 5 October 1937
Laid down 28 August 1936. Completed 9 December 1938. In September 1939 she had the misfortune to accidentally torpedo HMS *Oxley* off Norway. On 10 April 1940 in the Kattegat she sank German steamers *Friedenau* and *Wiebert*, along with patrol vessel *Rau*. Also claimed the sinking of an 8,000-ton Italian supply ship off Savona though this was never confirmed. She was lost, probably mined, in the South Adriatic in December 1940, although German sources say she was sunk by the Italian destroyer *Confienza* on 20 November 1940.

Yard No.731   HMS *Triumph*   Launched 16 February 1938
Laid down 19 March 1937. Completed 2 May 1939. On 23 September 1941 she torpedoed and sank the German freighter *Luvsee* off Sevenik. Sank the Italian submarine *Salpa* off north Egypt in June 1941. She was probably mined in the Aegean Sea off the island of Milo in January 1942, when failing to return from a cloak-and-dagger mission.

Yard No.736   HMS *Thistle*   Launched 25 October 1938
Laid down 7 December 1937. Completed 4 July 1939. Torpedoed and sunk by U-4 off Skudesnes, Norway, 10 April 1940.

Yard No.739   HMS *Triad*   Launched 5 May 1939
Laid down 24 March 1938. Completed 16 September 1939. Lost by unknown cause off Calabria, Mediterranean, 20 October 1940. Some sources say she may have been sunk by Italian submarine *Enrico Tòti* during a surface gun exchange – if true this would be the only time one submarine has sank another during such an exchange.

Yard No.740   HMS *Truant*   Launched 5 May 1939
Laid down 24 March 1938. Completed 31 October 1939. She sank enemy ships in three different battle theatres – Home waters, Far East and Mediterranean (the only British submarine to achieve this feat). In total sank 77,000 tons of enemy shipping. She was wrecked on the way to the breakers in December 1946, having been sold on the 19th of that month.

Yard No.745   HMS *Tetrarch*   Launched 14 November 1939
Laid down 24 August 1938. Completed 15 February 1940. She was lost (presumed mined) on passage from Malta to Gibraltar on 2 November 1941 in the Western Mediterranean.

HMS *Thistle* immediately after launch. *(Barrow Museum Service CAT 2358)*

Yard No.770   HMS *Trusty*   Launched 14 March 1941
Laid down 15 March 1940. Completed 30 July 1941. Scrapped at Milford Haven in July 1947, having spent the war in the Far East.

Yard No.771   HMS *Turbulent*   Launched 12 May 1941
Laid down 15 March 1940. Completed 2 December 1941. Depth-charged by Italian anti-submarine boat off Maddalena, Sardinia, on 12 March 1943.

Yard No.811   HMS *P311*   Launched 5 March 1942
Previously P91 and ultimately to have been renamed HMS *Tutankhamen*. Laid down 25 April 1941. Completed 7 August 1942. Mined and sunk off Maddalena, Sardinia, 31 December 1942.

Yard No.812   HMS *Trespasser*   Launched 29 May 1942
Originally named P92. Laid down 8 September 1941. Completed 25 September 1942. Renamed P312, then *Trespasser*. Scrapped at Gateshead, arriving there 26 September 1961. During her lifetime she sailed some 200,000 miles.

Yard No.813   HMS *Taurus*   Launched 27 June 1942
Laid down 30 September 1941. Completed 3 November 1942. Renamed P313, then Taurus. On 12 November 1943 she torpedoed and sank the Japanese submarine I-34 off Penang. Between 1948 and 1953 she was in the Royal Netherlands Navy as *Dolfijn* and reverted to the name *Taurus* on transfer back to the Royal Navy in 1953. She was scrapped at Dunston, April 1960.

Yard No.814   HMS *Tactician*   Launched 29 July 1942
Laid down 13 November 1941. Completed 29 November 1942. Renamed P314, then *Tactician*. From 1959 to 1961 she served in the Far East. She arrived at Newport, Monmouthshire, for scrapping by John Cashmore Ltd, 6 December 1963.

Yard No.815   HMS *Truculent*   Launched 12 September 1942
Laid down 4 December 1941. Completed 31 December 1942. Renamed P315, then *Truculent*. She sank after a collision with MV *Dvina* in the Thames Estuary (at Medway) 12 January 1950. After being raised on 14 March 1950 she arrived for scrap at Grays, Essex, 8 May 1950.

Yard No.816   HMS *Templar*   Launched 26 October 1942
Laid down 28 December 1941. Completed 15 February 1943. Renamed P316, then *Templar*. In January 1955 she was sunk in Loch Striven as a torpedo target practice ship. After being raised 4 December 1958 she arrived at Troon for scrap by the West of Scotland Shipbreaking Co. Ltd, 17 July 1959.

Yard No.817   HMS *Tally-Ho*   Launched 23 December 1942
Laid down 25 March 1942. Completed 12 April 1943. Renamed P317, then *Tally Ho*. On 11 January 1945 she torpedoed and sank the Japanese light cruiser *Kuma*. She served in the Mediterranean 1955 to 1960. Scrapped in February 1967.

Yard No.818   HMS *Tantalus*   Launched 24 February 1943
Laid down 6 June 1942. Completed 2 June 1943. Renamed P318, then *Tantalus*. Scrapped at Milford Haven November 1950.

HMS *Tantalus*. *(Barrow Museum Service CAT 0077)*

Yard No.819   HMS *Tantivy*   Launched 6 April 1943
Laid down 4 July 1942. Completed 25 July 1943. Renamed P319, then *Tantivy*. Expended as a target in Cromarty Firth, 1951.

Yard No.842   HMS *Telemachus*   Launched 19 June 1943
Laid down 25 August 1942. Completed 25 October 1943. Scrapped by Shipbreaking Industries Ltd at Charlestown, Fife, after arriving there 25 August 1961. During her life she sailed about 241,500 miles and was responsible for sinking the Japanese submarine I-166 off Penang in July 1944.

Yard No.843   HMS *Talent*   Launched 17 July 1943
Laid down 13 October 1942. Completed 4 December 1943. In 1944 she was transferred to the Royal Netherlands Navy and renamed *Zwaardvisch* (Swordfish). Decommissioned in December 1962 and sold for scrap to Antwerp Shipbreakers, July 1963.

Yard No.844   HMS *Terrapin*   Launched 31 August 1943
Originally called P323. Laid down 19 October 1942. Completed 22 January 1944. Declared a constructive total loss 19 May 1945 having been badly damaged by depth charges from Japanese surface craft. Scrapped at Troon, April 1946.

Yard No.845   HMS *Thorough*   Launched 30 October 1943
Laid down 26 October 1942. Completed 1 March 1944. Served in the Far East from October 1949 to December 1957. The first British submarine to circumnavigate the world. She arrived at Dunston for scrap by Clayton & Davis Ltd, 29 June 1961.

Yard No.868   HMS *Tiptoe*   Launched 25 February 1944
Laid down 10 November 1942. Completed 13 June 1944. Later converted to 1,310 tons/ 1,740 tons displacement. Overall length 293.5ft, six 21in tubes with homing torpedoes. Sold to Pounds of Portsmouth in 1975. In February 1969 (some twenty-five years after she was first completed) *Tiptoe* returned to Barrow on a courtesy visit. Featured in the film *We Dive at Dawn* starring John Mills. Her anchor was mounted on stone and erected at Blyth in 1969.

Yard No.869   HMS *Trump*   Launched 25 March 1944
Laid down 31 December 1942. Completed 9 July 1944. Later converted to the same specification as *Tiptoe* (Yard No.868). Scrapped August 1971.

Yard No.870   HMS *Taciturn*   Launched 7 June 1944
Laid down 9 March 1943. Completed 7 October 1944. Later converted to 1,280 tons/ 1,700 tons displacement. Overall length 287.5ft, six 21in tubes with homing torpedoes. Scrapped 8 August, 1971.

Yard No.871   HMS *Tapir*   Launched 21 August 1944
Laid down 29 March 1943. Completed 30 December 1944. Served in the Royal Netherlands Navy as *Zeehond* 1948 to 1953 when she returned to the Royal Navy and the name *Tapir*. She was later modernised and streamlined. Scrapped February 1966.

Yard No.872   HMS *Tarn*   Launched 29 November 1944
Laid down 12 June 1943. Completed 6 April 1945. Completed as *Tijgerhaal* for the Royal Netherlands Navy. Scrapped in 1966.

Yard No.873   HMS *Tasman*   Launched 13 February 1945
Laid down 21 March 1944. Completed 26 July 1945. Completed as *Talent*. Was later modernised and streamlined, and served until 1966. Scrapped in 1970.

Yard No.874   HMS *Teredo*   Launched 27 April 1945
Laid down 17 April 1944. Completed 13 April 1946. Served in the Far East 1959 to 1962. Scrapped June 1965.

U Class Submarines

Yard No.728   HMS *Undine*   Launched 5 October 1937
Laid down 19 February 1937. Completed 21 August 1938. Depth-charged and sunk 7 January 1940 in the Heligoland Bight.

Yard No.729   HMS *Unity*   Launched 16 February 1938
Laid down 19 February 1937. Completed 15 October 1938. Lost in collision in the Tyne area 29 April 1940.

Yard No.730   HMS *Ursula*   Launched 16 February 1938
Laid down 19 February 1937. Completed December 1938. Served in the Russian Navy 1944 to 1949. She was scrapped at Grangemouth in May 1950. She was the Russian V4.

Yard No.757   HMS *Utmost*   Launched 20 April 1940
Laid down 2 November 1939. Completed 17 August 1940. Completed as P42, then renamed *Utmost*. She was sunk by the Italian motor torpedo boat *Groppo* off Cape Marittimo, Western Sicily, on 24 November 1942.

Yard No.758   HMS *Upright*   Launched 21 April 1940
Laid down 6 November 1939. Completed 3 September 1940. Completed as P38 then renamed *Upright*. Scrapped at Troon March 1946.

Yard No.759   HMS *Unique*   Launched 6 June 1940
Laid down 30 October 1939. Completed 27 September 1940. Completed as P36 then renamed *Unique*. On 3 June 1941 she torpedoed and sank the Italian coaster *Arsia* off Lampedusa Island. She herself was lost by unknown causes west of Gibraltar 24 October 1942.

Yard No.760   HMS *Usk*   Launched 7 June 1940
Laid down 6 November 1939. Completed 11 October 1940. Completed as P41 then renamed later *Usk*. She is presumed to have been mined off Cape Bon, Tunisia, on 3 May 1941.

Yard No.761   HMS *Upholder*   Launched 8 July 1940
Laid down 30 October 1939. Completed 31 October 1940. Completed as P37, later renamed *Upholder*. She was sunk by depth charges from the Italian motor torpedo boat *Pegaso* off Tripoli, Libya, 14 April 1942. During her sixteen months' service she completed twenty-four patrols and sank or damaged twenty-two enemy ships.

Yard No.762   HMS *Unbeaten*   Launched 9 July 1940
Laid down 22 November 1939. Completed 20 November 1940. Completed as P33, reverting later to *Unbeaten*. She was accidentally sunk 11 November 1942 in the Bay of Biscay by a British aircraft.

Yard No.763   HMS *Urge*   Launched 19 August 1940
Laid down 30 October 1939. Completed 12 December 1940. Completed as P40, reverting later to *Urge*. She is thought to have been mined in the Eastern Mediterranean 28 April 1942, probably by the Italian torpedo boat *Pegaso*.

Yard No.764   HMS *Undaunted*   Launched 20 August 1940
Laid down 2 December 1939. Completed 30 December 1940. Completed as P34, reverting later to *Undaunted*. She was depth-charged and sunk by an Italian motor torpedo boat off Tripoli, Libya, 13 May 1941.

Yard No.765   HMS *Urchin*   Launched 30 September 1940
Laid down 9 December 1939. Completed 28 January 1941. She was renamed after launching P39, but on 19 January was renamed *Sokol* by the Polish Navy. In 1946 she was returned to the Royal Navy and renamed *Urchin*, being scrapped in 1949.

Yard No.766   HMS *Union*   Launched 1 October 1940
Laid down 9 December 1939. Completed 22 February 1941. Completed as P35, being later renamed *Union*. She was sunk 20 July 1941 by the Italian motor torpedo boat *Circe* between Tunisia and Pantellaria. (This MTB was also responsible for the sinking of P38 – Yard No.782 – on 23 February 1942.)

Yard No.775   HMS *Ullswater*   Launched 27 November 1940
Laid down 30 April 1940. Completed 2 April 1941. Renamed *Uproar* in 1943. Scrapped at Inverkeithing in February 1946.

Yard No.776   HMS P32   Launched 15 December 1940
Laid down 30 April 1940. Completed 3 May 1941. Presumed to have been mined off Tripoli, Libya, 18 August 1941.

Yard No.777   HMS P33   Launched 28 January 1941
Laid down 18 June 1940. Completed 30 May 1941. Presumed mined off Tripoli, Libya, 23 August 1941.

Yard No.778   HMS *Ultimatum*   Launched 11 February 1941
Laid down 19 June 1940. Completed 29 July 1941. Arrived at Port Glasgow for scrap, 23 December 1949.

Yard No.779   HMS *Umbra*   Launched 15 March 1941
Laid down 19 July 1940. Completed 2 July 1941. Scrapped at Blyth, July 1946.

Yard No.780   HMS P36   Launched 28 April 1941
Laid down 26 July 1940. Completed 24 September 1941. She was bombed and sunk in Lazarett Bay, Malta, by aircraft 1 April 1942. The wreck was raised and beached 7 August 1958 and, after patching, was taken to deep water off Malta and scuttled, 22 August 1958.

Yard No.781   HMS P37   Launched 9 July 1941
Laid down 30 August 1940. Completed as HMS *Unbending* 5 November 1941. Scrapped on the Tyne in May 1950.

Yard No.782   HMS P38   Launched 12 May 1941
Laid down 30 August 1940. Completed 5 November 1941. Depth-charged and sunk by the Italian MTB *Circe* on 23 February 1942. (The *Circe* also sank the *Union* – Yard No.766).

Yard No.783   HMS P39   Launched 23 August 1941
Laid down 14 October 1940. Completed 16 November 1941. Bombed and sunk by aircraft at Malta 26 March 1942. Salvaged and beached in June 1943 and eventually broken up in 1954.

Yard No.784   HM P41/*Uredd*   Launched 24 August 1941
Laid down 15 October 1940. Completed 12 December 1941. Completed as *Uredd* for the Royal Norwegian Navy. She was lost, believed mined off Bodo, Norway, about 24 February 1943.

Yard No.797   HMS *Unbroken*   Launched 4 November 1941
Previously named P42. Laid down 30 December 1940. Completed 29 January 1942. In the Russian Navy as V2 1944 to 1949. She was scrapped at Gateshead in May 1950.

Yard No.798   HMS *Unison*   Launched 5 November 1941
Previously named P43. Laid down 30 December 1940. Completed 19 February 1942. In the Russian Navy as V3 from 1944 to 1949. She was scrapped at Stockton-on-Tees in May 1950.

Yard No.799   HMS *United*   Launched 18 December 1941
Previously named P4 then P44. Laid down 25 February 1941. Completed 2 April 1942. Arrived at Troon for scrap, 12 February 1946.

Yard No.800   HMS *Unruffled*   Launched 19 December 1941
Previously named P46. Laid down 25 February 1941. Completed 9 April 1942. Scrapped at Troon in January 1946.

The shipyard's assembly shop and slipways viewed from Walney Island (*c.1942*). *(Barrow Museum Service CAT 6352)*

Yard No.801   HMS *Unrivalled*   Launched 16 February 1942
Previously named P45. Laid down 12 May 1941. Completed 3 May 1942. Scrapped at Briton Ferry in January 1946.

Yard No.802   HMS *Unshaken*   Launched 17 February 1942
Previously named P54. Laid down 14 June 1941. Completed 21 May 1942. Scrapped at Troon in March 1946.

Yard No.803   HMS P48   Launched 15 April 1942
Laid down 2 August 1941. Completed 18 June 1942. Sunk by the Italian MTB *Ardente* in the Gulf of Tunis, 25 December 1942.

Yard No.804   HMS *Unseen*   Launched 16 April 1942
Previously named P51. Laid down 30 July 1941. Completed 2 July 1942. Scrapped at Hayle in September 1949.

Yard No.805   HMS P47/*Dolfijn*   Launched 27 July 1942
Laid down 19 November 1941. Completed 8 October 1942. Completed as *Dolfijn* for the Royal Netherlands Navy. Scrapped in Holland in 1947.

Yard No.806   HMS *Unruly*   Launched 28 July 1942
Laid down 19 November 1941. Completed 3 November 1942. Scrapped at Inverkeithing in February 1946.

Yard No.807   HMS P52/*Dzik*   Launched 11 October 1942
Laid down 30 December 1941. Completed 16 December 1942. Completed at *Dzik* for the Polish Navy. In 1946 she was transferred to the Royal Danish Navy and renamed U1. She was later renamed *Springeren*. In 1957 she was returned to the Royal Navy and was scrapped at Faslane in April 1958.

Yard No.808   HMS *Ultor*   Launched 12 October 1942

Laid down 30 December 1941. Completed 31 December 1942. Scrapped at Briton Ferry in January 1946.

Yard No.837   HMS *Vandal*   Launched 23 November 1942

Laid down 17 March 1942. Completed 20 February 1943. Lost in the Clyde by accident, 24 February 1943. The shortest-living vessel built at Barrow. Located in October 2002 in Kilbrennan Sound by a team of sports divers.

Yard No.838   HMS *Upstart*   Launched 24 November 1942

Previously named P65. Laid down 17 March 1942. Completed 3 April 1943. Served in the Royal Hellenic Navy 1945 – 1952 as *Amfitrite*. After being returned to the Royal Navy in 1952 and reverting to the name *Upstart* she was expended as a target, 29 July 1957.

Yard No.839   HMS *Varne*   Launched 22 January 1943

Laid down 29 April 1942. Completed 3 April 1944. Completed as *Ula* for the Royal Norwegian Navy. Converted extensively in 1956. Sold for scrap in 1965.

Yard No.840   HMS *Vox*   Launched 23 January 1943

Laid down 29 April 1942. Completed 2 May 1943. Completed as *Curie* for the French Navy. In 1946 she was returned to the Royal Navy as P67 and was scrapped in April 1956.

Turkish Submarines

Yard No.751   *Oruc Reis*   Launched 19 July 1940

Laid down 24 May 1939. Completed 1 December 1941. Launched for the Turkish Navy but completed as HMS P611. In 1942 she was returned to the Turks, by whom she was renamed *Oruc Reis* and discarded as obsolete in 1957.

Yard No.752   *Murat Reis*   Launched 20 July 1940

Laid down 24 May 1939. Completed 7 January 1942. Launched for the Turkish Navy but completed as HMS P612. In 1942 she was returned to the Turks, renamed *Murat Reis* and was discarded as obsolete in 1957.

Yard No.753   *Burak Reis*   Launched 19 October 1940

Laid down 24 May 1939. Completed 10 March 1942. Launched for the Turkish Navy but completed as HMS P614. She was used for training purposes at Freetown, then in 1943 for similar uses in Home waters. In 1945 she reverted to the Turkish Navy as *Burak Reis* being discarded as obsolete in 1957.

Yard No.754   *Uluc-Ali Reis*   Launched 1 November 1940

Laid down 30 October 1939. Completed 3 April 1942. Launched for the Turkish Navy but completed as HMS P615. She was utilised for training at Freetown until torpedoed and sunk by U-123 on 18 April 1943 off the port of Freetown.

S Class Submarines

Yard No.789   HMS P72/P222   Launched 20 September 1941
Laid down 10 August 1940. Completed 4 May 1942. Completed as P222. Depth-charged
and sunk by the Italian MTB *Fortunale* off Naples, 12 December 1942.

Yard No.790   HMS P69/P219/*Seraph*   Launched 25 October 1941
Laid down 16 August 1940. Completed 10 June 1942. Completed as P219, later being named
Seraph. She had a most distinguished war record of secret landings, etc. Whilst awaiting
disposal in 1963, a periscope and various other items were removed and shipped to the USA
where they were incorporated into a monument at the South Carolina Military College. This
monument, dedicated in November 1963, commemorates Anglo-American co-operation
during the Second World War. Sold for scrap in 1965 to T.W. Ward of Brighton Ferry,
Swansea.

Yard No.791   HMS P71/P221/*Shakespeare*   Launched 8 December 1941
Laid down 13 November 1940. Completed 10 July 1942. Completed as P221, later renamed
Shakespeare. Following severe bomb damage by Japanese aircraft on 3 January 1945 in the
Nankaun Strait, *Shakespeare* was considered to be beyond economic repair and she was
scrapped at Briton Ferry in July 1946.

X Craft Submarines

A series of six X Craft. All the craft were ordered on 12 May 1942.

Yard No.883   X5   Commissioned 29 December 1942
Commissioned 29 December 1942. Sunk 22 September 1943 in the Kaa Fjord, Norway,
while attacking the *Tirpitz*.

Yard No.883   X6   Commissioned 21 January 1943
Commissioned 21 January 1943. Lost 22 September 1943 while attacking the *Tirpitz*. She
was scuttled after placing her charges.

Yard No.883   X7   Commissioned 14 January 1943
Commissioned 14 January 1943. Lost 22 September 1943 while attacking the *Tirpitz*. She
was scuttled after placing her charges.

Yard No.883   X8   Commissioned 18 January 1943
Commissioned 28 January 1943. Lost 17 September 1943. Scuttled after defects prevented
her from reaching *Tirpitz*.

Yard No.883   X9   Commissioned 29 January 1943
Commissioned 29 January 1943. Lost 16 September 1943 after breaking her tow and disappearing on the way to attack *Tirpitz*.

Yard No.883   X10   Commissioned 8 February 1943

Commissioned 8 February 1943. Prior to going on Operation Source X10 returned to Barrow for refitting after accidentally sinking in Kames Bay. She was scuttled while approaching the Norwegian coast on 23 September 1943.

XE Craft Submarines

Yard No.939   XE1   Launched between Dec 1943 and Jan 1945

One of a series of XE craft submarines built and completed between December 1943 and January 1945. Unable to execute the attack on *Nachi*, XE 1 assisted in the attack on the *Takao*. Scrapped at the Cockatoo Island breakers yard, Sydney Harbour, in October 1945.

Yard No.939   XE2   Launched between Dec 1943 and Jan 1945

Scrapped at the Cockatoo Island breakers yard, Sydney Harbour, in October 1945.

Yard No.939   XE3   Launched between Dec 1943 and Jan 1945

Sank the *Takao*. Scrapped at the Cockatoo Island breakers yard, Sydney Harbour, in October 1945.

Yard No.939   XE4   Launched between Dec 1943 and Jan 1945

Cut the Singapore – Saigon – Hong Kong submarine cable. Scrapped at the Cockatoo Island breakers yard, Sydney Harbour, in October 1945.

XE Craft submarine.

Yard No.939   XE5   Exact launch date unknown
Cut the Singapore – Saigon – Hong Kong submarine cable, two dates are commonly quoted: 30 July 1945 or 1 August 1945. Scrapped at the Cockatoo Island breakers yard, Sydney Harbour, in October 1945.

Yard No.939   XE6   Exact launch date unknown
Scrapped at the Cockatoo Island breakers yard, Sydney Harbour, in October 1945.

XT Craft Submarines

Yard No.927   XT1   Exact launch date unknown
Completed 18 January 1944. Scrapped 1945.

Yard No.927   XT2   Exact launch date unknown
Completed 26 January 1944. Scrapped 1945.

Yard No.927   XT3   Exact launch date unknown
Completed 4 February 1944. Scrapped 1945.

Yard No.927   XT4   Exact launch date unknown
Completed 15 February 1944. Scrapped 1945.

Yard No.927   XT5   Exact launch date unknown
Completed 25 February 1944. Scrapped 1945.

Yard No.927   XT6   Exact launch date unknown
Completed 15 March 1944. Scrapped 1945.

Second V Class Submarines

Yard No.860   HMS *Venturer*   Launched 4 May 1943
Laid down 25 August 1942. Completed 19 August 1943. In 1946 she was transferred to the Royal Norwegian Navy and renamed *Utstein*. In 1956 she was extensively modernised and in 1965 sold to the Sarpsborg Shipbreakers.

Yard No.861   HMS *Viking*   Launched 5 May 1943
Laid down 3 September 1942. Completed 30 August 1943. In 1946 she was transferred to the Royal Norwegian Navy and renamed *Utvaer*. In 1956 she was extensively modernised and in 1965 sold to the Sarpsborg Shipbreakers.

Yard No.862   HMS *Veldt*   Launched 19 July 1943
Laid down 2 November 1942. Completed 1 November 1943. Completed as *Pipinos* for the Royal Hellenic Navy. She was handed back to the Royal Navy at Malta 10 December 1957 and arrived at Dunston for scrapping by Clayton & Davie Ltd, 23 February 1958.

Yard No.863   HMS *Vampire*   Launched 20 July 1943
Laid down 9 November 1942. Completed 13 November 1943. Scrapped at Gateshead in March 1950 by J.J. King.

Yard No.864   HMS *Vox*   Launched 28 September 1943
Laid down 19 December 1942. Completed 20 December 1943. She was the second boat to be named *Vox* having replaced the U Class boat of the same name loaned to France. Scrapped at Cochin, India, May 1946.

Yard No.865   HMS *Vigorous*   Launched 15 October 1943
Laid down 14 December 1942. Completed 13 January 1944. Scrapped at Stockton-on-Tees, 23 December 1949 by Stockton Shipping & Salvage Co.

Yard No.866   HMS *Virtue*   Launched 29 November 1943
Laid down 17 February 1943. Completed 29 February 1944. Scrapped at Cochin, India, May 1946.

Yard No.867   HMS *Visigoth*   Launched 30 November 1943
Laid down 15 February 1943. Completed 9 March 1944. Scrapped at Hayle in April 1950 by T.W. Ward.

HMS *Venturer*. The first-of-class Second V Class submarine which was constructed at Barrow.

HMS *Upshot. (Barrow Museum Service CAT 0086)*

Yard No.886   HMS *Upshot*   Launched 24 February 1944
Laid down 3 May 1943. Completed 15 May 1944. Scrapped at Preston in November 1949
by T.W. Ward.

Yard No.887   HMS *Urtica*   Launched 23 March 1944
Laid down 27 April 1943. Completed 20 June 1944. Scrapped at Milford Haven in March
1950 by T.W. Ward.

Yard No.888   HMS *Vineyard*   Launched 8 May 1944
Laid down 21 May 1943. Completed 1 August 1944. Completed as *Doris* for the French
Navy. Returned to the Royal Navy as *Vineyard* in 1947. Scrapped in 1950 by Metal Industries
at Fife.

Yard No.889   HMS *Variance*   Launched 22 May 1944
Laid down 21 May 1943. Completed 24 August 1944. Completed as *Utsira* for the Royal
Norwegian Navy. She was extensively modernised in 1956. Sold to Eckhardt GmbH in what
was West Germany in December 1965 for breaking at Hamburg.

Yard No.890   HMS *Vengeful*   Launched 20 July 1944
Laid down 30 July 1943. Completed 16 October 1944. Completed as *Delphin* for the Royal
Hellenic Navy, being handed back to the Royal Navy at Malta 10 December 1957. She
arrived at Gateshead for scrapping by J.J. King & Co. Ltd, 22 March 1958.

Yard No.891   HMS *Vortex*   Launched 19 August 1944
Laid down 13 August 1943. Completed 1 December 1944. Completed as *Morse* for the
French Navy. In 1947 she was transferred to the Royal Danish Navy and renamed *Saelen*. She
was returned to the Royal Navy January 1958 and was scrapped at Faslane by Shipbreaking
Industries Ltd in August 1958.

Second A Class Submarines

Yard No.903   HMS *Amphion*   Launched 31 August 1944

Laid down 14 November 1943. Completed 27 March 1945. Laid down as *Anchorite*. She was streamlined and guppied, armament becoming six 21in tubes, sixteen homing torpedoes carried, seven MGs. Overall length 283ft. Scrapped 1971 at Inverkeithing by T.W. Ward.

Yard No.904   HMS *Astute*   Launched 30 January 1945

Laid down 4 April 1944. Completed 30 June 1945. Streamlined and guppied as HMS *Amphion* (Yard No.903). Refitted 1963. Scrapping date 1970 by Clayton & Davies Ltd, at Dunston-on-Tyne.

Yard No.905   HMS *Auriga*   Launched 29 March 1945

Laid down 7 June 1944. Completed 12 January 1946. Visited Barrow during June 1953 as part of the Coronation week celebrations. Streamlined and guppied as HMS *Amphion* (Yard No.903). Sold to J. Cashmore in 1970 for breaking at Newport.

Yard No.906   HMS *Aurochs*   Launched 28 July 1945

Laid down 21 June 1944. Completed 7 February 1947. Streamlined and guppied as HMS *Amphion* (Yard No.903). Only one of A Class not converted, broken up at Troon in February 1967 by West of Scotland Shipbreaking Co.

Yard No.907   HMS *Alcide*   Launched 12 April 1945

Laid down 2 January 1945. Completed 18 October 1946. Sold to A. Draper & Sons of Hull in 1974 for breaking up.

Yard No.908   HMS *Alderney*   Launched 25 June 1945

Laid down 6 February 1945. Completed 10 December 1945. Streamlined and guppied as HMS *Amphion* (Yard No.903) in 1957. Scrapped in 1972 by Shipbreaking (Queensborough) Ltd at Cairn Ryan.

HMS *Aurochs*. *(Barrow Museum Service CAT 0094)*

Yard No.909   HMS *Alliance*   Launched 28 July 1945
Laid down 13 March 1945. Completed 14 May 1947. Placed on permanent display at the Royal Navy Submarine Museum at Gosport.

Yard No.910   HMS *Ambush*   Launched 24 September 1945
Laid down 17 May 1945. Completed 22 July 1947. Streamlined and guppied as HMS *Amphion* (Yard No.903) at Chatham in 1957. Scrapped 1971 by T.W. Ward at Inverkeithing.

Yard No911   HMS *Anchorite*   Launched 22 January 1946
Laid down 19 July 1945. Completed 18 November 1947. Streamlined and guppied as HMS *Amphion* (Yard No.903). Scrapping date 1970 by West of Scotland Shipbreaking Co. at Troon.

Yard No.912   HMS *Andrew*   Launched 6 April 1946
Laid down 13 August 1945. Completed 16 March 1948. In June 1953 became the first Royal Navy boat to cross the Atlantic underwater. Streamlined and guppied as HMS *Amphion* (Yard No.903). Scrapped in 1977.

EX Class Experimental Submarines

Yard No.979   HMS *Explorer*   Launched 5 March 1954
Completed 28 November 1956. Cost over £2 million. Scrapped in 1965 at Barrow by T.W. Ward.

Yard No.980   HMS *Excalibur*   Launched 25 February 1955
Completed 22 March 1958. Scrapped in 1970 by T.W. Ward.

X Class Submarines

Yard No.1037   X51   Launched July 1954
Stickleback. One of a series of four. 1958 sold to Swedish Navy who renamed the boat *Spigger* (meaning Stickleback). Used for harbour defence exercises. Returned by Sweden in 1976 and is now exhibited at the Imperial War Museum at Duxford (Cambridge).

Yard No.1037   X52   Launched October 1954
Shrimp. Following satisfactory trials put into reserve at Portsmouth until 1966 when she was broken up at Faslane.

Yard No.1037   X53   Launched 30 December 1954
Sprat. Following satisfactory trials put into reserve at Portsmouth until 1966 when she was broken up at Faslane. Also used to test harbour defences in USA.

Yard No.1037   X54   Launched 5 May 1955
Minnow. Following initial acceptance trials returned to Barrow for testing with shrouded propeller. Further trials showed no appreciable performance improvement in this early application of a pump-jet. Put into reserve at Portsmouth until 1966 when she was broken up at Faslane.

Second Porpoise Class Submarines

Yard No.1029   HMS *Porpoise*   Launched 25 April 1956
Completed 17 April 1958. Used as a target by the navy. Sunk as a target by a Sting Ray torpedo in the Mediterranean in October 1985.

Yard No.1030   HMS *Rorqual*   Launched 5 December 1956
Completed 24 April 1958. Became alongside training boat at HMS Dolphin. Sold for scrap to Davies & Glenn at Plymouth in 1977.

Yard No.1031   HMS *Narwhal*   Launched 25 October 1957
Completed 4 May 1959. Deliberately sunk off Portland in June 1980 and raised as a salvage exercise by heavy lift ships. Sunk in 1983 off Falmouth as a diving training boat.

Oberon Class Submarines

Yard No.1059   HMS *Orpheus*   Launched 17 November 1959
Completed 25 November 1960. Cost £2,305,000. Superstructure of light aluminium alloy. Became a harbour training boat in 1993.

Yard No.1060   HMS *Olympus*   Launched 14 June 1961
Laid down March 1960. Completed 7 July 1962. Sponsor Mrs R.H. Wright. Sold to Canadian Navy as an alongside training boat in August 1990.

Yard No.1064   HMS *Osiris*   Launched 29 November 1962
Laid down 26 January 1962. Completed 11 January 1964. Sold to Canada, dismantled in UK and shipped to Canada as spares for that country's three Oberon Class submarines.

Yard No.1087   *Humaita*   Launched 5 October 1971
Ordered by Brazilian government August 1969. Keel laid 3 November 1970 by Admiral Nunes, Minister for the navy. Launched by Senora Nunes, wife of the Admiral. Contractors' Sea Trials February 1973. Commissioned 18 June 1973. Name commemorates naval action in Brazil's river war with Paraguay – 21 February 1868. Third Brazilian submarine to be named. Ninth Brazilian warship to be launched at Barrow. Broken up in 1996.

Yard No.1088   *Tonolero*   Launched 22 November 1972
Ordered by Brazilian government August 1969. Laid down 18 November 1971 by Admiral F.S. Alcantara, Director General, Naval Material, Brazilian government. Launched by Senora Nunes. Contractors' sea trials July 1977. Commissioned 10 December 1977. Sister ship of *Humaita* and name commemorates naval action in Brazilian naval war with Paraguay. Serious fire aboard 2 October 1973. Damage delayed completion of ship which was then almost ready for sea trials. In 2001 sank in 25ft of water at her mooring in Rio while under repair. Disposition not yet determined.

Yard No.1096   *Riachuelo*   Launched 6 September 1975
Ordered by Brazilian government and announced in August 1972. Laid down 6 December 1972. Keel officially laid by Vice Admiral J.C. de Souze, President of Brazilian Naval Mission in Europe, 26 April 1973. Commissioned 12 March 1977 at Barrow. Sailed July 1977. Now a museum/memorial ship at Rio de Janeiro.

Dreadnought Class Submarine

Yard No.1062   HMS *Dreadnought*   Launched 21 October 1960
SSN01. Laid down 12 June 1959. Launched by HM the Queen. Completed 17 April 1963. In July 1973 *Dreadnought* rescued thirty-five seamen from the 7,000-ton freighter *Carnation* after that vessel was in collision with the 20,000-ton tanker *Anson* in the Malacca Strait. Decommissioned 1982, laid up at Rosyth awaiting disposal.

Valiant Class Submarines

Yard No.1066   HMS *Valiant*   Launched 3 December 1963
SSN02. Ordered August 1960. Laid down 22 January 1962. Launched by Mrs Peter Thorneycroft. Completed 1965. The first all-British nuclear submarine adopted by the town of Barrow-in-Furness. Laid up in 1994 at Devonport awaiting disposal.

The shipyard's east shop at around the time *Dreadnought* was under construction. *(Barrow Museum Service CAT 6148)*

Yard No.1072   HMS *Warspite*   Launched 25 September 1965

SSN03. Ordered 12 December 1962. Laid down 10 December 1963. Launched by Mrs Mary Wilson, wife of Mr Harold Wilson, then Prime Minister. Commissioned 18 April 1967. A sister ship to *Valiant* (Yard No.1066) and third British nuclear-powered fleet submarine. Returned to Barrow 23 October 1968 with bridge fin damaged through underwater collision with ice. Damage repaired. Returned to service 20 November 1968. Damaged by an extremely serious fire on 11 August 1984 during a courtesy visit to Liverpool. In January 1990 the MoD announced hairline crack found in primary coolant system. Laid up in the same year at Devonport awaiting disposal.

Polaris Class Submarines

Yard No.1074   HMS *Resolution*   Launched 15 September 1966

SSBN01. Ordered 8 May 1963. Laid down 26 February 1964. Launched by HM Queen Elizabeth, the Queen Mother. Commissioned 3 October 1967 into 10th Submarine Squadron. First of five British Polaris submarines. One cancelled. Building of four shared by Vickers and Cammell Laird. Ship completed to time after great effort by builders and army of sub-contractors. Test firing of missiles on Atlantic range Spring 1968. Laid up at Rosyth in 1994 awaiting disposal.

Yard No.1075   HMS *Repulse*   Launched 4 November 1967

SSBN03. Ordered 8 May 1963. Laid down 26 February 1964. Launched by Lady Joan Zuckerman, wife of Sir Solly Zuckerman, Chief Scientific Adviser to the Government. Commissioned 28 September 1968. Test firing of missiles on Atlantic range March–April 1969. Vessel grounded in Walney Channel after launching. Refloated on midnight tide by six tugs. Undamaged. Contractors' sea trials May–June 1969 highly successful. Ship launch marked anti-Polaris demonstrations outside Shipyard on Walney Island. Sailed to join 10th Submarine Squadron 6 October 1968. Sailing delayed twenty-four hours due to tide not making predicted height. Ship completed three months ahead of schedule to take up delay in completing *Renown* (at Cammell Laird). Laid up at Rosyth in 1996 awaiting disposal.

Improved Valiant Class Submarines

Yard No.1076   HMS *Churchill*   Launched 20 December 1968

SSN04. Laid down 30 June 1967. Launched by Mrs Mary Soames, youngest daughter of the late Sir Winston Churchill and wife of the Rt Hon. Christopher Soames, the British Ambassador in Paris. Contractors' sea trials 6 March 1970. Commissioned 15 July 1970. Fourth submarine of her type for the Royal Navy and first to be named after the late Sir Winston Churchill. Returned to Barrow for routine docking and maintenance 24 May 1971. Sailed October 1971. Undertook trials in the early 1970s with the prototype pump-jet propulsor which would eventually be fitted as standard to future boats. In the late 1970s test fired the first Harpoon missile. Laid up at Rosyth in 1991 awaiting disposal.

Yard No.1077   HMS *Courageous*   Launched 7 March 1970
SSN05. Originally named *Superb*. Laid down 15 May 1968. Launched by Mrs Morris, wife
of Mr John Morris, Labour MP for Aberavon and Minister for Defence (Equipment).
Contractors' sea trials 22 May 1971. Commissioned 16 October 1971. Left Barrow
2 November 1971. Laid up in Portsmouth in 1992 (Cammell Laird-built *Conqueror* laid up at
same time) – both awaiting disposal.

Swiftsure Class Submarines

Yard No.1078   HMS *Swiftsure*   Launched 7 September 1971
Ordered as SSN07 on 3 November 1967. Laid down 15 April 1969. Launched by Lady
Pollock. Contractors' sea trials September-October 1972. Commissioned 17 April 1973.
Sailed 2 May 1973. Laid up at Rosyth in 1992 awaiting disposal.

Yard No.1086   HMS *Sovereign*   Launched 17 February 1973
Ordered as SSN08 in 1969. Laid down 17 September 1970. Launching scheduled for
September 1972 but set back because of effects of strike by the Boilermakers' Society April-
June 1972. Launched by Lady Ashmore, wife of Admiral Sir Edward Ashmore Commander-
in-Chief of the Fleet, Royal Navy. Contractors' sea trials February-March 1974.
Commissioned 9 July 1974. October 1976 surfaced at North Pole. Still in service.

Yard No.1090   HMS *Superb*   Launched 30 November 1974
Ordered as SSN09 and order announced on 20 May 1970. Contract worth £25 million. Laid
down 16 March 1973. Launched by Mrs Williams, wife of Admiral David Williams, Second
Sea Lord and Chief of Naval Personnel. In view of impending legislation to nationalise shipbuilding, the launch might well have been the last for the Royal Navy by Vickers Ltd. In that
event *Superb* was the 679th ship to be launched at Barrow, the 432nd vessel built by Vickers
for the Royal Navy and the 304th submarine to be built by Vickers for the Royal Navy (and
the 313th submarine to be built at Barrow since the 1886 Nordenfelt). Commissioned
13 November 1976. In 1977 took part in the Queen's Silver Jubilee Review of the Fleet in
late June. Wore flag of Flag Officer submarines. Nicknamed 'Super bee'. Still in service.

Yard No.1092   HMS *Sceptre*   Launched 20 November 1976
Ordered as SSN10 in November 1971. Laid down 25 October 1973. Launched by Lady
Audrey White, wife of Admiral Sir Peter White, Chief of Naval Support at Vickers Shipyard
Barrow. Commissioned 14 February 1978 at Barrow. Still in service.

Yard No.1097   HMS *Spartan*   Launched 7 April 1978
SSBN11. Order announced on 17 February 1973 by Admiral Sir Edward Ashmore after the
launch of HMS *Sovereign*. Laid down 24 April 1976. Launched by Lady Lygo. Sea trials
February 1979. Commissioned Saturday 22 September 1979. Refit at Rosyth 2000/01. Still
in service.

Yard No.1099   HMS *Splendid*   Launched 5 October 1979
SSBN12. Order announced on 26 May 1976. Laid down November 1977. Launched by Lady
Ann Eberle, wife of Admiral Sir James Eberle KCB, Commander-in-Chief of the Fleet.
Splendid last of Swiftsure Class submarines and 293rd submarine built for the Royal Navy at
Barrow. Still in service.

540 Class Submarines

Yard No.1093   *Gal* (Wave)   Launched 2 December 1975
Ordered by Israeli government April 1972. Built to a design produced by Ingenieurkontor
Lübeck, West Germany, for 500 and 1,000-ton submarines. Reports of order produced threat
of boycott by Arab States against Vickers. Laid down 4 December 1972. Launched by Mrs
Tamar Dror, wife of Capt. Dror, then Head of Israeli Commission. Completed 1976. First of
three submarines built to designs of German company IKL and Howaldstwerke under a
collaboration agreement. Ran aground off Haifa soon after arrival in Israeli waters. In 2001
was up for sale.

Yard No.1094   *Tanin* (Crocodile)   Launched 25 October 1976
Laid down 28 November 1972. Built on pontoon dock. Launched by Mrs Rafael, wife of
Israeli Ambassador to UK. Completed February 1977. Accident resulting in the death of
three crew members near Loch Gilphead created unwelcome national publicity and re-
generated Arab boycott. In 2001 was up for sale.

Yard No.1095   *Rahav* (Sea Monster) Launched 8 May 1977
Laid down 6 December 1972. Built on pontoon dock and launched without ceremony
Sunday 8 May 1977. Named alongside Buccleuch Dock works by Mrs Raananit Peer, wife
of Capt. Peer, Head of 540 Commission, 21 June 1977. At that time *Tanin* (Yard No.1094)
was complete and commissioned and berthed adjacent to *Rahav*. In 2001 was up for sale.

Trafalgar Class Submarines

Yard No.1100   HMS *Trafalgar*   Launched 1 July 1981
SSN13. Order announced on 7 September 1977, but construction began in advance of signed
contract. First of Improved Swiftsure Class submarine. Launched by Lady Fieldhouse, wife of
Admiral Sir John Fieldhouse, and commissioned on 27 May 1983. Left Barrow July 11 1983.
Still in service. In October 2001 launched a Tomahawk missile strike against Taliban strong-
holds in Afghanistan.

Yard No.1101   HMS *Turbulent*   Launched 1 December 1982
SSN14. Order announced on 28 July 1978 as second of Trafalgar Class. Launched by Lady
Cassidi, wife of Admiral Sir Desmond Cassidi, Commander-in-Chief Naval Home
Command (designate). Commissioned 28 April 1984. Left Barrow 30 July 1984. Still in
service.

Yard No.1103   HMS *Tireless*   Launched 17 March 1984
SSN15. Order announced 5 July 1979. Third of Trafalgar Class submarines. Launched by Mrs Sue Squires, wife of Vice Admiral Robert 'Tubby' Squires (Retired), a former Flag Officer Submarines. Commissioned 5 October 1985. Left Barrow 14 October 1985. Still in service.

Yard No.1104   HMS *Torbay*   Launched 8 March 1985
SSN16. Order announced 26 June 1981. Fourth of Trafalgar Class submarines. Launched by Lady Ann Herbert, wife of Admiral Sir Peter Herbert. Still in service.

Yard No.1105   HMS *Trenchant*   Launched 3 November 1986
SSN17. Order announced 22 March 1983. Fifth Trafalgar Class submarine. Launched by Lady Hunt, wife of Admiral Sir Nicholas Hunt, Commander-in-Chief of the Fleet. Still in service.

Yard No.1107   HMS *Talent*   Launched 15 April 1988
SSN18. Order announced 10 September 1984. Launched by HRH the Princess Royal (Princess Anne). Still in service.

Yard No.1108   HMS *Triumph*   Launched 16 February 1991
SSN19. Order announced 3 January 1986. Commissioned 12 October 1991. First Royal Navy nuclear submarine to visit Australia. Still in service. In October 2001 launched a Tomahawk missile strike against Taliban strongholds in Afghanistan. Damaged in November 2002 off the Isle of Skye after striking a rock at a depth of 165ft below the surface.

The launch of HMS *Talent*.

A hull section, containing a PWR2 Reactor Primary System and engine room, ready for 'launch' onto a semi-submersible barge. This type of reactor was fitted into a Trident submarine.

Type 2400 Class Submarine

Yard No.1106   HMS *Upholder*   Launched 2 December 1986
SSK01. Order announced 2 November 1983. The first Royal Navy Type 2400, Upholder Class submarine. Launched by HRH the Duchess of Kent. Commissioned on 9 June 1990. Mothballed at Barrow in mid–1990s, then leased to Canada in 1998 and renamed HMCS *Chicoutimi* (SSK879).

Trident Class Submarines

Yard No.1109   HMS *Vanguard*   Launched 4 March 1992
SSBN05. Laid down 3 September 1986. Commissioned 14 August 1993. Launched by HRH Prince of Wales in April 1990. She became the tenth ship to carry the name *Vengeance*. Her motto is 'We Lead' and in 1994 she launched the first UK Trident II D5 missile. Still in service.

Yard No.1110   HMS *Victorious*   Launched 29 September 1993
SSBN06. Ordered 1 October 1987. Launched by Lady Heather Newman. Commissioned 7 January 1995. Still in service.

Yard No.1111   HMS *Vigilant*   Launched 14 October 1995
SSBN07. Laid down 16 February 1991. Commissioned April 1997. Still in service.

Yard No.1112   HMS *Vengeance*   Launched 19 September 1998
SSBN08. Ordered July 1992. Laid down 1 February 1993. Commissioned March 1999. Was
originally to have been named *Valiant*. Still in service.

Astute Class Submarines (Not Yet Built)

Yard No.1122   HMS *Astute*   Ordered March 1997
Keel laid 31 January 2001, exactly 100 years after the keel of *Holland 1* was laid.

Yard No.1123   HMS *Ambush*   Ordered March 1997

Yard No.1124   HMS *Artful*   Ordered March 1997

Barrow-Built Submarines – A Perspective

On the facing page is a representation of the varying scales of a number of the submarine
classes featured in this book. The most noticeable absentees are the Trident and Astute
Classes.

   Taken from Shipyard Publication STP 305 9.85, these silhouettes give the reader an
approximate comparison of size across the various classes featured. Some of the class titles
used in the illustration are alternatives to the ones generally favoured by the authors. These
are: H21 Class (H Class); Odin Class (O Class); Parthian Class (P Class); Rainbow Class
(Second R Class); River Class (Thames Class); Churchill Class (Improved Valiant Class); and
Resolution Class (Polaris Class).

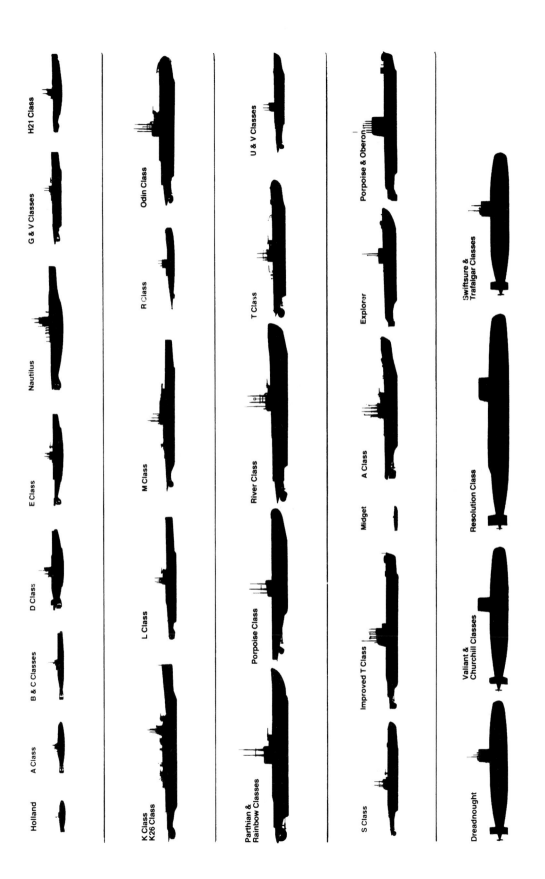

Holland

A Class

B & C Classes

D Class

E Class

Nautilus

G & V Classes

H21 Class

K Class
K26 Class

L Class

M Class

R Class

Odin Class

Parthian &
Rainbow Classes

Porpoise Class

River Class

T Class

U & V Classes

S Class

Improved T Class

Midget

A Class

Explorer

Porpoise & Oberon

Dreadnought

Valiant &
Churchill Classes

Resolution Class

Swiftsure &
Trafalgar Classes

Appendix II
The 'Nearly' Submarines

For completeness of this history and for those wishing to conduct further research we have recorded the Yard Number (and the name/identity where known) of submarine boats intended for construction at Barrow which, for the reasons given below, were never completed or constructed. All these submarines were originally ordered by the Royal Navy, except the private venture Oberon Class submarines. These were projected as a Vickers Shipbuilding Group private venture for possible sale to Argentina and/or Brazil. Argentina ultimately ordered smaller ships from West Germany, a move which attracted some attention in the British press (in early 1969) in view of Treaty limitations on German submarine building. It should be noted that the information in the list below is as recorded in the Shipyard's own listing of Yard Numbers and the authors have made no attempt to verify the information.

L28	L Class	(Yard No.543)	Contract cancelled
L29	L Class	(Yard No.544)	Contract cancelled
L30	L Class	(Yard No.545)	Contract cancelled
L31	L Class	(Yard No.546)	Contract cancelled
K27	K26 Class	(Yard No.565)	Contract cancelled
K28	K26 Class	(Yard No.566)	Contract cancelled
Unnamed	S Class	(Yard No.820)	Contract transferred to Scott's of Greenock
Unnamed	S Class	(Yard No.821)	Contract transferred to Scott's of Greenock
Unnamed	S Class	(Yard No.822)	Contract transferred to Scott's of Greenock
Unnamed	S Class	(Yard No.823)	Contract transferred to Cammell Laird of Birkenhead
Unnamed	S Class	(Yard No.824)	Contract transferred to Cammell Laird of Birkenhead
Unnamed	S Class	(Yard No.825)	Contract transferred to Cammell Laird of Birkenhead
Unnamed	S Class	(Yard No.826)	Contract transferred to Cammell Laird of Birkenhead
Theban	T Class	(Yard No.875)	Contract cancelled

Tabard	T Class	(Yard No.876)	Contract transferred to Scott's of Greenock, where she was built
Talent	T Class	(Yard No.877)	Contract cancelled
Threat	T Class	(Yard No.878)	Contract cancelled
P345	T Class	(Yard No.879)	Contract cancelled
P346	T Class	(Yard No.880)	Contract cancelled
P347	T Class	(Yard No.881)	Contract cancelled
P348	T Class	(Yard No.882)	Contract cancelled
Veto	Second V Class	(Yard No.892)	Contract cancelled
Virile	Second V Class	(Yard No.893)	Contract cancelled
Visitant	Second V Class	(Yard No.894)	Contract cancelled
Upas	Second V Class	(Yard No.895)	Contract cancelled
Ulex	Second V Class	(Yard No.896)	Contract cancelled
Utopia	Second V Class	(Yard No.897)	Contract cancelled
Andromache	Second A Class	(Yard No.913)	Contract cancelled
Answer	Second A Class	(Yard No.914)	Contract cancelled
Antagonist	Second A Class	(Yard No.915)	Contract cancelled
Antaeus	Second A Class	(Yard No.916)	Contract cancelled
Anzac	Second A Class	(Yard No.917)	Contract cancelled
Aphrodite	Second A Class	(Yard No.918)	Contract cancelled
Approach	Second A Class	(Yard No.919)	Contract cancelled
Arcadian	Second A Class	(Yard No.920)	Contract cancelled
Ardent	Second A Class	(Yard No.921)	Contract cancelled
Argosy	Second A Class	(Yard No.922)	Contract cancelled
Atlantis	Second A Class	(Yard No.923)	Contract cancelled
PV01	Oberon Class	(Yard No.1081)	Contract cancelled – private venture
Unnamed	Oberon Class	(Yard No.1082)	Contract cancelled – private venture
Unnamed	Oberon Class	(Yard No.1083)	Contract cancelled – private venture

Some 'Drawing Board' Submarines

Over the years, many boat designs have been produced by the Shipyard which never reached further than the drawing board stage. There are too many to describe in detail, but we offer a selection of exmaples with supporting information from their promotional brochures. One of these – *Piranha* – was lucky enough to reach the 'mock-up' stage.

In 1986 the Shipyard produced a small leaflet to promote their commercial submarines: the Piranha Class, 550 Class and Type 2400 Class. The 2400 Class was the only one of the three classes which was ever built (HMS *Upholder* being constructed for the Royal Navy) and we have covered this class of submarines in pages 192-96. However, the proposed Piranha Class and 550 Class boats did not reach construction stage.

The leaflet said of *Piranha*:

> *Despite the success of the nuclear submarine, particularly in long-range deep-water roles, they are too large and too costly to risk in shallow waters; and they are, of course, an unrealistic proposition for many maritime nations. Consequently there is still a considerable demand for diesel-electric submarines of which VSEL currently has three designs available – Piranha, 550 Class and Type 2400. Piranha is a small surveillance/attack vessel, with good tactical range and relatively high transit speed. The main armament is mines or two 2-man chariots armed with mines and limpet mines. The chariots can be launched and recovered while Piranha remains fully submerged. Combat swimmers and chariot operators are released and recovered through a diver lock-out chamber.*

Also according to the leaflet: 'The 550 Class is an up-to-date ocean-going submarine, capable of carrying out coastal and medium-range patrols. It can accept a weapon and sensor fit normally associated with the much larger ocean patrol submarines.'

Another commercial venture which never got past the design stage was the Type 2497, and it was promoted in a Shipyard leaflet in 1989. The text from the leaflet is reproduced below:

> *An Evolutionary Design that Meets the Exacting Requirements of the Future Through the Application of New and Advanced Technologies*

> *The Type 2497 is a long endurance, deep diving submarine for the 21st century. It embodies the very latest developments in submarine systems, sensors and weapons in a vessel which is equally at home in the shallow waters and in the deep oceans, and which has development potential for prolonged submerged operations with independent propulsion. The Type 2497 has four diesel generators and three battery sections, each of 240 cells, to provide a propulsion system that is characterised by its flexibility, reliability and economy. Part of all this installation can be replaced by a fuel cell system for full air independent operation. The major benefits of such a system are the ability to maintain extremely low noise signatures through the entire mission, prolonged submerged endurance and – because the submarine has no need to snort in order to recharge its batteries – dramatically reduced indiscretion rates and low vulnerability.*

> *The Type 2497 is designed to permit full operational effectiveness with the minimum possible level of manning. All systems are highly automated to allow a 3-watch patrol state and a 2-watch defence state. Carefully designed living and working spaces, optimal man/machine inter-faces, high reliability and minimal onboard maintenance combine to ease crew stress and fatigue throughout the mission.*

> *The computer-based energy management system provides the Command with fast, accurate information on the vessel's remaining energy resources, thus allowing power usage to be judged within very fine limits and extending submerged operations to the maximum.*

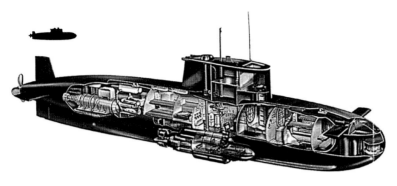

Piranha.

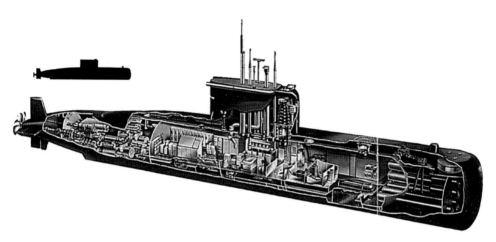

550 Class.

Type 2497.

The Type 2497 has a powerful and versatile combat system incorporated in a platform with outstanding stealth characteristics. A structured approach to the design ensures the full, system-wide integration of a variety of equipments according to operational requirements. Extensive use is made of multi-function consoles, divorced from the signal processing function, to reduce clutter and provide a spacious and effective working environment.

The submarine is equipped with large sensitive sonars at the bow, on the flanks and astern, together with a towed array, a comprehensive above-water sensor fit, high latitude navigation facilities and fast, secure external communications. The above and below-water sensors transmit information to the tactical data handling system computers via a VSEL-designed database which performs the following tasks: (1) Correlation of sensor data. (2) Generation of target parameters. (3) Production of fire control solutions. (4) Control of weapon launch. (5) Weapon guidance.

The Type 2497 can launch and control heavyweight torpedoes, anti-ship missiles and mines. Able to detect with absolute safety and at extreme range, and to deliver a potent weapon load with devastating accuracy, the Type 2497 has a remarkable strike capability making it a deadly and most effective adversary.

Length Overall	63 metres
Breadth	7.6 metres
Surface Displacement	2,200 tons
Complement	30
Designed Diving Depth	350 metres
Torpedo Tubes	6
Total weapons carried	20
Speed Submerged	24 knots
Endurance	2 hours at 20 knots or 120 hours at 3 knots

Appendix III
German Submarines at Barrow-in-Furness

This appendix records some of the events surrounding German submarines brought to Barrow-in-Furness though it is not claimed that all such boats have been identified. Of those reported here, the Second World War boats are well known and well documented while the First World War Type UB-III boat was identified during research into another matter. This third type of the UB series were constructed in 1917 and 1918 and had by then lost much of their original coastal characteristics but were nevertheless successful enough to serve as a prototype, some fifteen years later, for development of the design of the Type VII of Second World War fame.

A Type UB-III berthed alongside Devonshire Dock's town wharf on Saturday 17 January 1919. Her previous port of call had been Fleetwood and, following ten days at Barrow, she would motor up to Whitehaven. Her mission at each port of call was identical – to permit the public to view her in return for a small admission fee which would be donated to Royal Navy charities. The typical characteristics for a Type UB-III boat were: Surfaced displacement of 520 tons; submerged displacement of 650 tons; armament of five torpedo tubes (four bow and one stern) and one 4.1in gun; length 181ft, beam 19ft and draught 12ft; surface speed 13.5 knots, submerged speed 7.5 knots; twin diesel engines producing 1,100shp and electric motors producing 760shp; two propellers; surface endurance 8,500 miles at 6 knots; diving depth approximately 200ft; and complement thirty-four.

A water-line silhouette illustrating a Type UB-III submarine, a class which were originally designed as coastal boats.

★ ★ ★

U-570 berthed alongside the Ramsden Dock on 3 October 1941 and, following a rigorous inspection by Royal Navy specialists, was handed over to the Yard for refit on 9 October 1941. It was probably during that inspection that the young Yard caulker-burner Donald Craig was assisted in cutting away the crushed bow plates by one of the two navy officers assigned to making the torpedoes safe prior to removal. Those officers were Lts Ashe Lincoln (Directorate of Torpedoes and Mining) and Martin Johnson.

To add to the technical equipment already described on page 111 were a very sophisticated gyro-compass, attack calculator (this performed a function similar to the Royal Navy's famed

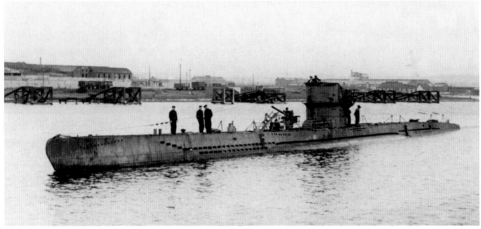

Above and middle: Views of German submarine U-570 under the White Ensign in the Barrow dock system. *Below*: U-570 undergoing trials at sea.

fruit machine but was much more advanced) and there was also a full set of drawings. These 'finds' would permit the Royal Navy to determine which areas they lagged in and as to how they should direct resources to catch up and improve on German brilliance; identify those areas where they were ahead and how they could maintain them; and how they could turn German technical know-how against Germany and make the hunter become the hunted. After the re-fit, U-570 (or HMS *Graph* as she had become) carried out extensive sea trials in the Clyde, which yielded more valuable information.

★ ★ ★

U-532, a Type IX C-40 boat, surrendered at Liverpool on 10 May 1945, unloading her cargo of strategic materials which included 8 tons of wolfram, 5 tons of molybdenum, 100 tons of tin and a deck cargo of 60 tons of rubber. The Type IXC-40 were double-hulled ocean-going submarine boats possessing good sea-keeping qualities and long range. Their characteristically wide and flat deck combined with bulwarks almost perpendicular to the surface made them a very stable platform. It did, however, increase crash-dive time.

From Liverpool, U-532 sailed under destroyer escort to Barrow and the *Barrow News* of 26 May 1945 described her arrival under the headline 'Nazi Submarine Comes to Barrow' as follows:

> In the Graving Dock at Barrow, within a stone's throw of homes wrecked by the Luftwaffe, lies the U-532, once the pride of the German under-water fleet. There was no demonstration, just a little curiosity, as the big submarine – she is 240ft long and designed for cargo-carrying – came up Walney Channel on Friday. LMS railway and naval officials watched the U-boat arrive off Piel with an escorting destroyer and enter the channel. She had come from Liverpool with a German crew aboard guarded by a British Naval party. Opposite the docks the destroyer left her and she was taken in tow by a tug while another steamed ahead.
>
> Workers ran out on the banks as the U-boat, with the White Ensign floating from her conning tower, passed the Shipyard. There were a few people on the Walney banks, and at one point a couple of women waved Union Jacks. On the bridge two or three hundred people awaited the passing of the submarine. The spans were opened and as she glided between the piers with three Nazi sailors fore and aft and armed British officers on the bridge, a woman called 'Boo them' but there was no demonstration. 'They're the blighters that stopped the bananas coming,' said another woman, amid laughter.
>
> At the entrance to the Graving Dock the tugs left the U-boat and she moved in under her own power. Wearing a light kind of khaki-coloured uniform, not unlike that of the US troops, half-a-dozen German sailors, one sporting an Iron Cross sign, busied themselves in mooring the ship. They looked in good condition, but in need of a haircut, and seemed to be very little embarrassed by their position. A gangway was slung aboard, and LMS dockmen went on to the U-boat and squared her into position preparatory to the dock being emptied of water.
>
> It is stated that the submarine has been brought to Barrow to have 'certain work' carried out. Rusted and pitted with all distinguishing marks removed, the submarine looks as if she were in need of several coats of paint. Mounted on her squat bridge is an anti-aircraft gun, and she carries a heavier gun aft.

German submarine U-532.

> *The public were excluded from the dock when she arrived and interviews with anybody on board were banned. In fact there was no sign of fraternisation, which is frowned upon by naval authorities. She was docked under the supervision of Harbour Master Coates and Trinity House and LMS pilots brought her up the channel. The U-532 is a cargo-carrying submarine, one of the type designed to run the blockade between Germany and Japan. It is hoped she will later be on view to the public, who will be admitted to the Graving Dock but not on board the ship.*

The *Barrow News* was granted its wish, the Barrow public being permitted to view U-532 on 2 and 3 June for a token admission fee later donated to a naval charity. Some 7,500 of the public took the opportunity to visit the Graving Dock and the *Barrow News* noted U-532 to be 'an object of interest remarkable not so much for its size as for the amount of internal equipment which was dispensed with to adapt it as an underwater cargo vessel.'

The Shipyard and the navy spent some time examining U-532 which later went to the U-boat assembly point at Loch Ryan prior to disposal by the Royal Navy in Operation Deadlight – the code name under which 116 U-boats were disposed of by the navy. In early December 1945 U-532 was towed north-west of Tory Island and sunk by the submarine HMS *Tantivy*.

U-532 – Details at a Glance

Constructed by	Deutsche Werft, Hamburg
Launched	26 August 1942
Dimensions	287ft x 24ft 6in x 17ft 9in
Machinery	2 x diesel engines (4,400hp) for surface propulsion and 2 x electric motors (1,000hp) for submerged propulsion

Speed	18.2 knots surfaced / 7.7 knots submerged
Range	13,850 miles at 10 knots surfaced / 63 miles at 4 knots submerged
Diving Depth	450ft
Torpedo Tubes	6 x 21in (4 forward, 2 aft)
Guns	1 x 4.1in, 1 x 37mm and 1 x 20mm
Complement	57

★ ★ ★

Below is a rather unsatisfactory photograph of U-1407, briefly referenced on page 140. Whatever the shortcomings of the picture, the story will more than make up for it. Scuttled at Cuxhaven on 2 May 1945 to prevent it falling into Russian hands, U-1407, and similar boats, had been known to Allied intelligence since 1943 but were never verified by sightings. The first sightings of these vessels, named 'Walterboote' after the designer Dr Rudolph Walter, were by members of a Royal Marine Commando Unit raised specially to ensure significant material of an operational or strategic use was made available to Britain. The marines, or more correctly, their 30 Assault Unit, located two badly damaged Walterboote (U-1408 and U-1410) at the Blohm and Voss works at Hamburg on 3 May 1945. The next day, they reached Kiel and occupied the Walterwerke itself (which, along with Dr Walter and his staff, revealed a number of prized items and materials). Weapons, materials, components (including the highly prized reduction gearing), chemicals and documents were readied for shipping to Barrow as indeed were Dr Walter and a number of his scientific staff. During meaningful discussion with Allied interrogators the German scientists revealed the location of U-1407 which, although scuttled, was not too badly damaged to be beyond use.

Once salvaged, U-1407 was made sea-worthy and prepared for towing to Barrow. A German tug, which was to become war reparation, towed U-1407 to Sheerness; from there the tow to the Barrow Shipyard was made by a British ocean-going tug. Apparently U-1407's entry to the Yard was undertaken with a degree of anonymity, at least as far as the local press were concerned.

German submarine U-1407

German submarine U-1407 (later HMS *Meteorite*).

The arrival of Dr Walter, his staff and the sealed crates, was altogether a different matter as the local press took delight in reporting the local furore:

German Hush-Hush Ship at Barrow

Secret Voyage Ended
The German cargo vessel Elisabeth, *which arrived in Barrow last week with a consignment of 'hush-hush' machinery after a secret voyage from Kiel, Germany, is now safely berthed at the rear of the aircraft-carrier* Majestic, *in Ramsden Dock and her precious cargo has been unloaded. The 'hush-hush' machinery, it is learned, is packed in wooden cases, some of which are stencilled 'Berlin' and 'Wien' (Vienna). Part of the cargo is believed to have come from the great Hermann Goering Works in the Ruhr. Certain of the cases are reported to be marked 'Absender-Siemens Schuckerwerke Weiner Mascchinen' and consigned thus: 'An gugegast, Bredenbek I Holst, Brandsbek'. The machinery has been unloaded by naval personnel and members of Messrs. Vickers-Armstrongs' staff who have been sworn to secrecy. A conference regarding the ship was held in London on Friday week, but so far no official statement has been forthcoming and she still remains a 'mystery' ship. It is believed, however, that the machinery may be an advanced delivery against reparation account.*

Attempted 'Seizures'
It is understood that the Customs attempted to 'arrest' the vessel, but she was ultimately cleared as an Admiralty ship, although it is possible that she may ultimately be seized as a prize and her fate decided by an International Prize Court. The Elisabeth *is a German vessel specially adapted for conveying machinery, and her arrival from the port of Kiel naturally aroused a good*

deal of curiosity. It has not been possible to get any official statement on the ship or her cargo. It will be remembered that some time ago submarine experts from Barrow, and the leading production chief of Messrs. Vickers-Armstrongs Ltd, left England to investigate the submarine bases of Northern Germany.

The official statement requested by the *Barrow News* was not long in coming and was offered to the public of Barrow on 5 January 1946:

German Key Men Coming to Barrow

The following official statement was handed to a 'News' representative on Friday by Admiralty representatives in Barrow, following our recent enquiries. 'The interest of Barrovians will be aroused by the arrival of a German vessel at Barrow, and the statement of the President of the Board of Trade in the House of Commons on 19 December, that it is the intention to extract from Germans any knowledge which may be of value to this country. In this connection it is learned that certain of these German scientists will be brought to work in the vicinity of Barrow. It can be safely assumed that whatever knowledge these Germans may have will be put to good use in this country'.

'Enemy Aliens'
'During their stay in the country they will be treated as enemy alien civilians, and housed in a standard Admiralty hostel. They will be given a certain amount of freedom, but will be subject to Admiralty and police supervision'. It is understood that the scientists have already been advised that they are not permitted to give any interviews to the Press or any other agency. They have also been told that they are not going to communicate anything to persons unless they are in uniform.

Statement in the Commons
In a written reply to a question in the House of Commons on the subject of bringing technicians and scientists from Germany, Sir Stafford Cripps, president of the Board of Trade, said on 19 December: 'Although Britain generally was ahead in scientific progress, in some fields Germany had a temporary lead and a strictly limited number of men of the highest grade would be brought over for service in this country'. He added 'all must be politically unobjectionable, and they will be subject to strict supervision while they are here. It is intended that in general these experts should work in Government establishments or for research associations sponsored by the Department of Scientific and Industrial Research. In approved cases their services may be available to individual firms. In no case will a German be brought in to undertake work that could equally well be performed by a British subject. Sir Charles Darwin will be chairman of a panel to examine the requirements of British industry and to scrutinise credentials of those whose names are put forward.'

Barrovians were by now indicating a certain amount of concern about the living conditions of the German scientists which were perceived as being considerably better than those of the 'victors'. Letters of complaint were being printed in the papers and, to be fair, so were some letters supporting the scientists and their work. The media determined on further enquiries and their findings, as far as the *Evening Mail* had pursued them, were reported as follows on 7 January 1946:

German Scientists

'Temporary Civil Servants'
'Top Secret' Work May Help Barrow Switch-Over
Making further inquiries into the arrival of the small party of German scientists who have taken up residence in Barrow, an Evening Mail *reporter was informed that their secret scientific research work, far from being detrimental to the town, will be a means of assisting its industrial development. In addition their work will, in all probability, be a means of attracting more work to the area, which, after the First World War, was severely hit by industrial depression in the switch-over to peace-time production.*

'Back Room Boys'
Much interest and curiosity has naturally been aroused as a result of the world-wide publicity accorded the arrival of these eminent German research workers, and the 'hush-hush' machinery which preceded them from the port of Kiel by about a month. As the work of the scientists comes under the heading of 'top secret' on the Admiralty list, it is considered that the development of the revolutionary inventions of these 'back room boys' will bring about will, in the national interest, have to remain a closely-guarded secret [for the] meantime.

Quiet Week-end
After settling down in the Admiralty hostel at 'Rocklea', Abbey Road, Barrow, which is furnished on austerity lines, the scientists quietly spent their first week-end in England by getting to know their whereabouts and admiring the beauty of their surroundings. On Saturday they were registered as enemy civilians, and afterwards issued with special identity cards and ordinary civilian rationing documents which placed them on more or less the same footing as British civilians.

Civil Servants
Our reporter was informed by an Admiralty official that the scientists had been placed in the category of temporary civil servants. It is therefore presumed that they will receive remuneration from the Admiralty for their work.

At Church Services
Three of the party, on Sunday morning, attended divine services at two Barrow churches and the remainder went on a sight-seeing tour of the town on foot. Apart from certain restrictions, the scientists are now more or less free men and will be able to do more or less as they please and be without escorts.

Statement Denied
Alderman J. Miller, secretary of Barrow Trades Council, which represents 65 trade unions,
when interviewed regarding a statement in a daily newspaper alleged to have been made by him
'that the men in the shipyards would not work with the Germans under any consideration,'
emphatically denied having made it.

Whatever that delivered report in the *Evening Mail* was intent on doing, it certainly didn't
calm matters and, by mid-January, the *Barrow News* would contain the following article:

German Experts Come to Barrow
Believed to be headed by the world-famous authority on torpedoes and inventor of synthetic
fuels, Dr Rudolph Walther, a small party of German scientists, holding high degrees, arrived
last week-end at Barrow-in-Furness from Germany. The arrival of the scientists was cloaked
in secrecy, and it is understood that they have been told not to communicate anything regarding
their secret scientific research work to the Press or any other agency. Admiralty officials have
intimated that the men will continue their work in the vicinity of the town.

Protest to Government
'Horror at the installation of the German technicians in Barrow,' was unanimously expressed
at a meeting of the Barrow Townswomen's Guild on Monday. Members agreed on an opinion
that the Government were very ill-advised to think for one moment that such recent enemies
could be trusted to reveal anything worthwhile. In any case, it was demanded, why house them
in more comfort than the majority of Barrow citizens? It was decided to write to Mr Monslow,
MP, on the matter expressing, in no uncertain terms, the intense dislike Barrow women felt
towards men who had so recently accomplished the destruction of their sons and husbands. It
was further decided that the Government should be requested to immediately derequisition
Rocklea, the house in which the Germans will stay, for housing purposes – rather than for
youth or any other movement – a policy to be pursued until Barrow's housing position is more
satisfactory.

Barrow Co-Op Youth Club and 'Rocklea'
The following resolution was carried unanimously by the Co-operative Youth Club at a
meeting on Wednesday. 'We appeal to the public of Barrow to support us in a campaign to
secure the removal of the German scientists from 'Rocklea'. This building was purchased by
the Barrow Co-operative Society last year for the housing of the Co-operative Youth
Movement, and we feel that the action of the Admiralty in installing the German scientists
there is most unwarrantable. 'Rocklea' was vacated by the Military authorities some three
months ago and strenuous efforts were being made to secure derequisition at an early date.
Alternative accommodation could have been found for the German scientists, even in the same
area of town and we hope that the citizens of Barrow will raise their voice in protest at this
flagrant piece of injustice.'

Mr Monslow would report the German scientists' surroundings 'as Spartan to a degree close to
unacceptable were Barrovians required to live the same way.' Asked what the scientists' opinions
were of Rocklea and Barrovians, Mr Monslow had replied 'acceptable' to the former and 'those
we have come into contact with have been professionally correct and courteous' to the latter.

Barrovians must have been satisfied with Mr Monslow's words, or the Press had worried the story enough, because the matter of the German scientists faded away. With no further information coming from the Admiralty or the Shipyard, the matter of the mysterious crates on the *Elisabeth* would also be forgotten. In the meantime, work was underway on U-1407 to re-fit, and in some areas substantially modify, her for tests and trials which, if successful, would lead to the Royal Navy's use of high-test peroxide (HTP) as a means of providing an extremely high speed for use in emergencies.

U-1407 was subject to a number of changes amongst which were the removal of torpedo tubes (the hull apertures being blanked), modification of the battery ventilation system for use as per the Royal Navy, an extra air compressor was fitted (although the original high-pressure air system for operating the main vents was discarded as was the snorkel) and, due to earlier scuttling, all electrical equipments were changed. The turbine plant was to be tested in a workshop test bed and would require almost two years of work – in fact it would be July 1948 before it was considered suitably reliable to be re-housed on the boat now named HMS *Meteorite*.

Meteorite's diesel-electric drive had been fully trialled by the Royal Navy who had a suitable opportunity to familiarise themselves with the operational handling characteristics of the boat while the turbine was on shore test. In Autumn 1948 a modification was undertaken to *Meteorite*'s conning tower to improve her performance at speed. Boat trials of the turbine proved satisfactory and, although her top speed of 18 knots didn't meet the design speed of 25 knots, valuable information was provided by the trials. By 1949 *Meteorite*'s usefulness had ended and she was sold to local ship-breaker T.W. Ward for breaking.

It would be several years after *Meteorite*'s demise that *Excalibur* and *Explorer* would be laid down (see pages 141-44). There is no doubt that the lessons learned from the captured *Meteorite* and also from Dr Walter and his team of German scientists paved the way for the building of *Excalibur* and *Explorer* though, as can be read on pages 141-44 the experiments with high-test hydrogen peroxide were less than successful and eventually the idea was to fade out.

Appendix IV
Pisces Mini-Submarines

The inclusion of this brief appendix on commercial mini-submarines is justified by virtue of the Yard acting as a sub-contractor for some activities related to the Pisces and the LR series boats (whose identification letters are in honour of Sir Leonard Redshaw – an early protagonist of mini-subs). The original Pisces were developed by Canadian company International Hydrodynamics Ltd, and their potential was recognised by what was, in the 1960s, the Oceanics Department at the Shipyard. Under a joint agreement, Hydrodynamics and the Oceanics Department operated *Pisces* in the late 1960s and at the same time sub-contracted the construction of two pressure hulls (manufactured from HY100 steel, and capable of operating in depths up to 6,500ft) to the Shipyard. A support/research vessel, *Vickers Venturer*, a stern trawler converted to lift *Pisces* into and out of the water, was operated by the well-known Barrow ship-owners Fisher & Sons. By 1970, Vickers' annual reports were able to state that '*Pisces* submersible has been employed on work for the MoD, fisheries, geological institute and the national Environmental Research Council' and in 1971: 'In oceanics, the *Pisces* submersible was in increasing demand for underwater search and research and a second submersible was accordingly being put into commission.' As the workload increased so did the support fleet, and sub-contract work of a modification and upkeep nature would fall to the Yard for both the *Pisces* and support vessels.

Pisces was described at that time as displacing 11 tons, being about 10ft wide and 19ft long and a little over 10ft high with a crew of two. Equipped with external front claw manipulator it was propelled by two 3hp electric motors. The crew pressure hull had an internal diameter of 6ft 6in, providing 72cu.ft per person – which was 10% to 20% greater than other similar spheres. The monitored atmosphere could last seventy-two hours by removal of carbon dioxide, replenishment of oxygen and air cleansing through an activated charcoal bed. Electronic equipment comprised VHF radio for surface use, underwater telephone communications with the support ship, magnetic and gyro-compass systems, sector scanning sonar for navigation, echo sounder depth gauge as well as temperature and ballast indicators. With new contracts came a new name for the company – Vickers Oceanics Ltd (VOL) – who were now operating three Pisces boats and were well established in the off-shore business.

In August 1973, *Pisces III* and the identities of her crew of two would become world-wide household names as in hour-by-hour broadcasts TV, radio and press reported on the 2½-day rescue operation mounted after the mini-sub plunged 1,575ft to the ocean bed. The Yard called for volunteers to assist in work of an unspecified nature and apparently the entire Yard volunteered. One well-publicised task was the construction of a special toggle to lock in the open hatch of the aft sphere, by which means *Pisces III* would eventually be raised. The rescue itself was conducted by an international team from both sides of the Atlantic. The two crew members were Roger Mallinson and Roger Chapman who the media would describe as

A Pisces mini-submarine.

'Aquanauts, a tough breed of men, superbly fit and mentally well adapted to undergo the plight they are in.' Lack of space precludes further description here, better anyway to read the full amazing story told by Roger Chapman in his book *No Time on Our Side*.

VOL continued to expand, obtaining from Perry Oceanographics a diver lockout submersible which became known as L1 and operated from a support vessel converted for diver lockout operations with a saturation diving system and transfer under pressure facility. The submersible fleet grew to ten, including three built by Vickers-Slingsby with hulls constructed from glass reinforced plastic (GRP) on which the Yard undertook some mechanical operations.

That use of GRP lead to the manufacture and testing of the first composite material dry transfer skirt designed to clamp directly to the lower trunking of L1's diver lockout compartment. Following a series of trials and exercises the transfer system was validated in August 1975 when L1 successfully locked onto Canadian Navy submarine HMCS *Ojibwa* and the transfer of personnel took place.

One very important mini-sub was LR 5, designed and manufactured in 1978 by Vickers-Slingsby in accordance with Lloyds Register requirements for the construction and classification of submersibles. With a crew of five, including two divers, LR 5 was originally intended for diver lockout operations at a maximum depth of 1,500ft but, in 1983, now in the role of Submarine Rescue Submersible, was modified and successfully trialled for retention as part of the MoD(N) submersible rescue contract operated by British Oceanics Ltd. The rescue contract was eventually awarded to Rumic, which runs the submarine rescue base operated from Renfrew, Scotland, where LR 5 is kept on permanent stand-by.

Rumic's head office is at Dalton-in-Furness, close to Barrow, from which it supplies personnel trained for various operations in the off-shore and nuclear industries, in particular ROV applications. This office also maintains the submarine rescue database which supplies up-to-date information on such matters as marine, road, rail and air transport availability for LR 5, as well as crews and support staff in the event of a submarine rescue either real or practice. Rumic have now maintained, modified and upgraded LR 5 for a number of years. In April 2000 LR 5 was certified to Lloyds Register requirements in submarine rescue operations to a maximum depth of 400msw (metres of sea water). From 2000, ownership of LR 5 has rested with MoD(N). Rumic Ltd currently hold the contract to maintain and operate LR 5 in its role as submarine rescue submersible, as they did in 2001 when they stood by the Russian Navy's *Kursk* desperately awaiting permission to undertake a rescue mission which Russian authorities ignored. The managing director of Rumic Ltd is Roger Chapman who, with Roger Mallinson, crewed *Pisces III* in those desperate 2½ days of August 1973.

In late 2002, as this book was being finalised, Rumic Ltd was taken over by the well-known shipping company James Fisher & Sons to form a new company names James Fisher Rumic Ltd.

Pisces III mini-submarine with diver aboard preparing the boat for hoisting onto a support vessel.

Appendix V
The Royal Commission on the
Private Manufacture of Arms

The scale of Vickers' activities is vast and of considerable interest. However, even more inter-esting is the part that the Admiralty agreement (illustrated opposite) and the Electric Boat Co. agreement (illustrated on page 270) would play in the evidence Sir Charles Craven (then Vickers' managing director) would give in the 1935 Royal Commission on the Private Manufacture of Arms. Included below is the relevant extract from the Commission's proceed-ings which was conducted in an atmosphere of press hostility to Vickers. The full proceed-ings, widely reported in the press at the time, are far too long to be covered here but they are excellently summarised in J.D. Scott's *Vickers – A History*.

Extract From the 1935 Royal Commission on the Private Manufacture of Arms
Electric Boat Co. of America

Sir John (Eldon Banks – Chairman of the Commission) next referred to the statement of a previous witness, who had said that a foreign subsidiary company of Vickers had provided torpedo boats, torpedoes, torpedo destroyers, and mines for Austria immediately before the world war. Sir Charles Craven replied that Vickers had been shareholders in the company. He was advised that it was at the request of our own Government that they took an interest in this torpedo company. In 1907 there was an incorporation under English law, but they still held a shareholding in the main company at the declaration of war. 'Our sole interests in torpedoes now is at Weymouth,' he added. Sir John Eldon Banks next referred to the agreement which Vickers made with the Electric Boat Company of America. This was a very long document, he said, and had to do with the business of making and selling submarines. It provided that as between Vickers and the Electric Boat Company certain countries should be excluded altogether from the agreement, and that certain other countries should be reserved for Vickers and certain others for the Electric Boat Company. There was a provision as to the payment which should be made from one to the other in the event of business being done in one of the reserved terri-tories or the common territories. Sir Charles Craven made a long statement on the relations between the Electric Boat Company and Vickers-Armstrongs. He said that negotiations in connection with the construction of the first five submarines for the British Navy were in the first instance conducted in 1899-1900 between the Admiralty and the Holland Torpedo Boat Co. which later became the Electric Boat Co. 'During the inquiry in Washington,' he added, 'Mr Carse, the present president of the Electric Boat Co., who perhaps does not know the whole history of the agreement between the Electric Boat Co. and Vickers, is reported to have stated, 'he believed the British Government had no knowledge of the agreements between Vickers-Armstrongs and the Electric Boat Co., but the Electric Boat Co. had advised the United States Navy Department of them.'

Example of a Vickers' agreement with the Admiralty dated 14 May 1906 replacing a previous agreement for building submarine boats.

'This evidence is incorrect,' said Sir Charles, who pointed out that two paragraphs of an Admiralty letter to Vickers dated 13 December 1900, proved that the Admiralty had full knowledge of the agreement between Vickers and the Electric Boat Company. In this letter the Admiralty offered Vickers the contract for the first five 'Holland' submarines. According to earlier correspondence between the Admiralty and Vickers, the construction of submarines for the Admiralty commenced in the year 1900. By an agreement of 17 May 1902, between the Admiralty and Vickers, the Admiralty agreed to confine submarine construction to Vickers for five years provided that Vickers did not build, design or sell to any other Government any submarine boat of any kind whatever before 1 April 1909. This agreement of May 1902 was cancelled by a further agreement dated 14 May 1906, which again tied Vickers to the Admiralty for five years, from April 1906, and precluded Vickers from foreign business for these five years and two years thereafter except with the consent of the Admiralty. 'Under this agreement, however, the Admiralty only bound themselves to give us half of the submarines ordered, but agreed not to invite other firms to compete, provided Vickers could give satisfaction regarding deliveries.' Went on Sir Charles: 'It will be seen that the closest possible liaison existed between the Admiralty and Vickers in connection with the construction of the 'Holland' type of submarine for the British Navy up to 1911. About that time the Admiralty desired to consider other foreign designs, and Scott's of Greenock made an arrangement with the Fiat san Giorgia Co. and Armstrong-Whitworths with Schneider.'

'Much has been made of the fact that profits are shared with the Electric Boat Company. To the best of my belief, the arrangement of profit-sharing instead of a fixed royalty in the original agreement with the Electric Boat Co. was due to the fact that Vickers were not prepared to put down the necessary capital for the equipment of special shops and the provision of the necessary special jigs and tools for the provision of a type of vessel the future of which was in doubt.' The statement then referred to a new agreement expiring 31 December, 1937, which provided for a Royalty of three per cent on British submarines built by Vickers and a division of foreign business between the two companies. 'Much has been made of this carving up of the world into zones of operation,' the statement continued, 'but it seems to me that the only reason for this arrangement was that the Electric Boat Company, in the meantime, had agreements with

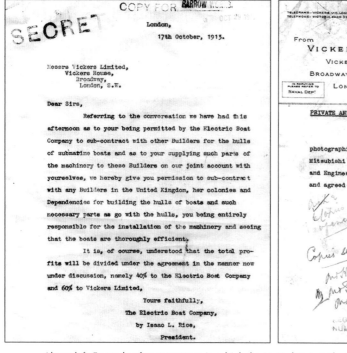

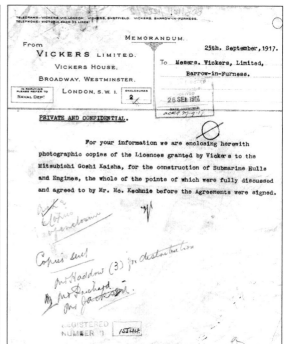

Above left: Example of an agreement in which the United States' Electric Boat Company granted permission to Vickers to sub-contract, with any builders in the United Kingdom, colonies and dependencies, for building submarine hulls and machinery.

Above right: Example of a Vickers' agreement granting a licence to the Japanese company Mitsubishi for the construction of submarine hulls and engines, dated 25 September 1917.

certain foreign countries and had associations with others and, therefore, in some cases they could not agree to our interference in others, such as Peru, for which country they had been building submarines in America. They did not feel disposed to give us a licence to compete with them. I wish to make it clear that in my opinion the "Holland" (USA) submarine was the first practicable submarine vessel produced in the world.'

'I would go further and say that in 1914, when the American 'H' boats were bought by the British Navy after assembly at Montreal, the design of these small submarines was the best in the world. Particular reference has been made to certain letters by me to Mr Carse, president of the Electric Boat Company, and Mr Spear, a vice-president, who really carries out the duties of managing director. I should like to make it clear that I have known Mr Spear intimately ever since I joined Vickers in 1912, and this accounts for the fact that my letters to him are written in a very free and friendly way. Naturally had I known that such letters would be published the wording would have been different, but there is nothing in the letters which will not bear close investigation, and practically every letter in my file was written with one object only – and that was to impress on the Electric Boat Company the vital necessity of their reducing the three per cent royalty paid on British submarines in order that I could more satisfactorily compete with the British wartime builders who had no such royalty to pay. The success of the efforts which I have made in this direction is evident when it is appreciated that in no case since the signature *of the new agreement has royalty in accordance with the agreed scale been paid on British submarines, but always a mutually agreed amount considerably less, thus enabling us to reduce the price quoted to the Admiralty.'*

'I am confident that at Barrow we can build submarines more cheaply, more quickly, and more efficiently than any other builder in the country and possibly in the world, but in order to place ourselves in this position we have spent very large sums of money since the war in fitting ourselves for this very special and difficult form of construction. During the periods of the agreements with the Electric Boat Company the closest relationship has existed between the two companies for the obvious reason that we wished to obtain all technical information from the Electric Boat Company. In no case has any secret information been divulged by Vickers to the Electric Boat Company or vice versa. It is of particular interest to note that for 13 years Vickers were precluded from building submarines for foreign navies."

In May 1937 the government of the day issued its Statement on the Report of the Royal Commission, the contents of which were, at their most basic, a recommendation that arms manufacture should not become a State monopoly. Additionally, the Commission censured Vickers for two matters concerning past business practices, which in the circumstances left both matters as non-starters.★

One matter which was not explained in the report was how the supply of boats to Japan in 1908 went through – presumably that contract was subject to Admiralty consent.

★ These two matters were as follows:
1. Widely reported in the press in 1914 was the case of two Japanese admirals, Admiral Matsumoto and Admiral Fujii, who were found guilty of accepting financial inducements to influence the building of the battlecruiser *Kongo* (Yard No.414) at Barrow. Admiral Matsumoto was from the Japanese company Mitsui Bussan Kaisha, the Admiral Fujii from Vickers.
2. An agent of an unnamed British armaments firm had, in the Commission's words, 'connived at a bribe' on a tank contract in China. Although not named by the Commission, Vickers were aware that the incident involved their agent although they took the view that the agent was lining his pockets. Vickers, on learning of the incident which took place in 1932, immediately brought the man home and dismissed him

Appendix VI
The Build Cycle of a Polaris Submarine

It is almost forty years since the Polaris Class boats were constructed and there have been numerous changes in the intervening years to equipment and construction methods. However, to represent the co-ordination of activities undertaken by Yard staff, MoD, several thousand suppliers and the Royal Navy, this appendix demonstrates some basic principles which have not changed too much. The following sequence of illustrations (and words) are a mixture collated from the commissioning brochures of *Resolution* and *Repulse* to provide an example of the boat build cycle. Rather than choose the name of either *Resolution* or *Repulse* to represent the example, the chosen title is 'boat', 'Polaris boat' or 'ship'. Similarly we have not elected to name a dignitary for the launch, but instead refer to a 'patron'.

Vickers Dumbarton Tank

Before a vessel was constructed, exhaustive tests were carried out to check hull design and to observe the vessel's reaction to varying service conditions. Such tests on the Polaris model were undertaken at a Royal Naval Establishment. In addition, tests were performed at the Vickers Dumbarton Tank to determine the amount of dredging to be carried out at the end of the slipway.

A model of the channel, local to the slipway at Barrow, was constructed on the bed of the experimental tank, and launch experiments were carried out to determine the depth of water

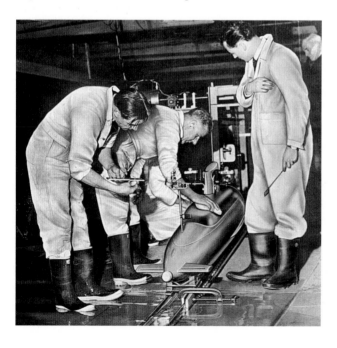

Figure 1: A Polaris model undergoing tank experiments.

required at the end of the slips to prevent the hull touching the bottom during launching. Subsequent measurement at the actual launch proved these experiments to be extremely accurate. (See **Figure 1**)

Studies had also been conducted on the stability of grounded submarines – intact and progressively flooded – in the context of escape. Consequently, when a Polaris boat grounded in Walney Channel on the sandbank after launch, those 'in the know' were aware that the boat could remain securely upright until, with the high tide and the assistance of tugs, she would be refloated intact (see pages 175-276).

Quality Control

The basic safety of the ship depended on the quality of design, materials and workmanship built into her. The Vickers' Quality Control Organisation was responsible for ensuring, by inspection, control procedures and audits, that the ship was built in accordance with drawings and specifications, also that the usual high standard of workmanship was maintained.

This included not only all the work carried out at Barrow, but also the many items of equipment which are manufactured throughout the country by sub-contractors. One type of inspection employed on the Polaris boats was the still widely used ultrasonic testing.

Tests and Trials

The Quality Control responsibilities were maintained during Contractor's Sea Trials as the rigorous programme of tests and trials, to which the boat was subjected, could have led to the removal and refurbishment of some components and equipment.

Tensile Testing

Tensile testing was conducted against a material 'batch', a sample being selected on a random basis or in accordance with a sequence determined by a standard or specification or possibly the customer – in this case MoD(PE).

On certain esoteric materials a 100% test was sometimes required. In the case of raw material the geometry of samples included plate, bar, rod or tube. The testing of finished material extends from fasteners through to test coupons on hull material such as castings and forgings, pipes and flanges. These are just a very few examples of the vast range tested.

Chemical Analysis

The general comments provided for tensile testing also hold true against chemical analysis. However, it should be noted that test and analysis was conducted against a variety of materials depending on their nature and use.

Just a few examples included electrical cable, shock mount rubber and various gases used in welding (argon and helium for instance). For all tests, of whatever nature, certification was required and in some cases reports. Consequently the Quality Control Department and the Test House and Laboratories maintained vast quantities of records, some for the lifetime of the item (in the case of the hull perhaps thirty years or more).

Figure 2: Machining of the main gearbox.

Main Gearbox

The main gearbox was machined (see **Figure 2**) with ultra-precision and advanced stress analysis techniques applied during the design. By these means good alignment and structural rigidity were obtained to ensure that the accurately produced gears mesh under ideal conditions during service – with the result that there is a uniform load distribution on the gear teeth and minimum generation of noise.

Main Machinery

Manufacture of the main machinery was arranged to be complementary to the submarine-building programme to ensure that the larger components could be built into the hull at the berth. To maintain the correct alignment between the units comprising the main machinery, and to reduce the effects of shock loading, the main machinery was mounted on a special jig. Workshop practice was to the highest standards to ensure the necessary reliability and quietness of operation, and all materials employed were subjected to the most stringent tests.

Skilled Staff

The complexity and size of the Polaris boats and the extremely tight timing of the delivery programme were of sufficient concern in themselves, but added to those was the necessity to further expand Shipyard facilities and to mount a huge recruitment drive to attract personnel with the appropriate abilities for the programme. In most cases that ability required additional training, sometimes of the 'on the job' variety and sometimes more formal.

Put simply, there were just not enough people with the experience necessary for building the biggest, most advanced nuclear submarine the world had, at that time, ever seen.

Take the case of fitters (although this applied equally to all tradesmen). It was difficult enough finding people with the requisite time-served apprenticeship ('chancer' applicants were numerous) but above and beyond that was a need for specialist skills – spot facing for instance.

Many of the high pressure pipe systems required the flanged connections to be spot faced finished and then mated, via spot facing, with the opposing flange. This was a technique unknown to many of the fitters who successfully applied to work on the boats. Nevertheless, it was one that would need to be acquired.

Structural welding on the hull and some welding of pipe systems, such as the reactor primary system, required the welder to be 'qualified' or 'coded'; that is, to have successfully completed a number of test welds replicating the materials, geometry, deposition rates and temperatures etc. required during production welding.

These and other problems were numerous amongst applicant tradesmen while other similar difficulties would occur with technical staff.

Construction

Towards the end of 1964 deliveries of steel for the construction of the boat were building up in the Barrow Shipyard and in September 1965 the first massive hull unit moved from the Assembly Shop to the building berth (see **Figure 3**). During 1966 the Assembly Shop continued to reverberate to the clatter of shipbuilding, and brilliant welding arcs spotlighted the huge units growing one by one towards completion (see **Figure 4**).

All units were delivered to the berth by January 1967, many of them already containing large items of machinery and equipment. From the latter half of 1966, outfit, electrical and fitter tradesmen began to install the very complex machinery systems and controls necessary for the safety and efficient operation of a Polaris-armed nuclear submarine.

Figure 3: Note the 'Temporary Strut' stencilling on the horizontal crossbeam. These temporary struts were able to support scaffolding so that various operations could be undertaken and they also assisted other diagonal crossbeams to maintain circularity of the unit until decks, tanks etc. were welded to position.

It was during this phase of construction that the vast contribution by so many departments and sub-contractors came to fruition – Drawing Offices, Equipment Procurement, Planning, Quality Control, Cleanliness, all contributing a vital link in the chain which was leading towards the timely completion of the contract to a delivery date specified.

Acrimonious Strike

In July 1968, the Yard's fitters commenced what would become an increasingly acrimonious strike that would not be settled until February 1969 – and then only by the mediation of a Court of Inquiry.

That there was a confrontational aspect to industrial relations throughout the shipbuilding industry in general had been reported by the 1966 Geddes Report – which noted ship-building's survival might well hang on improvements in the area of demarcation-generated disputes.

The fitters' strike of 1968 (which began on 3 July) involved almost 2,000 men and resulted in the loss to the company of around 200,000 working days. It would run into 1969 and consequently is often referred to locally as the six-month strike. This dispute ran almost parallel with a protest by apprentices against the introduction of a new pay structure. This had begun in June 1968 and was not resolved until December that year. 420 apprentices were involved and just short of 40,000 man hours were lost by this strike.

There isn't room here for the full story of the fitters' strike; suffice to say the dispute was triggered through pipe-testing work, which the fitters believed was theirs, being allocated to the plumbers.

The matter was indeterminately settled by a formula, developed by Sir Jack Scamp's Court of Inquiry, which the fitters accepted as a basis for their return to work but which did not actually resolve the matter which continued to have repercussions for many years after.

Figure 4: The 'elegant solution' devised by Leonard Redshaw for the insertion of missile tubes with minimal cut out of the hull.

Figure 5: Hull sections being built around formers.

Figure 6: Sections fitted onto mandrel.

Geddes Report

It is of interest to note that the Geddes Report of 1966 recommended the number of Shipyard unions be reduced to five – at the time of the referenced dispute Yard management were dealing with seventeen.

One other matter of concern emerged during the strike when, following certain allegations of the striking fitters' work being undertaken by office 'volunteers' (who had neither the training nor the ability to carry out the work correctly), members of the boat's crew aired their worry about the boat's safety via the local papers. Vickers subsequently threatened legal action if the allegations were repeated.

Figure 5 shows Polaris hull sections being built around formers in the Assembly Shed. In the foreground, lying flat on the shop floor, are two sets of cross-bracing jigs and lying flat on the left-hand jig is a section of bulkhead. Immediately behind that section is part of the submarine's fore-end structure under preparation (note the clearly visible taper on this unit). Various fore-end sections in different stages of construction complete the scene.

Figure 7: Equipment being 'fleeted' into position.

Figure 6 shows construction of the superstructure taking place on the centre of the three units depicted (again note the taper). The sections were fitted onto mandrels to enable them to be revolved for ease of working. The unusual absence of Shipyard personnel in both this and the top picture is a rare sight and it would appear to indicate that the photographer chose to shoot his photograph in the period between the end of day-shift and the start of night-shift – one of the few occasions when the bustle of the workshop would not interfere with his picture.

Figure 7 shows equipment being 'fleeted' into position prior to the unit's transport to the berth. Freon fridge units are seen being installed, with temporary protective shields covering the units to prevent them from being damaged. The purpose of these units was to cool the chilled water system which circulates through various pumps and air treatment units on the boat. Carefully watching the installation process is a white boiler-suited supervisor, almost certainly a foreman slinger. Visible between the two units, a Yard worker skilfully guides the port unit into position. On the top of the hull unit is a casually posed slinger carefully watching that the overhead crane wires do not foul against the hull and ready to call a warning to the crane driver if they appear in danger of doing so.

Note the total absence of guard rails, safety harnesses, construction helmets and other safety precautions which nowadays we take for granted. In those days, the rare occasions that safety helmets were worn would indicate that the wearer was working outdoors and it was raining.

There is nothing particularly unusual about such an apparent lack of safety knowledge – this picture is almost forty years old, well before today's highly sophisticated safety awareness.

Figure 8 shows a group of platers constructing the distinctively tapered aft end superstructure. On the left of the picture two platers (one of whom seems to have a somewhat precarious stance) hold platework in position awaiting the welder (to the left) to strike an arc. Again note the total absence of safety equipment, but equally note the casual confidence with which they go about their work.

The forward end superstructure is shown in **Figure 9**. Clearly visible on the bow or fore-end unit, is the immense aperture in which part of the bow array (belonging to the principal submarine sonar) is housed. The cut-away illustration of the boat (shown on pages 172-73) identifies the bow array against the title 'sonar transducer'.

Figure 8: Aft End.

Figure 9: Forward End.

Figure 10: Missile Tubes.

Figure 10 shows ongoing work on missile tube construction. The three white boiler-suited individuals are technicians from the Non-Destructive Examination (NDE) Department preparing equipment prior to undertaking ultrasonic examinations.

The NDE Department conducted examinations in accordance with written procedures complying with MoD requirements. The procedures, depending on their complexity and the nature of the examination, required approval by departmental heads, senior management and the MoD. In addition to inspections undertaken on platework (eg hull, bulkheads, seats, decks, etc.) welded and brazed pipework systems, forgings and castings also required inspections both prior to and after machining.

The workshops provide, in one covered area, all the necessary facilities and equipment for prefabrication of the massive hull sections. Huge rolling shafts (mandrels) enabled the sections to be rotated for ease of operation in any particular area. At such times, these workshops reverberated with the clatter of shipbuilding and brilliant, blinding welding arcs spotlighted the huge units as they grew, one-by-one, towards completion. When these workshops were busy the noise was, at times, deafening and there was a constant odour of burning metal caused by the activities of welders, burners, grinders, etc. as they went about their highly-skilled tasks.

Following the installation of the Freon fridges (see **Figure 7**) the unit had now been loaded onto the special transporter for transit to the berth (see **Figure 6**). The supervisor on the right would be giving instructions to the transporter staff and (as referenced earlier) has, in deference to inclement weather rather than any perceived safety risk, donned a construction helmet.

Once the unit had been positioned on the berth, giant portable U-shaped shelters (see **Figure 12**) were put in place. The purpose of these was to permit welding operations (and the pre-heating processes necessary for this work) and subsequent Non-Destructive Examination to take place regardless of weather conditions. Any welds found to be defective, following such inspection, were removed via 'gouging'. Re-welding then took place, followed by re-examination.

Although not visible in the picture (see **Figure 11**) it was necessary to lay steel plates over some areas adjacent to assembly sheds to protect underground systems from the weight of loads never previously envisaged by either the management or the workers of the Shipyard.

Over 500 manufacturers contributed to the design and production of equipment for a Polaris boat. Apart from the standard items installed in any submarine, from galley equipment to anchors and cables, some of the most advanced mechanical and electronic equipment in the world was fitted, much of it secret.

Long before construction began, a massive planning programme involving about 500,000 man-hours was initiated. All foreseeable problems were analysed and resolved, and overall programmes were sub-divided to the last screw.

The installation of every item had to be planned to conform to a flexible sequence because access to a particular location became progressively more difficult as each new item was fitted.

Apart from planning, every detail of design and construction also had to be recorded. Over 10,000 carefully detailed drawings, all of which were thoroughly checked to ensure the highest degree of accuracy and compatibility, were produced by the builders, contractors and the MoD (navy). Design and drawing office work had to be translated into the physical business of construction.

As a preliminary to the actual building, a full-scale wooden 'mock-up' was prepared to exact positioning of equipment and the routing of cables, piping and trunking throughout the complex contours of the hull.

Figure 11: A Polaris submarine unit being transported to the berth.

Figure 12: The giant portable U-shaped structures shielded welders and NDE technicians on the berth from the worst of Barrow's weather. The random bright dots seen against the open hull are temporary lighting systems.

The hull was assembled on the berth from fifteen pre-fabricated sections, each of which had been constructed in the Shipyard workshops and moved a short distance to the berth on a special transporter. The sections were then welded together using rigidly controlled welding techniques specially developed for this class of vessel. The fore and aft parts of the ship were built-up simultaneously with a space left between the two into which the pre-fabricated missile sections, complete with missile tubes, were fitted.

Polaris boats were on the slipway for approximately thirty months from keel laying to launch. During this time most of the machinery and equipment were installed and a large-scale test programme completed.

At the berth the sections were welded together, and the outer casing was completed. In **Figure 12** the outer shell (the superstructure) can clearly be seen surrounding the much thicker hull unit. Subsequently, piping runs, trunking, cabling and the final items of machinery were installed.

Every available inch of space in the submarine was used to the best advantage and as construction neared completion the importance of the pre-building programme became more and more evident. Access openings became fewer and smaller with surprising rapidity.

The Fin, which would later house the periscopes, masts and bridge platform was one of the largest items positioned by crane. The navigation of the ship, whilst on the surface, was controlled from the bridge platform. Despite the apparently roomy appearance, the bridge fin, as already described, was filled with a variety of equipment and, with relevant personnel in place, the bridge platform could feel extremely crowded.

Figure 13: A busy view of the Yard, c.1965, is shown in Figure 17 with Walney Channel the diagonal stretch of water in the foreground and, on the right, the bulk of the 100,000-ton tanker *British Admiral* (Yard No.1069) dwarfing all. To her left is *Resolution* in the early stages of build and further to the left *Warspite* is under construction. Behind the vessels, and occupying some 80% of the area leading to the docks, are assembly and joiners' shops, plate yards, engineering and ordnance shops, smithy and foundries, drawing and design offices, etc. The long, straight road on the right is Michaelson Road and the High Level bridge with Buccleuch Dock to the right containing two moored Isle of Man passenger ferries. To the left of the High Level bridge is Devonshire Dock with the top of her 'old' floating dock and her travelling crane just visible. Left again is the 250-ton hammerhead crane and further left, between the two cranes, the boiler barge and facilities barge can be seen. On the far side of the dock, on the left, is a bucket dredger. To the right and opposite the hammerhead crane is the Admiralty Floating Dock.

Figure 14: The confines of the interior.

Throughout the building programme, daily, monthly and bi-monthly meetings were held to examine progress and MoD overseers, builders specialists and contractors' representatives were continuously involved in checking details.

Close to 1,000 fully illustrated technical manuals containing descriptive, operational and maintenance information were prepared to serve as works of reference for trained personnel and as training aids for crews under instruction.

Dredging operations in Walney Channel and the erection of stands for guests indicated that launch day was approaching. Weather shields were cleared away and for the first time the boat looked ready for her natural elements.

On the launch day stands were few, the guests were not necessarily all the high and the mighty but they were most definitely the invited.

Walney Channel waited for the day's major guest, as did the tug sited midships to the berth.

Loose timbers were the residue of the launch. The timbers were valuable as they could be re-used by the Yard and they were also of a sufficient size and weight to do damage to the channel's general traffic if not secured and made safe.

The launching of the boat in the autumn of 1967 was highlighted by the presence of a major Patron, who had graciously consented to sponsor the ship.

As on other days when great ships have been launched at Barrow the workaday atmosphere of the Shipyard was suddenly transformed by the gaiety of the bunting and flags and the music of the brass band.

Crowds of Shipyard employees and their families, visitors and many guests made their way towards the slipway where the boat, already fitted with most of her complex equipment, was looking powerful and proud, dominating the scene.

For the men who planned and built the ship, this was the moment of conscious achieve-ment; for the men who were to sail in her, a feeling of pride and excitement in seeing 'the coming to life' of their boat – perhaps the largest submarine in the world.

Outbursts of cheering welcomed the Patron.

The example of a launch procedure (see **Figure 15**) – although quite obviously not for a Polaris boat – shows the minute-by-minute planning applicable to the event. Each of the operations were further broken down into even more closely detailed and defined events specific to the responsibilities of the recipient.

Bankfield was for many years the Yard's own private hotel, or country house, situated in the pleasant countryside near Urswick (some six miles from Barrow).

Today's era of video links and high-speed travel have rendered Bankfield superfluous and it has been sold.

The Old England Hotel refers to the world-famous Bowness-on-Windermere hotel, while Grange-over-Sands is the home of the Grand Hotel.

Grange was occasionally home to George William Garrett (whom we met on pages 18-22). During the good times – which were presumably before the Nordenfelts were launched – Garrett would sometimes sail or motor in his yawl *Lodestar* to Barrow. The *Lodestar* accom-

LAUNCH PROCEDURE	
LAUNCH OF	
H.M. SUBMARINE " SWIFTSURE "	
TRIGGERS RELEASE	1-00 p.m.
GENERAL PROGRAMME	
Main Party leave Offices for Launch Platform	12-35 p.m.
Sponsor's Party leave Offices for Launch Platform	12-45 p.m.
LUNCH	
Cocktails	1-10 p.m.
Lunch Commences	1-30 p.m.
TRAIN	
Leaving Station	3-30 p.m.
Leave Luncheon Room	3-05 p.m.
Leave Main Hall (Last of Guests)	3-15 p.m.
BANKFIELD (Guests Touring Works)	
Leave Bankfield	10-30 a.m.
Commence Tour	10-50 a.m.
Return to General Offices (Coffee)	11-50 a.m.
Leave General Offices for Launch Platform (Sponsor's Party)	12-45 p.m.
BANKFIELD (Not Touring Works)	
Leave Bankfield	11-30 a.m.
Arrive General Offices (Coffee)	11-50 a.m.
Leave General Offices for Launch Platform (Sponsor's Party)	12-45 p.m.
OLD ENGLAND HOTEL (Guests Touring Works)	
Leave Hotel	9-40 a.m.
Commence Tour	10-50 a.m.
Return to Coffee Room	11-50 a.m.
Leave Coffee Room for Launch Platform	12-35 p.m.
OLD ENGLAND HOTEL (Not Touring Works)	
Leave Hotel	10-40 a.m.
Enter Coffee Room	11-50 a.m.
Leave Coffee Room for Launch Platform	12-35 p.m.
GRAND HOTEL GUESTS	
Leave Hotel	10-40 a.m.
Enter Coffee Room	11-50 a.m.
Leave Coffee Room for Launch Platform	12-35 p.m.
LOCAL GUESTS	
Enter Coffee Room	11-50 a.m.
Leave Coffee Room for Launch Platform	12-35 p.m.

Figure 15: A typical launch day itinerary.

Figure 16: A Polaris Class boat under launch.

panied the second Barrow Nordenfelt on its doomed trip to Russia and was wrecked in the same circumstances, time and place.

Some additional information may be of interest before the launch itself is described. As the aft end became water-borne, the boat would pivot on the clearly seen white-painted cradle under the bow (see **Figure 16**), the 'poppit', as it is known, imposing an immense strain – just one good reason for using a shiplift.

The reasons for launching stern-first were tied into technical reasons related to forces and stresses but, as a matter of practicality, the very heavy timbers of the cradles (which broke up as the boat entered the water) cannot damage the vulnerable propeller and control surfaces. As a matter of further interest some yards, where there is a limited width to the waterway, launched sideways.

Barrow last launched by that method in 1913 for the Brazilian river monitors *Javery*, *Solimoes* and *Madeira* (Yard Nos 433, 434 and 435, respectively) which would eventually be sold to the Admiralty to become HMS *Humber*, *Severn* and *Mersey*.

When the launch began, the boat gathered speed, her stern dipping into the water and, with startling effect, the drag chains jerked into action to take the weight off the boat. The waiting tugs nosed towards their stations through masses of floating timber which, a few moments before, had supported the boat on the slipway. The last link with the building berth was broken as the drag chains were released and the watching crowd, not without some emotion, realised the boat was afloat for the first time.

When the boat had been towed to the fitting-out berth after the launching ceremony (see **Figure 17** and **Figure 18**), the two crews who would later man the boat on alternate operational patrols had the opportunity to practise their drills in earnest. Instead of classroom theory, the wooden mock-up and text books, they would finally have the equipment which they would operate at sea.

While the few remaining items of machinery were being installed and equipment and systems repeatedly tested, the builders worked to complete the accommodation areas. Particular attention was given to ventilation, air conditioning and other essential domestic services, such as fresh water supplies and waste disposal.

High voltage precipitators kept dust out of the ship's atmosphere; an air-treatment unit maintained air temperature and humidity at predetermined levels; an electrolyser supplied oxygen; and air conditioning equipment ensured adequate circulation of pure air. Atmosphere conditions throughout the ship were continuously monitored and a close watch was kept for any radiation content. Fresh water supplies were obviously vital and these were maintained by two distilling plants each having an output of over 5,000 gallons per day. Distilled water was required for the reactor systems, main feed system, auxiliary systems, batteries and domestic services.

Figure 17 (above) and *Figure 18* (below) show a Polaris boat under tow to the fitting-out berth following launch.

Considering the complexity of the ship and the conditions under which it operated, amenities for the crew were considerable. Meals were served on a cafeteria system, the well-equipped galley enabling several choices of hot and cold dishes to be offered at each meal. A daily newspaper was published on board to keep the crew informed of international news and also local news from their base area. Each crew member may also have received several family messages while on patrol.

Work continued day and night as the boat was secured in the Admiralty Floating Dock.

After the launch the boat was taken in tow to the fitting-out berth of Devonshire Dock, one of three enclosed docks forming the docks system for the port of Barrow-in-Furness. These three docks – Devonshire, Ramsden and Buccleuch – were constructed by the former Furness Railway Co. under statutory powers granted in 1863. A fourth dock (Cavendish) was completed with the system in 1879 but was never developed.

All four docks are interconnected and have a total water area of 280 acres and 13,750ft of quays. Access is via a 100ft-wide entrance at Ramsden Dock Basin, and this entrance has a depth on the sill of 31ft 6in at high water (ordinary Spring tides) and 24ft at high water (ordinary neap tides).

Access to the dock system from the Irish Sea is via the six-mile-long Walney Channel.

The vessel stayed in Devonshire Dock for the next few months while the final items of equipment were installed and the ship and missile systems were completed. A short period was spent in the floating dock while such items as the propeller, rudder and hydroplanes were fitted. Throughout this period extensive testing was carried out until every item had proved its reliability and efficiency.

When all was satisfactory, final tidying-up operations were completed and the submarine was provisioned for her sea trials.

Figure 19 shows the missile tube inspection/maintenance hatches. In **Figure 20** attention is drawn to rudimentary safety precautions. Careful scrutiny, particularly of the tube in the right foreground, shows the mesh of the safety netting fitted for such circumstances.

Figure 19: Inside the missile compartment area.

MENU

Minestrone Soup

***

Roast Beef and Yorkshire Pudding

Curried Chicken

Ham Salad

Roast, Creamed or Chipped Potatoes

Peas, Carrots, Cauliflower

***

Apple Crumble

Pineapple and Cream

Cheese and Biscuits

***

Coffee

Figure 20 (left): Fitting-out in progress on the outside of the missile compartment area. Note the open muzzle hatches.
Figure 21 (right): A specimen menu.

This view looking aft shows the boiler barge in position adjacent to the engine room. The barge's function was to supply steam to test the main steam system and the turbines prior to the reactor going critical.

The inverted V between the boiler barge and the boat is the temporary steam pipework supply line. The apex of the V is a flexible connection permitting movement of both boat and barge.

Even with a Polaris boat's vast size there was so much machinery to be fitted into the available space that compactness was essential. Despite this, the standard of accommodation was far higher than that in conventional submarines. No space was wasted and yet good lighting and careful layout resulted in accommodation decks which were extremely comfortable and pleasant.

The galley, fitted out in gleaming stainless steel, could produce meals for more than 140 persons and offered a choice of several hot and cold dishes at all meals. The crew ate their meals in the comfortable dining area and could choose from a wide-ranging menu. A specimen menu as served on a Polaris submarine is shown above.

Entertainment during patrols was provided by a good stock of films, a library and a choice of three piped radio programmes. The crew were provided with a daily newspaper and a weekly magazine both of which were printed onboard. Experience during trials showed that there would be no lack of contributors to the magazine.

Onboard Training

While the shipbuilder fitted out and completed the boat, the crews commenced their onboard training (see **Figure 22**). They could now apply what they had learned in classrooms and finish their training in what would be their own boat.

Each officer and rating had to have a perfect knowledge of his own job and had to be familiar with the workings of the entire boat. To assist in training, operational and maintenance instruction handbooks, together with bound copies of training aid diagrams (prepared by the Technical Publications Departments), were supplied to the crew.

A gradual build-up of step-by-step tests, ranging from small single items to the complexities of the nuclear reactor and its associated systems, ensured complete and proven readiness for long operational periods. This testing ran in parallel with (and in conjunction with) the training of the crew to ensure that both the submarine and those who would man it were fully ready for the task ahead.

A special phase of the programme was the testing and tuning of the highly sophisticated Fire Control, Navigation and Launcher systems associated with the Polaris missiles. This was conducted by a specially formed team of American-trained Shipyard engineers, various UK weapons contractors and a support team of American technical advisers.

Test instruments used and carried on the boat, particularly those associated with the missile equipment, were calibrated to international standards in the Shipyard Calibration Laboratory.

With the ship almost ready for sea, the crew made the most of their opportunities to master the many operating drills, while Shipyard personnel of all disciplines were still available to give assistance.

One of the most important final tests concerned the complex missile launching system.

The maze of pipe runs, trunking and cabling had now been 'dressed' and coded, but, as the view between the missile tubes clearly illustrates, the specialist engineers had an incredible amount of information to assimilate. By contrast the torpedo flat (see **Figure 23**) looks empty. Nevertheless every inch of this space was vital under operational conditions.

Figure 22:
Onboard training.

Figure 23: View of the torpedo flat.

Missile Checks

For the Polaris missile to function as required, six key components were necessary. The Ship's Inertial Navigation System (SINS) was required to maintain a constant plot of the boat's position for both navigation and fire control. Next, the fire control computers had to be in receipt of information from SINS in respect of the relative bearing of True North and the boat's actual position. The fire control computers calculated (on a continuous basis) the trajectory for each missile in order for them to acquire their targets – and that information was transmitted into the memory of the missile. Missile readiness and the readiness of all associated equipments were then checked via the Missile Test and Readiness Equipment (MTRE). Launcher control prepares each of the sixteen missile tubes for launch – which includes equalising the pressure to ensure that each tube remained free of water until its missile was launched. Each missile's memory had to receive and store the trajectory computations originated from the fire control system prior to launching.

At the Missile Control Panel, where the status of all sixteen missiles was displayed, the firing sequence was selected, and the final launching circuit was closed after the captain had given permission to fire.

In the final sequence, the firing key was closed and the gas generator ignited to form exhaust gases which ejected the missile upwards from the tube.

After leaving the tube, the solid-fuel motor ignited and the missile left the water. Once launched, the missile's inertial guidance system would keep it on course without the need for external control.

When the Polaris boats went on patrol in the 1960s and 1970s the warheads were of the type known as A-3 with a range of approximately 2,900 miles.

In 1979 the Royal Navy had a new 'Semi-Multiple Independently Targeted Re-Entry Vehicle', the code name for this war-head being 'Chevaline'. This was basically a triple war-head which could be programmed to hit three targets up to forty miles apart, something which the British A-3 could not do. The missile compartments were nicknamed 'Sherwood Forest' by the boat crews.

In deference to the original United States' supply of all missile components and equipments, when the Polaris boat was first commissioned, a notice reading 'You are now entering the American Zone' hung in the missile compartment.

Amenities

Accommodation space aboard any warship is necessarily limited and this is particularly true of submarines. However, in Polaris boats, equipment and materials were carefully chosen to provide best use of the space available and to provide as pleasant an environment as possible for the crew on their long patrols. The areas shown below were typical of the standard achieved.

The galley (**Figure 24**) was fitted with many modern aids to cater for the 130 crew members, including potato-peeling, slicing, mixing, dishwashing and ice cream-making machines. The food served was good, as was the choice available. Many of the meals were given nicknames by the crew members – one example being 'Babies' Heads' (steak puddings). Accommodation and bunk spaces were equally well appointed although bunk space was functional rather than spacious.

The ship carried cinema equipment, with a selection of some fifty films, and a comprehensive library. Facilities were available for crew members to take a variety of correspondence courses to further their education. In addition to their bunk spaces, junior ratings had a recreation area and a dining hall, while senior ratings had a lounge, coffee bar and dining hall. It is worth noting that all living/recreational areas were decorated with neutral colours. This apparently helped make life aboard the submarine more pleasant during the potentially extremely long operational tours of duty which the crews had to endure.

Figure 24 (above): The kitchen galley.

Figure 25 (right): The laundry on a Polaris submarine.

From top:
Figure 26: A Polaris boat carefully works her way through the dock system …
Figure 27: … then finally exits the system …
Figure 28: … before heading out to sea.

Sea Trials

The reward for two years of hard work came when the boat sailed for Faslane in 1968 for Contractors' Sea Trials, leaving Barrow-in-Furness under her own power for the first time (see opposite). With Walney Island on the starboard quarter and the open sea ahead, her blunt bow ploughed into the short swell.

For the next sixty days the ship's company, the shipbuilder and contractors worked together testing and tuning the many complicated systems, generally putting the submarine through her paces and discovering her capabilities.

Two hundred and ten men lived aboard during this time – one and a half times the normal complement. As a consequence, meal times, off-duty relaxation and sleeping arrangements while at sea called for a great deal of patience, give-and-take and (in the case of sleeping arrangements) a great deal of ingenuity.

Fitters, electricians and Dockside Test Organisation (DTO) staff hoping to carry out remedial work in quiet hours would frequently find the work place occupied by recumbent sleeping bag-clad figures catching up on their sleep.

The DTO, briefly referred to above, requires some further explanation so it can be seen in its true setting. Complementing the overall quality control effort (but not integrated into the Quality Control Organisation) the foundations of the DTO lay in an Admiralty requirement for the establishment of a competent organisation for testing and operating boat equipment and systems following their installation. Considerations for safety lay uppermost, followed by actual performance requirements.

The Admiralty's intent for such an organisation stemmed from the experience of *Dreadnought* but was further refined for the Polaris project.

DTO were responsible for the overall administrative direction, coordination and documentation of the satisfactory testing of all boat systems prior to the MoD's acceptance, and for preparing the test forms requiring the Polaris Technical Directorate's approval.

Additionally, DTO organised and programmed all the test operations and finally executed the tests (in conjunction with relevant Installation Departments), recorded and evaluated the data and certified the tests.

The organisation comprised five test groups, each made up of Yard technical staff, naval overseers and appropriate contractors.

Test Groups

The test groups and their responsibilities were:

Propulsion	Main machinery and associated equipment
Ship	All systems not part of the reactor plant, main machinery or tactical/Polaris weapons
Reactor	Nuclear plant and its containment
Polaris Weapon	The ballistic missile system
Tactical Weapons	All weapon systems except Polaris.

The Tidal Window

There were concerns with regard to the tidal window which, because of the necessity for the boat to leave for trials in June and return in August would leave only the very tightest margins for work to be completed or go by default. It may not be widely known but tidal predictions are just that – predictions. Consequently, a tide may be of the predicted height or (depending on weather and atmospheric conditions) greater or lesser than anticipated.

To ensure that the Polaris boat could leave and enter the docks as required, a false bow was built on the floating dock so that she could 'piggy-back' the boat through the dock system and out to sea where the boat could be floated off. This didn't become necessary but it shows the problems to be resolved.

Intensive Programme

With forward hydroplanes folded to reduce her beam while surfaced, the boat departed for sea trials off the north-west coast of Scotland (see opposite). For six weeks her crew, together with engineers from the Shipyard and various contractors, carried out an intensive programme of fully operational tests. On completion of trials the boat was commissioned and left Barrow to join the 10th Submarine Squadron.

Commissioned

Ten months following the naming ceremony and launch of the submarine, the boat was commissioned.

The commissioning of the submarine was a formal affair attended by many dignitaries and Shipyard workers – some 1,000 guests in total. The traditional service of dedication preceded the actual commissioning ceremony and this service, conducted by the Chaplain of the Fleet, assisted by other naval chaplains, included the Sixteenth Century Gaelic Blessing.

The Commissioning Warrants were signed by Commander-in-Chief Western, who charged the two commanders of the new submarine with their specific duties. Royal Marine buglers sounded the Alert and the National Anthem was played as the White Ensign and Union Jack were broken (at the ship's ensign and jack staffs) to signify that she had been commissioned.

From top:
Figure 29: The boat heads towards clear water.
Figure 30: The casing party go below and the boat gathers speed on her first outing.
Figure 31: The boat finally departs for sea trials.

Appendix VII
Devonshire Dock Hall and Shiplift

The Devonshire Dock Hall (DDH), with the adjacent synchronised shiplift, is one of the world's major shipbuilding facilities. Opened by Prime Minister Margaret Thatcher, on 3 September 1986, the Hall and shiplift cost about £280 million. The Hall was built at the northern end of Devonshire Dock, which required 2.5 million tons of sand to fill the area required for the Hall and adjacent areas. The sand was pumped, in a pipeline about 1.5km long, as slurry from the nearby Roosecote Sands.

The Hall is approximately 269m long, 67m wide and 51m high. The internal available build area is, to give some impression of size, twice the size of Manchester United's Old Trafford ground. With its associated supporting workshops, offices and six amenity towers (housing mess rooms, changing areas, toilets, showers, etc.) the complex covers 25,000sq.m. The Hall offers tremendous advantages when compared with the traditional methods of the building berths. Amongst the more obvious advantages are construction commencing from a horizontal plane and no requirement to plan for bad weather. Berth declivity did not cause insurmountable problems, but fleeting major and very expensive items of equipment into position required care and thought, and even more thought was required when dimensional inspection requiring plumb-lines was necessary. Climate no longer played a part in the duration of the build. Cranes would not be out of use due to high winds. Painting, tiling and welding would not be delayed because of adverse weather conditions. Services are supplied via purpose-built gantries so that gases, electricity and other services can be delivered exactly where required. Units, sections, jigs, rigs and complete hulls are moved on transfer cars (powered bogies) within the Hall, on the shiplift and adjacent hard standing, via a matrix of some 3km of rails, permitting forward, reverse and lateral movement. Two 180-ton cranes and four 30-ton cranes provide heavy lift facilities within the Hall and these are controlled from the Hall floor by operators using radio control.

From the reference to weather and climate no longer playing a part in construction schedules it can be seen that the construction programme could be shortened. Additional reductions in the construction programme would come from reductions in hull and bulkhead weld duplication. Because weight restrictions require no more than 75% of a boat's equipment to be installed when undergoing a dynamic launch, completed hull and bulkhead welds need to be opened, the relevant areas removed and the missing equipments installed when the boat is resident at the fitting-out dock. Following installation, hull and bulkheads are replaced, re-welded and re-tested. Hall construction negates all these removal and re-weld requirements.

The Hall and shiplift offer other advantages such as a 'dry-docking' facility as in the case of *Talent* and *Trenchant* and the Canadian SSKs, with ready-made construction, maintenance and/or refit facilities immediately available. Although *Upholder*, *Trenchant* and *Talent* were early guests of the shiplift, the first true baptism was with that of *Triumph* in February 1991. Perhaps surprisingly, for all its size, the Hall does not loom large over the town. It is true that the inhabitants of the closest streets are not particularly enamoured of its presence, but this is mainly due to the disruption caused during the transport of units. The Hall can be seen by fell-walkers from some of the Cumbrian hills and holidaymakers enjoying the delights of some of the Cumbrian and Lancastrian beaches.

★ ★ ★

The reality of moving units or sections which may weigh in excess of 2,000 tons over a distance of a kilometre – from and to a specific datum – is a serious and complex business. Units are prepared in the assembly shed from a number of pre-fabrications and one or more units may comprise the section which will eventually be transported to the DDH to form the hull.

The units are constructed on what Yard personnel call a 'temporary rig' which is a cradle suitably supported on blocks at a height sufficient to permit a very powerful and sophisticated flat bed twin ninety-six-wheeled transporter (each set of wheels has independent manoeuvrability) to manoeuvre to a specific datum under the cradle. The transporter's hydraulic capability lifts the cradle and unit clear of the support blocks and drives from the assembly shed and transits the public highway to the DDH. Once there the transporter manoeuvres to a specific datum within the matrix of rail lines, aligned with which are temporary sets of support blocks, then the transporter lowers the cradle onto the blocks and vacates the area. The appropriate number of remotely-operated bogies are then directed under the cradle and the bogies' hydraulic capability accepts the cradle and its load.

The DDH and Devonshire Dock run diagonally right to left. The assembly shed is at the top right-hand corner of the figure with the transfer route depicted by the thick line to the right-hand-side of the picture.

The bogies, if not already in a pre-determined position in the build-line, will be driven to the location where the units will be subject to further operations. Machinery or equipment not already fitted to position in the assembly shed will now be installed and the units or sections will be welded up into longer sections until hull construction is complete. Almost immediately prior to, or following weld completion of the hull, the bogies will move down the build-line to locations at the east end of the DDH for fitting out and the completion and acceptance of various tests and inspections. The bogie wheels are then turned through ninety degrees and the hull is moved to the transfer position for eventual location on the shiplift.

The dimensions of the DDH are sufficient to allow a maximum of four hulls, submarines or surface vessels, to be constructed at any one time. The cranage complement includes two 150-ton cranes (high level), two 30-ton cranes (low level) and two 15-ton cranes. There are also additional auxiliary hoists.

The synchronised shiplift is 162m long and activated by 108 electric winches, each with a lifting capacity of 224 tons – giving a total lift of 24,300 tons. This equates to a Lloyds nominal lifting capacity of 16,200 tons. Adjacent to the lift is the wet basin in which work on submarines and surface vessels (eg destroyers) can take place. The shiplift is served by a 15-ton crane and the wet basin by a 40-ton crane.

Ancillary buildings include substations, boiler house, compressor house, gas storage, ambulance rooms and a firefighting centre. Workshops and stores exist along part of each side of the DDH on two floors to provide support facilities adjacent to the construction and outfit positions. Offices are located above the workshops and the Amenity Towers house stairways, lifts, locker rooms, toilets, showers, mess rooms and conference rooms.

Vessels are accessed by gangways and there is provision for full supporting facilities to be made on an 'as and when required' basis.

Once in position on the shiplift, the bogies lower their loads, the cradle supports the hull and the bogies are returned to the DDH. It should be noted that there are variations on this

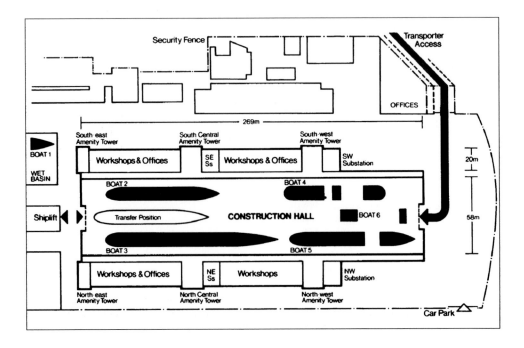

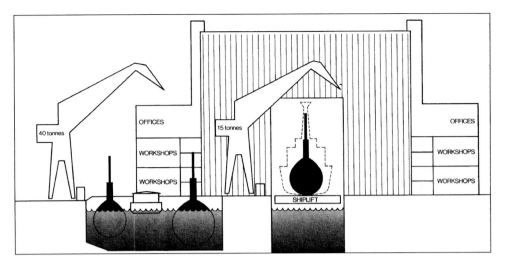

Above: Two hulls in the wet basin and a hull on the shiplift; either submarines or surface vessels can use the facility.

Below: A cradled hull on the shiplift.

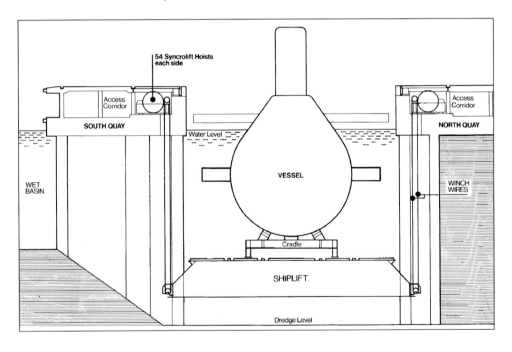

Opposite: An overhead view of the build-lines and (at the east end of the DDH) the shiplift and the wet basin. Note that both submarines and surface vessels can be built in the construction hall. The arrow indicates the transit route from the assembly shed to location in the build-line.

Inside Devonshire Dock Hall.

operation such as retrieval of a hull lifted by the shiplift, and transfer between the DDH, shiplift and the hardstanding adjacent to the shiplift.

In the event that the hull to be lifted is new to the shiplift, support profiles manufactured from hull drawings are pre-positioned on the cradles deposited by the bogies. Hull location prior to lift would be determined against specific data to ensure correct seating in the cradles once contact between hull and cradles is established. In some circumstances divers may assist the hull to cradle alignment.

★ ★ ★

In February 2002, four office suites in the Devonshire Dock Hall were named after four of the Royal Navy's VC heroes to commemorate their deeds while they were in command of Barrow-built submarines.

The names of the VC winners were chosen, following a competition organised by BAE, as a means of establishing a fitting and permanent reminder of the 2001 Submarine Centenary.

The named offices are the Sandford multi-media suite, the Linton Room, the Cameron Room and the Fraser Room. The citations of those VC recipients are referenced in the relevant sections in the main body of this book.

HMS *Triumph*, the last of the Barrow-built Trafalgar Class submarines, on the bogies outside of the Devonshire Dock Hall. Note the Yard's temporary swan-necked battery vent pipe atop the bridge fin.

Appendix VIII
The Barrow-in-Furness Shipyard

The purpose of this appendix is to give the reader a brief idea about the town of Barrow-in-Furness and its Shipyard. The map above shows the location of the town, while on the page opposite is an interesting aerial view of the Shipyard and surrounding area. The table below gives a very rough outline of how the Yard has developed (in terms of ownership) down the years while the text in this appendix gives an insight into how the town developed in the late 1800s and contains examples of secrecy and industrial unrest at the Shipyard.

Year	The Shipyard's Development	Significant Milestones
1871	The Barrow Shipbuilding Co. established.	The first order received: *Duke of Devonshire* – a passenger/cargo vessel of 3,000 gross tons, engined by the company.
1876		The first Admiralty contract received: HMS *Foxhound* – a second-class gunboat.
1886		The first submarine (*Nordenfelt I*) launched at Barrow.
1888	The Naval Construction and Armament Co. formed (by the amalgamation of the Barrow Shipbuilding Co. and the Nordenfelt Gun & Ammunition Co.).	The first order for the 'new' company was for a lifeboat – the *Edith and Annie* – for the RNLI (sailing out of the Southport Lifeboat Station).
1897	Vickers Sons & Maxim Ltd formed by Vickers Sons & Co. Ltd on their purchase of the Naval Construction & Armament Co. and the Maxim Gun Co. (The iron and steel firm of Naylor Hutchinson & Vickers was formed in 1829 and reformed as Vickers Sons & Co. Ltd – a public company – in 1867.)	Construction of HIJMS *Mikasa* (the world's most powerful battleship) and construction of HMS *Hogue* (a Cressy Class cruiser).
1901		The first submarine for the Royal Navy (HMS *Holland 1*) launched at Barrow (built to an American design).
1902		The first Vickers submarine design (the A Class boats) for the Royal Navy.
1911	Company name changed to Vickers Ltd.	The first naval airship (HMAS No.1 – *Mayfly*) built at Barrow.

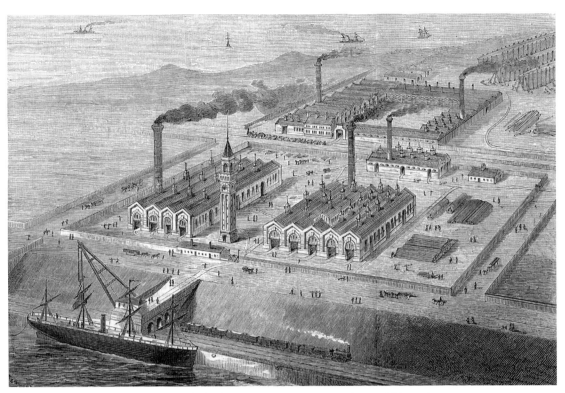

A view of Barrow Shipyard as it looked in 1874. *(Barrow Museum Service CAT 6208)*

Year	The Shipyard's Development	Significant Milestones
1927	Vickers-Armstrongs Ltd formed (within Vickers Ltd) from the amalgamation of the Vickers engineering works at Barrow and elsewhere, the Barrow Shipyard, the Armstrong engineering works at Newcastle and their shipyard at Walker-on-Tyne.	Construction of HMS *Medway* (a submarine depot ship) and construction of the *Strathnaver* and *Strathaird* liners for P&O.
1955	Vickers-Armstrongs (Shipbuilders) Ltd formed into a company separate from Vickers-Armstrongs (Engineers) and Vickers–Armstongs (Aircraft) – all within Vickers–Armstrongs Ltd. The Barrow Engineering Works was included in Vickers-Armstrongs (Engineers).	Construction of two oil tankers – *San Gregoria* (for Eagle Oil) and *British Glory* (for the Tanker Charter Co. Ltd, a BP subsidiary).
1959		*Oriana* (at 42,000 tons the largest passenger liner built in England) launched at Barrow.
1963		The first British nuclear-powered submarine (HMS *Dreadnought*) launched at Barrow.
1964		The first liquefied natural gas carrier in Europe (*Methane Princess*) launched at Barrow.

Year	The Shipyard's Development	Significant Milestones
1965	Vickers Ltd Shipbuilding Group established (with its headquarters at Barrow).	The first 100,000-ton tanker in Europe (*British Admiral*) launched at Barrow.
1967		The first British Polaris missile-carrying submarine (HMS *Resolution*) commissioned at Barrow.
1968	Barrow Engineering Works transferred from Engineering Group to Shipbuilding Group.	HMS *Churchill* (Improved Valiant Class nuclear submarine) launched at Barrow.
1975		The first British guided-missile destroyer (HMS *Sheffield*) launched at Barrow.
1977	Vickers Shipbuilding Group Ltd adapted as new company name on nationalisation – the Group becoming a member company of British Shipbuilders.	HMS *Sceptre* (nuclear-powered submarine) under construction at Barrow.
1978		The first deliveries of the FH70 field howitzer (a joint project between VSEL – UK, Rheinmetall – West Germany, and OTO Melara – Italy) to the armies of all three countries.
1980		The first anti-submarine carrier (HMS *Invincible*) accepted at Barrow.
1981	A new company name (Vickers Shipbuilding & Engineering Ltd) adopted in accordance with British Shipbuilders organisational requirements.	SSN13 – HMS *Trafalgar* (nuclear-powered submarine) – launched at Barrow.
1986	Vickers Shipbuilding & Engineering Ltd (a British Shipbuilders subsidiary) becomes the takeover target of several companies. The bid is won by the VSEL Consortium who also obtain Vickers, Cammell Laird Shipbuilders Ltd and Warship Design Services. Together they became the VSEL Group.	Keel laying of HMS *Vanguard* (the Royal Navy's first Trident-armed boat) to be followed by *Victorious*, *Vigilant* and *Vengeance*.
1995	VSEL bought by GEC to become one of their marine companies.	A return to surface ships with the building of *Ocean* (a Landing Platform Helicopter vessel) for the Royal Navy.
1998	Several changes take place within the GEC subsidiary Marconi now heading up VSEL as a Marconi Marine Company. This was swiftly followed by a change to Marconi Marine (VSEL) Ltd, following which it became Marconi Naval Systems.	Commercial vessels are under construction following orders from James Fisher & Sons for three 'clean products' tankers.
1999	BAE become the new owners of the Barrow Shipyard.	Steel to form the hulls of the Astute Class boats is being cut.

In 1845 Barrow-in-Furness was just a village. Less important than Rampside, Hawcoat and Newbarns villages, it comprised only thirty houses, though there was a blacksmith, smithy, grocer, butcher, shoemaker and a malt kiln. For a number of years it had been utilised as a port, and a number of jetties had been constructed to cope with this business, but it was the opening of the Furness Railway in 1846 (and the choice of Barrow as its headquarters) that sparked the growth into a town. A large dock system was built as the trade and population grew simultaneously, and industry soon followed. Industry on a large scale arrived in the town in 1857 with the opening of the steelworks in Hindpool, while in 1870 the Jute Works were opened. Iron shipbuilding was introduced in 1871 with the arrival of the Barrow Shipbuilding Co. and this is the one industry prevalent in the late 1800s which remains with us to this day. By 1861 the population had risen to the 16,000 mark and, in the ensuing two decades, the success of both the port activities and the new industries saw this figure rise to 47,000 in 1881. The growth of the town had seen it officially incorporated as the municipal borough of Barrow-in-Furness in 1867.

The Barrow Shipbuilding Co. grew along with the town, though one man above all others was a major contributor in the overall success of the area. That man was James Ramsden, the town's first mayor in 1867, who had great hopes for the future of Barrow. In 1872 he became Sir James, by which time he had visions of a docks system stretching as far as Piel Island and an ultimate population of 100,000. His ambitions are reflected in the way the town is planned, with its wide streets, tree-lined entrance to the town, the magnificent Town Hall and the potential for development on the outskirts. Although Ramsden's dreams were never totally fulfilled, the town eventually boasted four large docks and in the early 1920s the population briefly touched 80,000 before settling down at around the 65,000 figure at which it has remained for the last seventy or so years. However, throughout the long history of the town, and through all the changes, the one enduring feature has been the Shipyard.

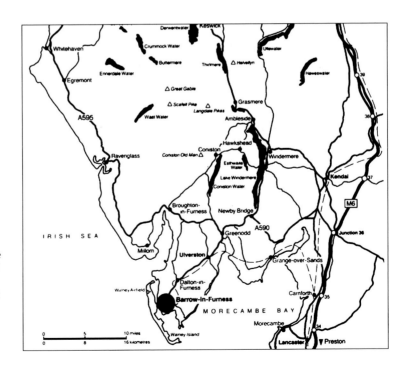

A map showing the isolated location of Barrow-in-Furness and its Shipyard (at the end of the Furness Peninsula in south-west Cumbria.

A 1990s aerial photograph of the Barrow-in-Furness Shipyard and surrounding areas.

There has always been a great deal of secrecy surrounding the Shipyard. New developments, war-related activities and experimental work are fairly obvious reasons for this. Throughout the text of this book there are examples of secrecy, and with regard to more modern boats there are many stories and details which have yet to emerge into the public domain. Often such stories and events go completely unreported, though on occasions the local newspaper will report what it can. One such example is the extract below taken from an article in the *North West Evening Mail* of 2 October 1954. (For further details on the X51 and the rest of her class refer to pages 144-45).

Secret 'Mini-sub' Launched
Ceremony at Barrow

Latest addition to the strength of the Royal Navy, a hush-hush 'mini-sub' – the X51 – was launched from Barrow Shipyard yesterday afternoon, but the outside world knew nothing about it until today. The launching was preceded by a short religious service conducted by the Rev John Mills, vicar of St John's, Barrow, but the secrecy surrounding the new ship's 'birth' was reminiscent of wartime secrecy. In a brief statement issued today, the Admiralty said that the first of a new and unproved small submarine 'was completed and launched at the Barrow-in-Furness yard of Messrs Vickers-Armstrongs Ltd yesterday.' The statement continued: 'Designated the X51, she is a boat of nearly 54ft in length and is propelled by diesel-electric machinery, the prime mover being by E. Perkins Ltd of Peterborough. She will have a complement of five.'

There was nothing new or surprising in such articles; indeed they continue to this day and will continue for as long as the Shipyard builds warships of any description. The fact that there have been very few security leaks or even scares down the years is a testimony to the integrity of the workers at the Yard (and to the townspeople of Barrow) who have, on occasions, been privy to information of utmost importance in maintaining both national and international security and world peace.

Industrial Disputes

Throughout its long history the Shipyard has known many industrial disputes, some short and easily and amicably resolved but some long and bitter. Some of the disputes of the 1960s are briefly touched upon on page 276, including the infamous 'who does what' dispute of 1968 which resulted in a protracted and acrimonious withdrawal of labour, a strike lasting six months which is still talked about in the town to this day. Such disputes though are not a new thing as the letter, reproduced on page 308 and published in the *Barrow Herald* in February 1886, clearly shows. In contrast is an article from the *North West Evening Mail* of August 1988 (reproduced on page 309) which outlined the company's offer to the workers in an attempt to end the dispute over fixed holidays. This particular strike, the last major one to hit the town, lasted some seventeen weeks and saw most of the Shipyard workers withdraw their labour.

The letter to the *Barrow Herald* in February 1886 – an example that these disputes have always occurred:

The Strike at the Shipbuilding Company's Works

Dear Sir

Would you kindly allow me space in your widely-spread journal to lay before the public a few statements by way of enlightenment as to the manner in which sundry strikes are caused and conducted. Take for instance the present one at the Barrow Shipbuilding Company, that of the strikers (angle iron smiths) and I think it will soon be clear to any impartial mind that they have a just grievance and therefore just cause for discontinuing work. The facts are these. A reduction of 7½ per cent has been lately announced in the yard specially affecting the above (angle iron smiths), but only to have an effect on future contracts – those now in hand to remain until completed at old rates. Now, the strikers to the angle iron smiths having already submitted to a reduction of 3s and 2s per week respectively do really think it hard lines to find themselves further bound to sacrifice the first quarter of each day's work when the smiths are not disposed to attend work. It will be thus easily seen that what with the 7½ per cent conceded and the lost time, viz, the early quarters referred to (and through no fault of theirs) make a loss of something like 40 per cent. And further it has always been the rule for strikers to be paid first quarter of each day's work whether the smiths attended or not, providing the tools and fires were all found in working order. It is all very well to get men out of their beds at six o'clock in the morning, and make up a fire and put the tools all right for starting (and this is repeated in some instances morning after morning); it is all right I say to wait until they come in, and then on Saturday to be paid the paltry sum of 6½d for the quarter. I say it is only an incentive for the smiths to lose these quarters, seeing that it takes one hour at the least to get in working order, leaving one hour and half to work upon, or if the smith is not in to knock about as though time was nothing to a striker only to use in waiting for their pleasure in starting. It becomes monotonous for a striker to attend two out of three mornings in the week for the sum of 6½d a turn, and when we consider that three days a week is the rule and not the exception, we think the quarters should stand as they have stood for a period of 13 years, and the smiths be contented with the reduction to which the strikers have already conceded, viz, 2s in the boiler shop and 3s respectively in the shipyard, and we take this opportunity of thanking the tradesmen, shopkeepers and publicans of Barrow for the support they have already given us, and to say that we only wish things to be put in a proper light so that men who are contesting their rights may not be condemned through any false reports which we know are going about.

THE HAMMER.

Opposite is the *North West Evening Mail* article of August 1988 by Colin Edgar, outlining the company's offer to the strikers.

Emslie Spells Out His Peace Offer to 12,000

The most crucial week of the Vickers strike dawned today with both sides going through the company's peace formula point by point. Personnel director Rick Emslie has sent a letter spelling out the exact terms of the management package to all 12,000 strikers. And union leaders were today going through the small print of the 'Cash for fixed holidays' offer with VSEL directors. In the back of their minds is the knowledge that national union officers have unanimously advised their members to accept the package. The week's timetable is:

Today: Confed officials meet directors to clarify the offer, or 'get it down in black and white' as one union chief said.

Tomorrow: The full Confed meets in the morning before reporting to shop stewards and office representatives in the afternoon.

Wednesday: A mass meeting of the whole workforce gathers at Cavendish Park at 11am.

There are three alternatives for the local Confed at Wednesday's mass meeting: to recommend acceptance, to recommend rejection or to make no recommendation. The first and last seem most likely. Both unions and management are trying to gauge people's current feelings on the offer.

Relief

Initial optimism and relief that an offer had at last been put on the table were dampened in some quarters, with strikers counting their losses in four figures. Many pounced on the company's £200 compensation offer and slammed it as 'derisory'. Others saw it as better than nothing and reckoned that if the strike drags on the equation of lost wages against compensation would only weigh heavier against them. 'I think people are disappointed and it isn't the world's best offer but it is an honourable settlement', one striker said today. 'We would be going back with more than we came out with.' Meanwhile strikers were mulling over their 'Dear Colleague' letters from Mr Emslie. Among points published for the first time is the offer of a £125 ex-gratia payment to the apprentices on top of the £200 compensation offered to all employees. 'This is a recognition of the fact that the apprentices were caught up in the dispute rather than taking a part in it,' said company spokesman Mike Smith today.

Summer

It has been revealed the summer shutdown would apply to the yard's directors as much as to anyone else. Other points in the offer are:

One fixed summer week in 1990, with two days extra pay.

Two fixed weeks from 1991, with three days extra pay.

Whit week floated from 1991.

Dates of summer shut-down to be chosen by ballot of all employees.

Agreement to let some sections return to work at least two days before everyone else to restore safety cover and catch up on the payroll backlog.

Workers wanting to be credited with one week's holiday taken during the strike will be paid one week in lieu.

Levels allowed off outside shutdown period to be reduced to 20 per cent next year and 15 per cent after that.

'The package which is described in this letter was reached after tough negotiations and provides a fair basis for settlement for us all,' Mr Emslie says in the letter.

Bibliography

This bibliography is selective in that it concentrates upon publications which are directly relevant to the text, or referred to therein. It is also a guide to further reading.

Newspapers – Periodicals – Journals

Barrow Herald
Barrow News
Daily Express
Daily Telegraph
The Engineer
The Guardian
Link magazine
The Mirror
Navy News
North West Daily Mail
North West Evening Mail
Ships of the World (Special Issue No.37 (1993))
Sunday Observer
The Times
Warship World
Western Daily Mercury
Vickers News

Shipyard Technical Publications

1886-1986 A Century of Barrow-Built Submarines STP 305 9.85
HMS *Dreadnought* (Not Dated)
HMSO Fleet Submarine 12.72 239473
Submarine *Humaita* (Not Dated)
HMS *Repulse* (Not Dated)
HMS *Resolution* (Not Dated)
HMS *Sceptre* STP 2 2/78
HMS *Sovereign* (Not Dated)
HMS *Spartan* STP 87 9/79
HMS *Splendid* TP 3.81
HMS *Superb* STP 182 11/76
HMS *Swiftsure* (Not Dated)
Type 2497 STP 214-89

Submarine *Tonelero* STP 136 12/77
HMS *Torbay* STP 509.861/87
HMS *Turbulent* STP 141 84
HMS *Upholder* STP 93 5 90
HMS *Valiant* STP 4/72

Books

Allfrey, Anthony, *Man of Arms: The Life and Legend of Sir Basil Zaharoff* (Weidenfeld &
    Nicholson, 1989)
Archibald, E.H.H., *The Metal Fighting Ship in the Royal Navy 1860-1970* (Blandford, 1971)
Bacon, Admiral Sir Reginald H.S. (Editor), *Britain's Glorious Navy* (Publisher and year
    unknown)
Bagnasco, Erminio, *Submarines of World War Two* (Weidenfeld & Nicholson, 2000)
Blake, George, *British Ships and Shipbuilders* (Adprint, 1946)
Bowers, Paul, *The Garrett Enigma and the Early Submarine Pioneers* (Airlife, 1999)
Boyd, Carl and Yoshida, Akihiko, *The Japanese Submarine Force and World War II* (Airlife,
    1996)
Brassey, *The Naval Annual* (Brassey's, various years)
Chant, Christopher, *Naval Forces of the World* (Collins, 1984)
Chapman, Roger, *No Time on our Side* (Nautical Pub. Co., 1975)
Clark, Tom, *A Century of Shipbuilding: Products of Barrow-in-Furness* (Dale Press, 1971)
Cocker, Maurice P., *Observer's Directory of Royal Naval Submarines 1901-1982* (Warne,
    1982)
Compton-Hall, Richard, *Submarines and the War at Sea 1914-1918* (Macmillan, 1991)
— *Submarine Boats: The Beginnings of Underwater Warfare* (Windward, 1983)
Conway's All the World's Fighting Ships
Critchley, Mike, *British Warships and Auxiliaries* (Maritime Books, year unknown)
— *British Warships since 1945* (Maritime Books, year unknown)
Electric Welding in Shipbuilding (Admiralty, 1943)
Erol, Turgay, *Ottoman Navy 1828-1923* (Denizler Kitapevi: 2000)
Evans, Harold, *Vickers Against the Odds 1956/77* (Hodder & Stoughton, 1978)
Everitt, Don, *K Boats: Steam-powered Submarines in World War I* (Airlife, 1999)
Friedman, *The Post-War Naval Revolution* (Conway Maritime Press, 1986)
Gray, Edwyn, *Few Survived: A History of Submarine Disasters* (Leo Cooper, 1986)
Harris, Nigel (Editor), *Portrait of a Shipbuilder: Barrow-built Vessels from 1873* (Silverlink,
    1989)
Hervey, Rear Admiral J., *Submarines* (Brassey's Sea Power Series, Volume 7, 1994)
Jane, Fred T., *The British Battle Fleet* (Conway Maritime Press, 1997)
Jentschura, Hansgeorg; Jung, Dieter and Mickel, Peter, *Warships of the Imperial Japanese
    Navy 1869-1945* (Cassell military, 1977)
Kemp, P., *Midget Submarines (Wartime Fotofax)* (Arms & Armour Press, 1990)
Lawrence, Peter, *A Century of Submarines* (Tempus Publishing, 2001)
Lipscomb, Com. F.W., *The British Submarine* (Conway Maritime Press, 1977)
Mackenzie, Sir Hugh, *Sword of Damocles* (Royal Navy Submarine Museum, 1995)

Mars, Alistair, *British Submarines at War, 1939-1945* (William Kimber, 1985)

Meister, Jurg, *Soviet Warships* (Macdonald & J, 1977)

Mitchell, Pamela, *The Tip of the Spear: The Midget Submarines* (Richard Netherwood Ltd, 1993)

Moore, Capt. J.E. (Editor), *Jane's Pocketbook 8 – Submarine Development* (McDonald & Jane's, 1976)

— *The Impact of Polaris* (Richard Netherwood Ltd, 1999)

Murphy, William Scanlon, *Father of the Submarine* (William Kimber, 1987)

Nailor, Peter, *The Nassau Connection: The Organisation and Management of the British Polaris Project: the Organisation and Management of the British POLARIS Project* (The Stationery Office Books, 1988)

Neuman, Robert, *Zaharoff the Armaments King* (Reader's Union, 1938)

Parker, R.G., *Cockatoo Island* (Thomas Nelson, 1977)

Polmar, Norman and Carpenter, Dorr, *Submarines of the Imperial Japanese Navy* (Conway Maritime Press, 1986)

Preston, Antony, *Submarines* (Octopus/Phoebus, 1975)

Redshaw, J.S., *Ships* (Frederick Mueller, 1947)

Ring, Jim, *We Come Unseen: The Story of Britain's Cold War Submariners* (John Murray, 2001)

Scott, J.D., *Vickers – A History* (Weidenfeld & Nicholson, 1962)

Smith, Geddis, *Britain's Clandestine Submarines 1914-1915* (Yale University Press, 1964)

Sontag, S., Drew, S. and Drew, A. *Blind Man's Bluff* (Hutchinson, 1999)

Stafford, Edward P., *The Far and the Deep* (Arthur Barker Ltd, 1968)

The Activities of Vickers-Armstrongs Limited (Barrow-in-Furness) (In-house publication, year unknown)

Treadwell, Terry, *Strike from Beneath the Sea* (Tempus Publishing, 1999)

Turner, John Frayn, *Periscope Patrol* (Airlife, 1997)

Vickers, Sons & Company Limited (Barrow-in-Furness) (In-house publication, year unknown)

Wilson, Michael and Kemp, Paul, *Mediterranean Submarines: Submarine Warfare in World War One* (Crecy, 1997)

Wilson, Michael, *Baltic Assignment: British Submariners in Russia, 1914-19* (Secker & Warburg, 1985)

Other Sources

Yard Build List
Various Shipyard Records

Index

This index details only those submarines and classes of submarines which were constructed, intended to be constructed or (in the case of the German submarines) handled by the Barrow Shipyard. Basically it details those submarines which the authors consider to be 'Barrow built', the 'nearly submarines' (Appendix II), the 'German submarines' (Appendix III) and *Pisces* (Appendix IV).

There are of course references to countless other submarines, vessels and personalities throughout the text. These are not referenced below. Prefixes (e.g. HMS, HMAS, etc.) have been omitted from the list below, though the Class (or type) has been included in brackets after the boat's name.

With regard to boat names (rather than classes) the list below includes only pages where the boat is specifically referenced by its name.

Other Submarine Titles by Tempus: